D1365234

THE BIOLOGICAL ACTION OF THE VITAMINS

THE UNIVERSITY OF CHICAGO PRESS
CHICAGO, ILLINOIS

*

THE CAMBRIDGE UNIVERSITY PRESS
LONDON

THE BIOLOGICAL ACTION OF THE VITAMINS

A Symposium

EDITED BY

E. A. EVANS, JR.

Associate Professor of Biochemistry
The University of Chicago

THE UNIVERSITY OF CHICAGO PRESS
CHICAGO · ILLINOIS

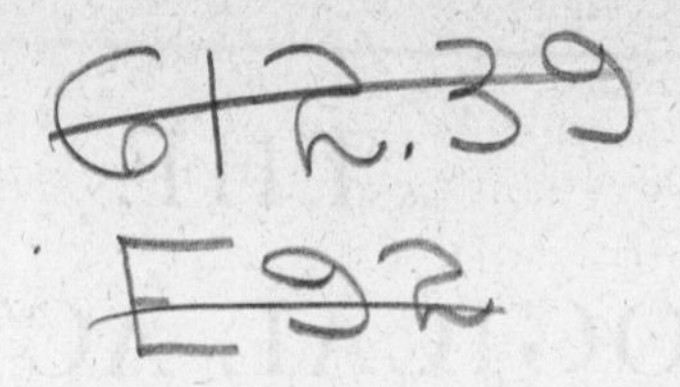

THIRD IMPRESSION FEBRUARY 1944

*

COMPOSED AND PRINTED BY THE UNIVERSITY OF CHICAGO PRESS
CHICAGO, ILLINOIS, U.S.A.

PREFACE

EVEN though the papers gathered in this volume were planned and presented in a less critical time than that of the moment, their value is enhanced by circumstances which make information as to what constitutes optimal human nutrition of great practical importance. Currently, the most striking advances in nutritional knowledge center about the vitamins. If we knew nothing more of these substances than their therapeutic value for such gross pathological conditions as scurvy, beriberi, and pellagra, the interest and extensive experimentation which they have evoked would be amply justified. However, as interest has turned to the specific action of these substances in the cell, their role has become more significant than first suspected. At the clinical level, also, conditions more subtle in their manifestation than the classical deficiency diseases now appear to be caused by functional disturbances associated with vitamin deficiencies. Perhaps even more striking is the fact that within the last decade investigations of the most varied type—studies of the growth requirements of bacteria, examinations of the nature of cellular respiration, clinical investigations of human nutritional deficiencies—have come to solutions involving the vitamins as a common denominator.

In recognition of this common interest in vitamins on the part of investigators in many fields, the universities of Chicago and Wisconsin joined in a Symposium on the Respiratory Enzymes and the Biological Action of Vitamins in connection with the Fiftieth Anniversary celebration of the University of Chicago. The symposium was organized and directed by Professor T. R. Hogness, of the University of Chicago, with the co-operation of Professor C. A. Elvehjem, of the University of Wisconsin. The papers concerned with respiratory enzymes were presented at sessions held at Madison, September 11–13, 1941; the papers on the biological action of vitamins were presented at Chicago, September 15–19, 1941. The symposium is being printed in two volumes, the papers presented at Madison being published by the University of Wisconsin Press under the editorship of Professor Perry Wilson and the vitamin papers given at Chicago constituting the present volume.

Both the Chicago session of the symposium and the publication of this volume were made possible by the financial aid of the Abbott Laboratories. It is a pleasure to acknowledge their generous support.

THE EDITOR

March 11, 1942

TABLE OF CONTENTS

THE BIOLOGICAL ACTION OF THE VITAMINS

C. A. ELVEHJEM
Department of Biochemistry, University of Wisconsin

RELATIVELY little attention has been given to the specific function of vitamins in metabolism until very recently. However, the increased momentum during the past few years has more than compensated for any previous lag in this field.

Early clinicians, I suppose, observed the biological action of vitamins when they found that an abundance of liver was a remedy for night blindness or when they found that green vegetables or fresh fruit juices gave relief in scurvy. They were interested, however, in healing the patient and gave little thought to the mechanism of these recoveries.

The pioneer experimental workers in the field of vitamins did give some attention to the cause of the symptoms observed in the deficient animals. Eijkman (1), in 1897, on the basis of systematic experiments, was able to refute the theories that beriberi might be due to the presence of pathogenic organisms in rice, to a lack of mechanical stimulation of the intestine, or to an insufficiency of total food. He suggested that beriberi is a state of intoxication brought about by the metabolism of excessive quantities of starch and that the silver skin of the rice contained a substance which would counteract the toxic products of the disturbed metabolism. Later, in 1906, Eijkman (2) agreed with Grijn's conception of beriberi, that there is present in rice polishings a substance indispensable to health.

In 1911 Hart, McCollum, Steenbock, and Humphrey (3), from studies with calves on rations balanced from restricted sources, were led to postulate an inherent toxicity in the wheat grain. This toxicity was overcome by something in a variety of forages. In 1924 they (4) were able to show conclusively that these results, observed by them seventeen years previously, represented a typical vitamin-A deficiency brought about by the very low amount of vitamin A in wheat grain.

More recently we have seen a similar story in the case of egg-white toxicity and biotin. Practically all workers who have studied this syndrome since it was first described by Boas (5) in 1927 have referred to it as some form of toxicity. Parsons and Kelly (6) concluded that the dermatitis in rats fed egg white was dependent upon an interrelation between a positive toxicity and a relative absence of a protective factor. Today, owing to the work of György, Rose, Eakin, Snell, and Williams (7), we know that egg white does not effect the metabolic processes in the animal itself but that egg white combines with biotin in the intestinal tract, preventing absorption and thereby producing a biotin-deficiency syndrome. The conclusions reached by many of the early workers were not surprising, since at the end of the past century Pasteur had shown that epidemic diseases were caused by microörganisms, and it seemed that every disease must have its positive causative agent.

Interest in the biological action of vitamins became secondary when concentrates of these illusive substances were made. In 1911 Funk (8) obtained a potent concentrate of what we know today as "thiamine." It is interesting to note that Funk used beriberi in pigeons for his assay work. He was more interested, however, in the chemistry of his concentrates than in the physiological action of the vitamins.

Shortly after these studies by Funk we reached another stage in the experimental work on vitamins. Here, the activity of these factors was evaluated in terms of growth. I imagine the real impetus for such studies came from Hopkins (9) when he showed the very significant effect of the addition of a few centimeters of milk to a synthetic diet. I am quite sure that the carefully drawn curves published by him in the *Journal of Physiology* did much to stimulate the extensive use of growth curves by nutrition workers. About the time I entered the nutrition field, half of our time was spent with graph paper and India ink.

It remained for McCollum and co-workers to show that both vitamin A and vitamin B could be measured on the basis of growth in rats on purified rations. All the early work on the additional members of B complex was based on growth responses in rats and chicks. Even vitamin C was measured to some extent through growth experiments with guinea pigs. The vitamins were called "growth factors," and Sherman did much to put these growth responses on a quantitative basis. Sherman and Smith (10) state:

> Thus by 1920 it was well established that the normal growth of the young, at least in the human and some other species, demands adequate supplies of at least three substances believed to be identical with the substances which are essential to the prevention of the three "deficiency diseases" of scurvy, beriberi, and the characteristic ophthalmia.

It was convenient to use growth, since this procedure did not require the actual production of symptoms or the necessity of purifying the basal rations to such a great extent. We now know that these methods produced results because they allowed the isolation and production of pure vitamins. Great effort went into the work on the chemistry of the vitamins, but progress was not phenomenal until the scientific efforts in this field and those in the field of respiratory enzymes collided. We are still busy following the sparks from this impact.

I should like, therefore, to divide my paper into two parts: first, a discussion of the studies on the biological action of vitamins before the relationship between vitamins and respiratory enzymes was recognized; and, second, a brief outline of the developments during the past few years.

Among the first attempts to understand the action of vitamins was the histological study of tissues from vitamin-deficient animals. These studies had a profound effect on all future work since they indicated how the absence of a minute trace of a nutrient could produce a complete change in the structure of certain tissues. We must not underestimate the significance of the knowledge which has accumulated from histological studies on deficiency diseases, but I believe we are safe in saying that these studies alone have not allowed us to elucidate the exact mechanism of vitamin activity.

The degeneration of the myelin sheaths of peripheral nerves described from forty to fifty years ago both in human cases of beriberi and in birds suffering from polyneuritis represents a classical observation. However, such observations did not help to stimulate interest in the action of vitamin B in every tissue of the body—an effect we know to be true today. They also tended to relate all the structural changes occurring in beriberi to a lack of vitamin B_1. There may still be some differences of opinion on this point, but I believe everyone is willing to recognize that many of the deficiency diseases in both humans and experimental animals are multiple deficiencies.

Histological studies in vitamin-A deficiency are more recent than those involving vitamin B, and they have been more extensive. The characteristic metaplasia which epithelial tissues in any part of the body may undergo in this deficiency did help in delocalizing the action of vitamins, but to date we still do not know how a molecule of vitamin A functions.

It is well known that vitamin D is specifically concerned with the calcification of growing bones; and I suppose few tissues have been studied more thoroughly, from both a histological and a chemical point of view, than this tissue, but we still do not know how vitamin D is related to the final stage of calcification. The histological studies on vitamin-C deficiency have produced a somewhat clearer picture. The lack of formation of intercellular material may depend upon the specific effect of vitamin C on the physical character of the intercellular fluids. However, the function of vitamin C in plant cells cannot be explained on this basis. In the case of vitamin E, we need only to mention the fact that much of the early work was limited to histological changes during embryonic growth and in reproductive organs, while today the action of vitamin E is also extended to other tissues as well.

Since most of the early work on vitamins was carried out in relation to animals, it is not surprising that a functional relation between vitamins and hormones was suggested. As late as 1935 Pende, quoted by Rolleston (11), considered that vitamin A stimulated the sex hormones and inhibited the thyroid, that vitamin B stimulated the secretion of insulin and inhibited that of the adrenals, that vitamin C stimulated the adrenal cortex to secrete, and that vitamin D stimulated the thyroid to secrete. As far as I know, none of these relationships has been established. Baumann and Moore (12) state that stringent proof would appear to be necessary before a specific and constant, as opposed to an accidental and occasional, relationship between vitamin A and thyroxine is assumed. It is true that both vitamin D and parathormone are related to calcium metabolism; but Kozelka, Hart, and Bohstedt (13) showed, as early as 1933, that vitamin D functions normally in the absence of the parathyroid glands. The supposed relationship of vitamins to the hormones of the adrenal gland has been based upon the high concentrations of certain vitamins in this gland and the changes in the adrenals during avitaminosis. Grollman and Firor (14) have presented evidence against the view expressed by many workers that there exists a particularly intimate relation between the vitamins and the adrenals. There has been much interest in the connection of vitamin E with the sex hormones, but at present the most significant relation is the change in the pituitary during vitamin-E deficiency. There appears to be a change in both the thyrotropic and gonadotropic activity of the pituitary in the absence of vitamin E. While these studies have given us no clear-cut evidence on the action of vitamins, it is logical to assume that definite relationships will be established when we know more about the specific action of both the hormones and the vitamins. Thus hyperthyroidism is known to reduce the cocarboxylase and cozymase content of rat tissues.

The relation of vitamins and enzymes was suggested not merely from a functional point of view but on the basis of chemical similarity. Seidell (15), in 1921, stated that, aside from a possibly significant degree of dialyzability, there is no outstanding evidence that vitamins should not be classified with the enzymes. This statement is interesting in light of our present knowledge that at least some of the vitamins function as prosthetic groups in enzymes. When methods were developed for determining the enzyme content of various tissues, it was not surprising that these methods were applied to tissues from vitamin-deficient animals. Green (16) reported in 1934 that vitamin-A deficiency brings about a pronounced fall in the esterase content of the blood serum. Sure *et al.* (17), in 1939, verified this finding and also observed a decrease in liver esterase and lipase. However, Green concludes that there is reason for considering the change in the serum a secondary change, and one unlikely to throw direct light on the physiology of vitamin A. A more specific relation of vitamin A and enzymes comes from the work of Wald which suggests that visual purple is a conjugated protein with vitamin A as the prosthetic group. Whether vitamin A functions as a prosthetic group with proteins in other tissues is, of course, unknown.

There has been good reason to associate vitamin C with various enzymes. Both ascorbic acid and dehydroascorbic acid exert stimulatory or inhibitory effects on many of the proteolytic and oxidizing enzymes. The fact that vitamin C can be readily oxidized and reduced and that specific enzymes have been demonstrated for both its oxidation and its reduction by SH-glutathione certainly suggests that it may serve as a hydrogen carrier. Crook (18) has recently given special emphasis to its role in this connection. Its close connection to glutathione, which for a time was the only so-called "autoxidizable" material extracted from animal tissues, further emphasized its role in oxidative mechanisms. Although much has been learned about the chemical role of vitamin C in these reactions, its function in animal tissues is still not clear. The recent paper by James, James, and Bunting (19), who find that lactic acid is not oxidized by cell-free barley sap alone, but that upon the addition of ascorbic acid rapid oxidation takes place, gives this vitamin a definite role in plant metabolism.

A high plasma phosphatase in vitamin-D deficiency has been recognized for ten years, but this is undoubtedly a secondary effect due to loss of phosphatase from the rachitic bones rather than to a direct relationship between the vitamin and the enzyme. Presnell (20) has reported a decrease in the oxygen uptake of the skin of rachitic rats, and other workers have reported a stimulatory effect of vitamin D on general metabolism; but no direct effect on any enzymes has been observed.

The most fruitful studies on the relation of vitamins to enzymes were those involving vitamin B_1. Early *in vitro* studies yielded conflicting results due largely, I believe, to the fact that total respiration, rather than changes in individual systems, was studied. During the first part of the last decade, work in Peters' laboratory at Oxford and in our laboratory at Madison led to the slow accumulation of data showing that the rate of metabolism of lactic and pyruvic acids was reduced in brain tissue from polyneuritic animals and that the addition of vitamin B_1 concentrates stimulated both oxygen uptake and removal of these substrates. Another important observation was the fact that similar changes were found to take place in other tissues, such as kidney, heart, and liver. Thus, vitamin B_1 did not function specifically in nervous tissues but affected metabolism in general.

At this point it might be well to mention the role that yeast and microörganisms played in emphasizing the relation of vitamins to enzymes. The part played by microörganisms in the recent work—not only on the biological action of vitamins but also on the actual recognition of vitamins—is well known; but, if we look back twenty years, we find that studies even at that time had some influence. In 1919 Williams (21) concluded that the substance or substances which stimulate the growth of yeast are identical with the substance or substances which in animal nutrition prevent beriberi, or polyneuritis. Similar results were obtained by Abderhalden and by Bachmann. These announcements resulted in much controversy, due undoubtedly to variations in the strains of yeast used and to the lack of other growth factors, but I have found no criticism based on the fact that yeast cells did not have a nervous system. This indicates perhaps the extent of interest in the mechanism of vitamin activity at that time. Conclusive evidence for the effect of vitamin B_1 on yeast growth did not come until 1930, but the fact that yeast was such a good source of vitamin B_1 did lead to certain suggestions regarding the general influence of vitamin B_1 in metabolism.

The early studies on the anaerobic breakdown of carbohydrates in both yeast cells and muscle tissue, which led finally to the Embden-Meyerhof-Parnas scheme of glycolysis, did much to help transfer ideas from yeast studies to those involving vitamin activity in animal cells. In 1906 Harden and Young emphasized the importance of organic dialyzable substances in yeast fermentation and called these substances "coenzymes." In 1918 Meyerhof found the coenzyme of yeast in a number of animal tissues. Work on the nature and number of natural activators participating in fermentation processes continued with little interest from the vitamin workers. Myrbäck and von Euler by 1931 had a fairly pure preparation of cozymase and showed that it was different from yeast and muscle adenylic acid as well as adenosine triphosphate, which had been characterized about the same time by Lohmann. About this same time considerable attention was being paid to the dehydrogenase type of enzymes, but more information was available about the dehydrogenases in bacteria than those in yeast. In spite of the meager knowledge concerning dehydrogenases in yeast, the more or less direct relation between dehydrogenases and the coenzymes was soon recognized. The necessity of a coenzyme for the oxidation of lactic acid by lactic dehydrogenase of animal tissues was shown by Szent-György in 1925. Banga and Szent-György obtained a fairly pure preparation of this coenzyme and concluded that it was not identical with muscle adenylic acid or adenosine triphosphate. The relation between vitamin B_1 and lactic acid dehydrogenase coenzyme was suggested in papers from Peters' laboratory in both 1932 and 1933. However, both Boyland and Birch and Mann (22) showed that coenzyme preparations showed little or no vitamin-B_1 activity. Thus, as late as 1934 there was no clear-cut evidence for a direct relationship between vitamins and enzyme systems.

While the vitamin workers were busy with their animals, a relatively new subject was being introduced into the field of enzymes—respiratory enzymes. Oxidases had been studied, but the importance of these in total tissue respiration were not recognized until the work of Warburg. According to his theory, the primary reaction of respiration is the reaction between molecular oxygen and iron. Warburg used the name *Atmungsferment* for the catalytically active iron compounds involved in cellular respiration. This was followed by Keilin's work on cytochrome, which not only emphasized the importance of iron compounds but showed that bacteria, yeast, plants, and animals contained similar respiratory pigments. Even glutathione, the first auto-oxidizable material to be isolated from living matter, was found to be oxidizable only in the presence of traces of iron or copper. Catalase and peroxidase were shown to be iron compounds. These results gave little stimulus to studies on biological action of vitamins.

Then came the discovery of Warburg and Christian (23) in 1932 which opened an entirely new group of relationships. That this discovery came from Warburg's laboratory is especially interesting, because no one had championed a single iron-containing respiratory enzyme in all aerobic cells more than Warburg. Warburg and Christian found that a combination of a preparation of the yellow enzyme from yeast, a second enzyme prepared from yeast, and a coenzyme obtained from the red blood corpuscles of horse blood was capable of catalyzing the oxidation of hexose monophosphate. The yellow enzyme, by virtue of its ability to be reduced and oxidized, acted as an oxygen transport agent between molecular oxygen and the substrates.

This yellow enzyme contained riboflavin as the prosthetic group. The relation of the observations on the yellow enzymes to vitamin studies was not obvious until Kuhn and co-workers demonstrated that pure riboflavin stimulated growth in rats on diets low in vitamin B_2. The real significance of these findings was not accepted as rapidly as one would expect in light of our present knowledge, largely because riboflavin was considered to be vitamin B_2 and because vitamin B_2 had been firmly related to the antipellagra factor. It was evident from work in our laboratory that riboflavin concentrates would not cure blacktongue in dogs. However, the rapidity with which riboflavin became available in pure form made it possible to establish its physiological function in a variety of animal species. At first, uncomplicated riboflavin deficiencies in animals were not easy to produce, but we now have a greater variety of symptoms noted for riboflavin deficiency than for any of the other vitamins.

Although there is considerable question about the role of the yellow enzyme described by Warburg and Christian in living tissues, there is no question about the importance of other riboflavin-containing enzymes, such as *d*-amino acid oxidase, xanthine oxidase, and cytochrome reductase. Axelrod (24) has demonstrated a very significant decrease in the *d*-amino acid oxidase and xanthine oxidase content of tissues from rats suffering from riboflavin deficiency. Very recently Axelrod and Potter found a decrease in the succinoxidase activity in tissues from rats on low riboflavin diets, which may indicate that succinic acid dehydrogenase is a flavoprotein. As far as I know, no studies have been made on cytochrome reductase changes during a riboflavin deficiency. This would also be an interesting problem.

Orla-Jensen *et al.*, in 1936, and Wood, Anderson, and Werkman, in 1937 (reviewed by Snell, Strong, and Peterson [25]), found riboflavin to be essential for the lactic and propionic acid bacteria; but I know of no studies on the specific function of riboflavin in microörganisms except those of Pett (26) which show changes in the riboflavin content of yeast grown with cyanide and those of Lipmann (27) involving the bacterial pyruvate oxidase system.

Warburg, in his enzyme system, used a coenzyme prepared from red blood corpuscles. Today we recognize this compound as coenzyme II. In 1935 he isolated and characterized the coenzyme as a dinucleotide consisting of adenine, pentose, phosphoric acid, and nicotinic acid amide. Von Euler and his co-workers had been working on cozymase from yeast, and in the same year both von Euler and Warburg isolated nicotinic acid amide from the cozymase after hydrolysis. The two coenzymes differed only in the number of phosphoric acid molecules. This work then introduced a new chemical component of the coenzymes and naturally attracted attention in nutrition circles, especially since nicotinic acid had been isolated by Funk from yeast concentrates which possessed antineuritic activity. In our laboratory I well remember the enthusiasm with which Max Schultze suggested that we try nicotinic acid in some of our rat studies. Frost did try both the acid and the amide, but the results were far from encouraging. It is easy to understand now why our results, as well as those in several other laboratories, were negative.

The bacteriologists were more successful in demonstrating the nutritional significance of these compounds. In 1937 Lwoff and Lwoff (28) showed that the growth factor V for *Hemophilus parainfluenzae* could be replaced by either cozymase or Warburg's coenzyme but that nicotinic acid or amide were inactive. They also showed that the oxygen uptake and aerobic and anaerobic glycolysis could be increased by adding the coenzyme to the bacteria grown in the presence of only small amounts of the V factor. Similar results were obtained when they used specific substrates such as pyruvate, fumarate, malate, alcohol, etc. Knight (29) showed that nicotinic acid could function as a growth factor for *Staphylococcus aureus*, and Mueller (30) showed it to be active for diphtheria bacillus. The activity of nicotinic acid in blacktongue was demonstrated the same year. It is interesting that nicotinic acid as such was fed to blacktongue dogs just one month before nicotinic acid amide was isolated from liver concentrates showing high anti-blacktongue activity. Thus it appears to be just as difficult to devise the proper conditions in which to demonstrate the physiological role of a known compound as it is to find the compound in a preparation known to have physiological activity.

As soon as the nutritional significance of nicotinic acid was recognized, it was assumed that its function in the animal body must be related to coenzymes I and II. In our laboratory no changes could be detected in the blood, but significant decreases were found in the cozymase content of the liver and muscle from dogs and pigs kept on nicotinic acid deficient diets. Similar results were observed by Kohn, Klein, and Dann (31), who measured the V-factor values of the tissues. Comparable data have been obtained in the case of humans. Studies on coenzyme II have not been carried out. These results would suggest that nicotinic acid functions specifically as a precursor of the coenzymes.

Working with dysentery bacilli, Saunders, Dorfman, and Koser (32) have come to the conclusion that nicotinamide is concerned in cellular metabolism in some way in addition to the formation of the pyridine nucleotides. Mann and Quastel (33) have recently reported that brain tissue and, to a lesser extent, liver and kidney are able to break down cozymase at a rapid rate. The presence of nicotinamide inhibits the breakdown of cozymase probably by competition with cozymase for the nucleotidase. This work may have some bearing on the results of Saunders *et al.* and certainly emphasizes the precautions necessary in cozymase determination in tissues.

We may now return to vitamin B_1 for a moment. While these studies were being carried out, Williams and co-workers isolated, characterized, and synthesized thiamine. Synthetic thiamine became available in 1936 and did much to further the work on the biological action of this compound. In 1912 Neuberg reported the presence in yeast of an enzyme, called carboxylase, which catalyzed the decarboxylation of α-keto acids. In 1932 Auhagen, working in von Euler's laboratory, split the enzyme into a protein component and a thermostable factor cocarboxylase. In 1932 Simola investigated the coenzyme content of the tissues from rats suffering from a complicated vitamin-B deficiency and concluded that the cozymase content was not reduced but that the cocarboxylase content was lowered. The significance of this work was not realized until five years later, when Lohmann and Schuster found that cocarboxylase was the pyrophosphoric acid ester of thiamine. There is today no question about the reduction in the cocarboxylase content of tissues from animals suffering from uncomplicated vitamin-B_1 deficiency, but we still do not have a complete understanding of the action of cocarboxylase in the animal body. Green, Herbert, and Subrahmanyan (34) have isolated carboxylase from brewers' top yeast and found it to be diphosphothiamine-magnesium-protein. Carboxylases have recently been prepared from bacteria by Silverman and Werkman (35), and animal tissues by Green *et al.* (36).

Pyridoxine is one factor which was recognized purely on a nutritional basis. Its existence was first suggested by György in 1934, based on the fact that certain concentrates from yeast cured a specific dermatitis in the rat. Orthodox chemical procedures led to its isolation and synthesis. As far as I know, its specific biological action is not known. Its function has been associated with a specific dermatitis in the rat, but in our laboratory we seldom see any dermatitis in rats fed on diets low in pyridoxine but containing adequate linoleic acid and the usual 18 per cent casein. Halliday (37) has reported an increased fat content of the liver from rats deficient in pyridoxine, and McHenry and Gavin (38) have reported an increased amount of body fat after feeding pyridoxine to rats on diets high in protein. Thus it appears that this vitamin may be related both to protein and to fat metabolism.

In dogs a low intake of this vitamin produces a typical microcytic hypochromic anemia which responds rapidly to the administration of pyridoxine. It is most interesting that serum iron increases to very high levels during the anemia and decreases to normal as soon as the vitamin is given. Swingle, in our laboratory, has studied the various respiratory enzymes during a pyridoxine deficiency both in rats and chicks, but to date he has obtained no significant changes. Pyridoxine has a stimulatory effect on the growth of yeast and many bacteria, but again no suggestions regarding its action have been obtained.

The first indication of the existence of pantothenic acid comes from work on yeast by Williams in 1931. Later it was shown to be essential for lactic acid bacteria, and in 1939 it was shown to be active in the prevention of a chick dermatitis which had been recognized since 1930. It is now known to be essential for growth in rats, dogs, pigs, and monkeys. However, we still know little about its biological action. The relation of pantothenic acid to dermatitis in chicks is interesting, especially since a lack of biotin also produces a dermatitis in chicks. In rats we have an interesting relationship between pantothenic acid and the adrenals. Pratt and Williams (39) have shown that pantothenic acid affects fermentation by both nonliving and living systems. Last fall Axelrod was studying the respiratory enzymes in tissues from rats suffering from pantothenic acid deficiency and obtained a very significant increase in the succinoxidase system in liver when he added calcium pantothenate. Unfortunately, this response turned out to be a calcium, rather than a pantothenic acid, effect.

It is unnecessary in this introductory paper to continue to list the newer factors, since other papers in the symposium will bring out information about these compounds.

I might mention the early paper by Allison, Hoover, and Burk (40) on coenzyme R, since it is now well established that coenzyme R and biotin are identical. They showed that the root-nodule bacteria failed to reproduce or to grow appreciably in the absence of coenzyme R because of their inability to respire. Although these observations were made eight years ago, the exact function of biotin in tissue respiration is still unknown. Friedman and Mattill (41) have observed an increased oxygen uptake in the muscle tissues during vitamin-E deficiency.

Although this survey is very incomplete, I think it is obvious that definite relationships have already been established between certain vitamins and certain enzyme systems, and there are numerous indications that additional similar relationships will be established in the future. However, we should not be too elated over the progress that has been made so far, for two reasons: First, we must recognize that, of the entire group of vitamins, a direct relationship with enzymatic function has been established only in the case of three vitamins: thiamine, riboflavin, and nicotinic acid. Second, in spite of the fact that these definite relationships have been established, we still do not know how the enzymatic changes are related to the symptoms observed.

In the case of thiamine, the mechanism is fairly clear; and we must return, to some extent at least, to the older idea of toxicity. Thus Peters (42) states: "Surely it is more possible to understand how pathologically the brain in its metabolism may not only be subjected to the action of toxins (the usual view) but occasionally fail owing to self poisoning with its own misguided machinery."

The large number of enzymes which appear to contain riboflavin may explain the variety of symptoms that have been observed during riboflavin deficiency. However, we still do not know if it is a decrease in the *d*-amino acid oxidase which causes degeneration of the sciatic nerves, if the xanthine oxidase decrease causes cheilosis, if a decrease in the cytochrome reductase causes cataract, or if the ocular symptoms are related to changes in succinoxidase.

In the case of nicotinic acid, the level of coenzymes is definitely reduced in striated muscle and in liver, and changes in the oxidative metabolism of liver, muscle, and kidney can be detected; but we do not understand the relation of these phenomena to the onset of blacktongue in dogs or pellagra in humans. However, exact studies on the relation of these changes to the actual infection of the tissues in the mouth of a blacktongue dog by microörganisms may do much to help explain the larger problem of the relationship of nutrition to infectious diseases.

In conclusion, I want to mention one additional biological effect of vitamins in the animal organism, and that is the effect of vitamins on the growth of microörganisms in the digestive tract. We know that many vitamins stimulate certain microörganisms and that, in turn, certain of these organisms can synthesize additional vitamins. In many cases the compounds formed by the bacteria or yeast must be available for assimilation by the animal. In our laboratory, Black has shown that sulfaguanadine inhibits the growth of rats given the known synthetic vitamins. More work is necessary to explain this effect completely. On the other hand, we have the very interesting results of Williams on the interrelation of various vitamins on yeast. He states that a balance, or even an antagonism, between various nutrilites is repeatedly observed. Further studies in this field may not elucidate the fundamental mechanisms, but I am sure such information will be very helpful in our understanding of complete nutrition.

BIBLIOGRAPHY

1. EIJKMAN, C., Arch. path. Anat., **149**:187, 1897.
2. EIJKMAN, C., Arch. Hyg., **58**:150, 1906.
3. HART, E. B.; MCCOLLUM, E. V.; STEENBOCK, H.; and HUMPHREY, G C., Wisconsin Agric. Exper. Sta. Res. Bull. 17 (1911).
4. HART, E. B.; STEENBOCK, H.; HUMPHREY, G. C.; and HULCE, R. S., J. Biol. Chem., **62**:315, 1924.
5. BOAS, M. A., Biochem. J., **21**:712, 1927.
6. PARSONS, H. T., and KELLY, E., J. Biol. Chem., **100**:645, 1933.
7. GYÖRGY, P.; ROSE, C. S.; EAKIN, R. E.; SNELL, E. E.; and WILLIAMS, R. J., Science, **93**:477, 1941.
8. FUNK, C., J. Physiol., **43**:395, 1911.
9. HOPKINS, F. G., J. Physiol., **44**:425, 1912.
10. SHERMAN, H. C., and SMITH, S. L., The vitmains, p. 20. 2d ed. New York: Chemical Catalog Co., 1931.
11. ROLLESTON, H. D., The endocrine organs in health and disease. London: Oxford Univ. Press, 1936.
12. BAUMANN, C. A., and MOORE, T., Biochem. J., **33**:1639, 1939.
13. KOZELKA, F. L.; HART, E. B.; and BOHSTEDT, G., J. Biol. Chem., **100**:715, 1933.
14. GROLLMAN, A., and FIROR, W. M., J. Nutrition, **8**:569, 1934.
15. SEIDELL, A., J. Indust. & Engin. Chem., **13**:72, 1921.
16. GREEN, H. N., Biochem. J., **28**:16, 1934.
17. SURE, B.; KIK, M. C.; BUCHANAN, K. S.; HARRELSON, R. T., JR.; and THEIS, R. M., Arkansas Agric. Exper. Sta. Bull. 373 (1939).
18. CROOK, E. M., Biochem. J., **35**:226, 1941.
19. JAMES, W. O.; JAMES, G. M.; and BUNTING, A. H., Biochem. J., **35**:588, 1941.
20. PRESNELL, A. K., J. Biol. Chem., **121**:5, 1937.
21. WILLIAMS, R. J., Biol. Rev., **16**:49, 1941.
22. BIRCH, T. W., and MANN, P. J. G., Biochem. J., **28**:622, 1934.
23. WARBURG, O., and CHRISTIAN, W., Biochem. Z., **254**:438, 1932.
24. AXELROD, A. E.; SOBER, H. A.; and ELVEHJEM, C. A., J. Biol. Chem., **134**:749, 1940; and AXELROD, A. E., and ELVEHJEM, C. A., J. Biol. Chem., **140**:725, 1941.
25. SNELL, E. E.; STRONG, F. M.; and PETERSON, W. H., Biochem. J., **31**:1789, 1937.
26. PETT, L. B., Biochem. J., **30**:1438, 1936.
27. LIPMANN, F., Nature, **143**:436, 1939.

28. LWOFF, A., and LWOFF, M., Proc. Roy. Soc., London, **122**:352, 1937.
29. KNIGHT, B. C. J. G., Biochem. J., **31**:731, 1937.
30. MUELLER, J. H., J. Biol. Chem., **120**:219, 1937.
31. KOHN, H. I.; KLEIN, J. R.; and DANN, W. J., Biochem. J., **33**:1432, 1939.
32. SAUNDERS, F.; DORFMAN, A.; and KOSER, S. A., J. Biol. Chem., **138**:69, 1941.
33. MANN, P. J. G., and QUASTEL, J. H., Biochem. J., **35**:502, 1941.
34. GREEN, D. E.; HERBERT, D.; and SUBRAHMANYAN, V., J. Biol. Chem., **138**: 327, 1941.
35. SILVERMAN, M., and WERKMAN, C. H., J. Biol. Chem., **138**:35, 1941.
36. GREEN, D. E.; WESTERFELD, W. W.; VENNESLAND, B.; and KNOX, W. E., J. Biol. Chem., **140**:683, 1941.
37. HALLIDAY, N., J. Nutrition, **16**:285, 1938.
38. MCHENRY, E. W., and GAVIN, G., J. Biol. Chem., **138**:471, 1941.
39. PRATT, E. F., and WILLIAMS, R. J., J. Gen. Physiol., **22**:637, 1939.
40. ALLISON, F. E.; HOOVER, S. R.; and BURK, D., Science, **78**:217, 1933.
41. FRIEDMAN, I., and MATTILL, H. A., Am. J. Physiol., **131**:595, 1941.
42. PETERS, R. A., Chemistry and industry, **59**:373, 1940.

COCARBOXYLASE

SEVERO OCHOA
Department of Pharmacology, Washington University School of Medicine, St. Louis

IN 1911 Neuberg and Karczag (1) reported the presence in yeast of carboxylase, an enzyme which catalyzed the decarboxylation of pyruvic acid to acetaldehyde and carbon dioxide; the crude enzyme also attacked other α-ketoacids (2, 3). Auhagen (4, 5) showed in 1932 that carboxylase required for its activity a thermostable coenzyme, cocarboxylase, which could be removed from yeast

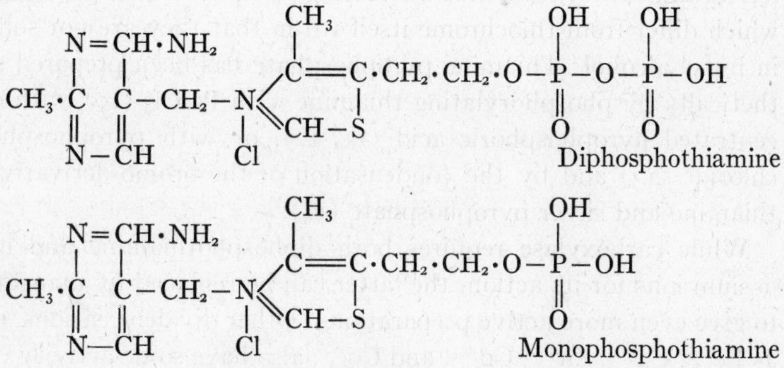

```
                                  CH3                    OH     OH
   N=CH·NH2                       |                      |      |
   |    |                       /C==C·CH2·CH2·O-P-O-P-OH
CH3·C   C-CH2-N<                  |                      ||     ||
   ||   ||         |  \CH-S                              O      O
   N-CH            Cl                                 Diphosphothiamine
```

```
                                  CH3                    OH
   N=CH·NH2                       |                      |
   |    |                       /C==C·CH2·CH2·O-P-OH
CH3·C   C-CH2-N<                  |                      ||
   ||   ||         |  \CH-S                              O
   N—CH            Cl                                 Monophosphothiamine
```

Fig. 1

by washing with alkaline phosphate; he also demonstrated the presence of cocarboxylase in animal tissues. Simola (6) observed in the same year that there was a decreased content of cocarboxylase in the tissues of animals suffering from a deficiency of the vitamin B complex. In 1937 Lohmann and Schuster (7) isolated cocarboxylase from yeast as the crystalline hydrochloride and demonstrated that it was a pyrophosphoric ester of vitamin B_1.[1] In the following pages cocarboxylase will be referred to as "thiamine pyrophosphate" or "diphosphothiamine." One of the two molecules of phosphoric acid in diphosphothiamine (Fig. 1) is easily hydrolyzable; it is split off

[1] Kinnersley and Peters (8) observed in 1928 that there was a form of thiamine in yeast which, unlike free thiamine, was precipitated by lead acetate.

in 15 minutes by hydrolysis in 1.0 NHCl at 100°, and more slowly by the action of phosphatases prepared from kidney. The resulting compound (thiamine monophosphate) will not function as cocarboxylase. The second phosphoric acid molecule is difficult to hydrolyze, although it is removed after long incubation with phosphatase preparations when thiamine can be isolated from the reaction mixture. Upon saponification with alkali the two molecules of phosphoric acid are partly split off as inorganic pyrophosphate. When split by Williams' sulfite treatment, diphosphothiamine yields the same pyrimidine sulphonic acid as does thiamine together with thiazole pyrophosphate (7). Owing to esterification of the alcoholic group of the thiazole, the thiamine phosphates do not give the formaldehyde-azo reaction of free thiamine; but, by oxidation with alkaline ferricyanide, they form blue fluorescing phosphorylated thiochromes which differ from thiochrome itself (9) in that they are not soluble in butyl alcohol. Thiamine pyrophosphate has been prepared synthetically by phosphorylating thiamine with $POCl_3$ (10), with concentrated pyrophosphoric acid (11, 12), or with pyrophosphoryl chloride (13) and by the condensation of the bromo-derivative of thiamine and silver pyrophosphate (14).

While carboxylase requires both diphosphothiamine and magnesium ions for its action, the latter can be replaced by manganese to give even more active preparations. Other divalent cations, such as Fe^{++}, Ca^{++}, Zn^{++}, Cd^{++}, and Co^{++}, also have some activity (15). Carboxylase has recently been obtained in a highly purified form by Green, Herbert, and Subrahmanyan (15) and by Kubowitz and Lütgens (16) and has been found to be a protein-diphosphothiamine-magnesium compound. The molecular weight of the protein portion is given by Kubowitz and Lütgens as 75,000. The three components are firmly united between pH 5 and pH 6 but dissociate at pH higher than 8.0. Diphosphothiamine is apparently attached to the enzyme protein in part through its pyrophosphate group. Both adenosine triphosphate (17) and thiazole pyrophosphate (18) inhibit carboxylase, presumably by competing with diphosphothiamine for the enzyme protein. The mechanism of action of cocarboxylase is still unknown. Weil-Malherbe (19) proposed a hypothesis based on the mechanism of decarboxylation postulated by Langenbeck (20), but

Stern and Melnick (13) could find no evidence in favor of a Langenbeck cycle involving the amino group of diphosphothiamine.

Although both thiamine and monophosphothiamine are inactive as cocarboxylase, they can increase the effectiveness of the latter in certain preparations of alkaline-washed yeast. The pyrimidine portion of thiamine produces the same effect, provided that its amino group is intact (21). This "activation" seems to be due to inhibition of a yeast phosphatase which deposphorylates diphosphothiamine (22, 23), or to combination with proteins which convert diphosphothiamine into an inactive compound (24), or possibly to both causes. The effect seems to have no physiological significance. Nevertheless, the "activation" has proved of value in a method using yeast for the separate determination of cocarboxylase and thiamine in biological materials (25).

The discovery that cocarboxylase is a thiamine derivative was of enormous significance, since the work of R. A. Peters and his associates in Oxford (26, 27) had shown that thiamine is concerned with the metabolism of pyruvic acid in animal tissues. This work was confirmed by Sherman and Elvehjem (28). Apparently, animal tissues and certain bacteria do not decarboxylate pyruvic acid to acetaldehyde and carbon dioxide, as yeast does, but by a process in which the decarboxylation is accompanied by dehydrogenation. The simplest reaction is an oxidative decarboxylation of pyruvic acid to acetic acid and carbon dioxide (29, 30); anaerobically, two molecules of pyruvic acid may react by dismutation to give lactic acid, acetic acid, and carbon dioxide (31, 32, 33, 29, 30, 34). In most animal tissues pyruvic acid is completely oxidized to carbon dioxide and water (35, 36). Green *et al.* (37) have reported quite recently that certain tissue preparations can bring about a pure decarboxylation of pyruvic and α-ketoglutaric acids.

Lipmann showed in 1937 (29) that dry acetone preparations of lactic acid bacteria (*Lactobacillus delbrückii*), which catalyze the oxidative decarboxylation as well as the dismutation of pyruvic acid, could be inactivated by washing with alkaline phosphate and reactivated by the addition of diphosphothiamine but not by free thiamine. In animal tissues, likewise, thiamine pyrophosphate, and not thiamine, is the active agent in pyruvate oxidation.

The main object of this paper is to make a study of the role of diphosphothiamine in animal-tissue metabolism, a study which can conveniently be divided into the following sections: (1) the distribution of thiamine and diphosphothiamine in normal and polyneuritic tissues; (2) the enzymatic phosphorylation of thiamine; (3) the active form of thiamine in pyruvic acid oxidation; (4) the pyruvic acid oxidation system; and (5) the metabolic function of diphosphothiamine.

DIPHOSPHOTHIAMINE IN TISSUES

Ochoa and Peters (25) determined thiamine and thiamine pyrophosphate in the tissues of rats and pigeons by a carboxylase method based on the activation of cocarboxylase by thiamine, previously mentioned. They found that all the tissues examined, including brain, skeletal muscle, liver, and heart, contained much more thiamine pyrophosphate than thiamine. Thus, brain and liver contained little or no free thiamine, whereas about 70 per cent of the total thiamine in muscle and heart was thiamine pyrophosphate. Since thiamine monophosphate "activates" cocarboxylase just as thiamine does, it was possible that the noncocarboxylase fraction in muscle tissues might be partly or entirely thiamine monophosphate. In fact, no free thiamine could be detected in pigeon-breast muscle; the whole of the thiamine extracted from it was found to be precipitated with lead acetate and to yield a butyl alcohol–insoluble thiochrome (38). Westenbrink and Goudsmit (39), who determined thiamine and its phosphoric esters by a thiochrome method, found very little thiamine in the muscles of rats and pigeons (cf. 40).

In thiamine deficiency the quantity of diphosphothiamine in the tissues is markedly decreased. Administration of thiamine to deficient animals leads to a large accumulation of thiamine and a marked increase of diphosphothiamine in the liver within 30 minutes; little increase of either compound occurs in brain, muscle, and heart in this time. However, when polyneuritic pigeons received small daily doses of thiamine for 3 days, the content of thiamine pyrophosphate of these tissues approached the normal values, whereas it was well below normal in the liver, as if the other tissues had replenished their diphosphothiamine stores at the expense of the diphosphothiamine previously stored by the liver (25). The lowest level of diphosphothiamine in pigeon brain (average 0.4 μg. per gram of tissue) is found in animals with symptoms of acute beriberi, whereas the brain of birds maintained on a diet of polished rice for 25 days, but not yet showing symptoms, contained an average of 1.2 μg. of diphosphothiamine (as against 3.0 μg. for normal brain). It is worth recalling, in this connection, that, whereas the brain of the former animals shows a catatorulin effect (*in vitro* activation of oxygen uptake, with pyruvate as substrate, upon addition of thiamine), the brain of the latter does not. Thus the appearance of nervous symptoms seems to be associated with the lowering of the diphosphothiamine content of the brain below a certain level when oxidation of pyruvic acid can apparently no longer be maintained at the necessary rate.

Results similar to those just discussed were independently obtained by Westenbrink and Goudsmit (39) with the thiochrome method. The Dutch workers added the important observation that administration of thiamine to polyneuritic animals produced, in a short time, a large increase of both thiamine and diphosphothiamine in the kidney as well as in the liver, an observation which was confirmed in Oxford (41). The fact that most of the thiamine in animal tissues is present in the form of its pyrophosphoric ester was subsequently confirmed by other workers (42, 43, 44, 45, 46, 47).

According to Goodhart and Sinclair (48), diphosphothiamine is present in nucleated blood cells, including nucleated red cells, but is absent from blood plasma, which contains only small amounts of unphosphorylated thiamine. The blood diphosphothiamine is decreased in thiamine deficiency (48). Cerebrospinal fluid contains thiamine (but not diphosphothiamine) in concentrations of the same order as in blood plasma (49, 50).

ENZYMATIC PHOSPHORYLATION OF THIAMINE

The work discussed in the previous section shows that liver and kidney phosphorylate thiamine to thiamine pyrophosphate *in vivo*. Earlier observations had indicated that such a phosphorylation could be achieved *in vitro* by yeast and by some animal tissues (9, 51, 52, 53, 54). Ochoa (55) found, in *in vitro* experiments, that the liver is the most active tissue as regards phosphorylation of thiamine; brain and muscle are much less so. Synthesis of diphosphothiamine from added thiamine readily occurs in various preparations of respiring liver from thiamine-deficient pigeons. Figure 2 shows the time curve of such a synthesis with liver brei and slices respiring in phosphate solution. The synthesis stops after about 30 minutes and is replaced, when the rate of respiration begins to fall, by a gradual breakdown of the diphosphothiamine formed.

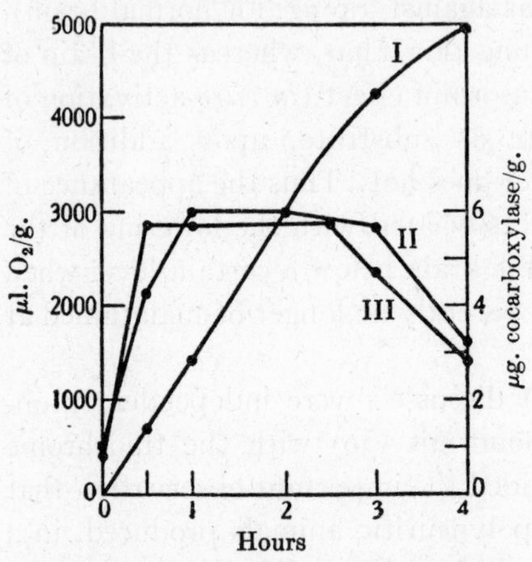

FIG. 2.—Phosphorylation of thiamine in liver from pigeons fed on polished rice for 25 days (no symptoms yet). Liver tissue suspended in Ringer phosphate; 10 μg. of thiamine hydrochloride added at time 0. Curve *I*, O_2 uptake at 28° (brei); pH 8.5. Curve *II*, change in diphosphothiamine at 28° (brei); pH 8.5. Curve *III*, change in diphosphothiamine at 38° (slices); pH 7.3. Gas O_2. (From Ochoa [55].)

The synthesis of diphosphothiamine requires that the synthesizing tissue be actively respiring, and there is little or no synthesis in the absence of oxygen. Iodoacetic acid is strongly inhibitory, but fluoride inhibits only slightly. The synthetic reaction has an optimum at about pH 8.5. The amount of diphosphothiamine synthesized by the liver rarely surpasses that normally present in the tissue; and, consequently, little synthesis can be observed with tissue of normal animals (55).

Goodhart and Sinclair (48) found that the blood of thiamine-deficient pigeons synthesized diphosphothiamine from added thiamine *in vitro*, and concluded that all nucleated cells are able to effect the synthesis to a greater or lesser extent. Various bacteria have been found to phosphorylate thiamine to thiamine pyrophosphate (56, 30). Ochoa and Rossiter (41) and Ferrebee (57) could find no support for a claim by Laszt (58) that the adrenal cortex is essential for the phosphorylation of thiamine.

The mechanism of phosphorylation of thiamine to thiamine pyrophosphate has been elucidated with yeast preparations by Lipton and Elvehjem (59) and by Weil-Malherbe (17). Phosphorylation occurs by transfer of the labile phosphate groups of adenosine triphosphate to thiamine or thiamine monophosphate. However, just as with animal tissues, only very small amounts of diphosphothiamine are formed, of the order necessary to saturate the carboxylase present; this is unfortunate, as it makes it impossible to study the reaction in detail. Both of the known reactions which cause a phosphorylation of adenylic acid or of adenosine diphosphate to adenosine triphosphate can cause a synthesis of diphosphothiamine in yeast when thiamine and catalytic amounts of adenine nucleotide (adenylic acid, adenosine polyphosphate) are present. Thus, synthesis has been obtained by using phosphoglyceric or phosphopyruvic acid as phosphate donor (59, 17), or in connection with the dehydrogenation of triose phosphate (59), a reaction which causes phosphorylation of adenylic acid or adenosine diphosphate with uptake of inorganic phosphate (60).

It would seem that the aerobic synthesis of diphosphothiamine in animal tissues occurs only after the phosphorylation of adenylic acid to adenosine polyphosphate; if so, the synthesis should be associated with the oxidation of triose phosphate or of pyruvic acid. This seems probable in view of the recent work on the mechanism of aerobic phosphorylation, which will be discussed later.

Brain, muscle, liver, and kidney contain enzymes which dephosphorylate diphosphothiamine (55), liver and kidney being the most active of the four. When liver preparations are incubated *in vitro*, the concentration of diphosphothiamine is maintained at the original level for long periods, provided that the tissue is respiring actively, but it decreases when oxygen is withdrawn or when the rate of respiration falls (55).

THE ACTIVE FORM OF THIAMINE IN PYRUVIC ACID OXIDATION

Lohmann and Schuster (7) observed that cocarboxylase cured polyneuritis, and they claimed that it was as effective as thiamine in activating the oxidation of pyruvic acid by brain slices of thiamine-deficient pigeons. This claim could not be confirmed in Oxford, where diphosphothiamine was found to be much less active than thiamine when small concentrations of the catalysts were used with brain brei (53) and slices (38; cf. also 30). However, by using finely ground preparations (dispersions) of brain of polyneuritic pigeons, it could finally be proved that diphosphothiamine is the physiologically active substance (38). In these preparations thiamine has either no activity or much less activity than diphosphothiamine (Fig. 3). Thiamine monophosphate is not more active than thiamine itself.

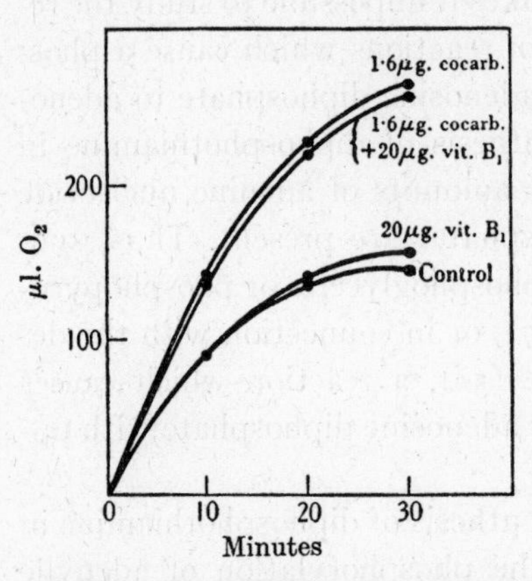

FIG. 3.—Comparison of the effects of thiamine and diphosphothiamine on the oxidation of pyruvic acid in dispersions of brain from thiamine-deficient pigeons. Air, 38°. (From Banga, Ochoa, and Peters [38].)

These experiments indicate that the failure of diphosphothiamine to display full activity in brain brei and slices must be due to its poor penetration into the tissue, so that access to the enzyme is rendered difficult. Such an explanation had already been tentatively advanced by Peters (53). It remained to be explained why thiamine is active in brei, slices, and some dispersions. The answer is that such activity is subsequent to its phosphorylation to thiamine pyrophosphate. Table 1 illustrates an experiment with a brain dispersion in which thiamine had little, although definite, activity. In the presence of 10 μg. of thiamine, 0.05 μg. of diphosphothiamine was synthesized in 40 minutes. In a separate experiment (lower part of Table 1) it was observed that either 10 μg. of thiamine or 0.05 μg. of diphosphothiamine activated the oxygen uptake of deficient brain dispersions, with pyruvate as substrate, approximately to the same extent. This was especially true in the period from 20 to 30 minutes. The effect of thiamine rose sharply in the first 20 minutes, supposedly as the amount of diphosphothiamine formed increased, whereas the effect of diphosphothiamine was maximum from the beginning. Barron and Lyman (30) observed that in bacteria which can phosphorylate thiamine the unphosphorylated vitamin was as active as diphosphothiamine in stimulating pyruvate oxidation but that only diphosphothiamine was active in bacteria that are unable to phosphorylate thiamine.

TABLE 1

PHOSPHORYLATION AND ACTIVITY OF THIAMINE ON PYRUVIC ACID OXIDATION IN DISPERSIONS OF BRAIN FROM THIAMINE-DEFICIENT PIGEONS

One and one-half cc. of undialyzed dispersion (320 mg. of brain) to 2.0 cc. with additions including phosphate buffer pH 7.3, pyruvate, and fumarate. O_2, 38°. (From Banga, Ochoa, and Peters [38].)

A

	Micrograms of Diphosphothiamine
Sample incubated 40 minutes without thiamine	0.16
Sample incubated 40 minutes with 10 μg. of thiamine	0.21
Diphosphothiamine synthesis	0.05

B

Time Period in Minutes	Rate of O_2 Uptake (Cubic Millimeters per Hour over Control without Coenzyme)	
	In Sample with 10 μg. of Thiamine	In Sample with 0.05 μg. of Diphosphothiamine
0–10	60	190
10–20	186	130
20–30	100	114

The effect of increasing concentrations of diphosphothiamine is shown in Figure 4. Under optimum conditions 1 mole of diphosphothiamine caused the uptake of 1,500 moles of oxygen per minute with pyruvate as substrate. The minimum effective concentration of diphosphothiamine was 5×10^{-9} M. Maximum effects were obtained with 1.5×10^{-7} M. The latter concentration corresponds to that found in the brain of "rice-fed" pigeons without symptoms (1.2 μg. per gram of brain), so that the pyruvic acid oxidase in 1 gm. of brain must be saturated when about 1 μg. of diphosphothiamine is present.

The dissociation constant of the diphosphothiamine-pyruvate oxidase complex in brain, calculated from the data in Figure 4 by the method of Lineweaver and Burk (61), is 0.6 × 10^{-7} *M* per liter. This is a lower value than that found by Lipmann (2.7 × 10^{-6}), at approximately the same pH (7.3), for the pyruvate dehydrogenase of *L. delbrückii* (62).

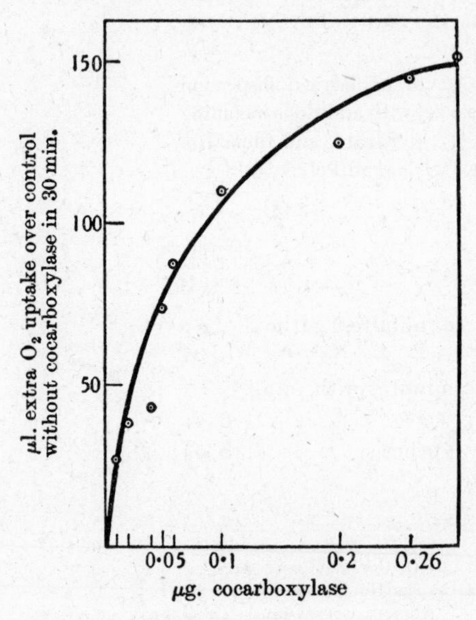

FIG. 4.—Effect of increasing concentrations of added diphosphothiamine on the rat of oxidation of pyruvic acid in dispersions of brain from thiamine-deficient pigeons. O_2, 38°. (From Banga, Ochoa, and Peters [38].)

Diphosphothiamine metabolism.—The urine contains neither diphospho- nor monophosphothiamine (48, 43, 63, 64, 65). When these substances are injected into human beings (64) or rats (65), an increased amount of thiamine is excreted in the urine. Borsook *et al.* (66) injected thiamine containing radioactive sulfur in the thiazole ring into human subjects and found that there was a rapid increase in the urinary excretion of thiamine but that no radioactivity appeared in the urine until the second day after the injection; destruction of thiamine in the tissues was indicated by the appearance of radioactive neutral sulfur compounds and inorganic sulfates in the urine and feces.

Evidence discussed in previous sections indicates that thiamine reaching the blood stream from the intestine is taken up mainly by the liver and kidney, where it is phosphorylated and stored as diphosphothiamine (25, 39). All tissues, but mainly the liver and kidney, can dephosphorylate diphosphothiamine (55, 63) and supply free thiamine to the blood; this is transported in the plasma (48) to other tissues, which rephosphorylate it more slowly (25), or it is excreted in the urine. Phosphorylated thiamine would not pass easily across cell membranes (38).

An increased catabolism of thiamine and diphosphothiamine in experimental hyperthyroidism is indicated by increased thiamine requirements and by a decrease of diphosphothiamine in the tissues (67, 68, 69).

According to Abderhalden (70), animal tissues possess some ability to synthesize thiamine from a mixture of its pyrimidine and thiazole components.

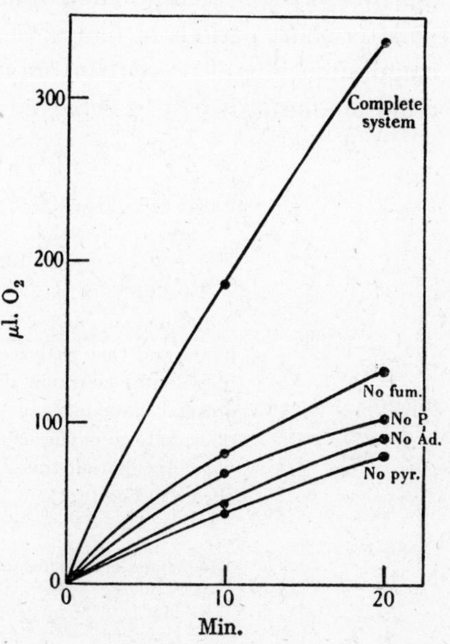

Fig.5.—Effect of phosphate (0.05 M), fumarate (0.005 M), and adenylic acid (0.00014 M) on the oxidation of pyruvic acid by dialyzed dispersions from normal pigeon brain. One and one-half cc. of enzyme (dialyzed 2 hours) to 2.0 cc. with additions including 0.1 mg. of Mg^{++} (as $MgCl_2$). The complete system contains enzyme + Mg^{++} + phosphate (*P*) + fumarate (*fum.*) + adenylic acid (*Ad.*) + pyruvic acid (*pyr.*). The brain dispersion contains optimal amounts of diphosphothiamine. Air, 38°. (From Banga, Ochoa, and Peters [71].)

THE PYRUVIC ACID OXIDATION SYSTEM OF BRAIN

A study of dialyzed brain dispersions (71) has shown that at least five substances are essential components of the pyruvate oxidation system: (*a*) diphosphothiamine; (*b*) a C_4-dicarboxylic acid, such as succinic, fumaric, or malic acid (cf. also 72, 73); (*c*) inorganic phosphate; (*d*) adenylic acid or adenosine polyphosphate; and (*e*) magnesium or manganese ions (74). Diphosphopyridine nucleotide is probably another component of the system, but the evidence for this is not conclusive (71).

Evidence that diphosphothiamine is essential has already been presented above. That a C_4-dicarboxylic acid, inorganic phosphate, and adenylic acid are necessary is shown in Figure 5. Concentrations of inorganic phosphate as high as 0.05–0.1 M are required to secure an optimum rate of pyruvate oxidation; all the other components of the system are active in catalytic amounts.

After short periods of dialysis against dilute potassium chloride, magnesium is still present in brain dispersions in practically optimum amounts; it can be removed, to a large extent, by precipitation with an excess of pyrophosphate, which can subsequently be removed by dialysis. After this is done the rate of oxidation of pyruvate is greatly decreased, but it is brought back to normal by addition of magnesium or manganese salts.[2] This is illustrated in Table 2.

TABLE 2

EFFECT OF MAGNESIUM AND MANGANESE IONS ON PYRUVIC ACID OXIDATION IN DISPERSIONS OF BRAIN FROM NORMAL PIGEONS

Dispersion treated with sodium pyrophosphate and then dialyzed 8 hours. The samples contained brain dispersion (containing optimal amounts of diphosphothiamine), phosphate, adenylic acid, fumarate, and pyruvate. Incubation time, 30 minutes; air, 38°. (From Ochoa [74].)

Micrograms of Mg^{++} Added (as $MgCl_2$)	Micrograms of Mn^{++} Added (as $MnCl_2$)	Cubic Millimeters of Oxygen Uptake
0	0	175
100	0	400
150	0	455
0	100	345

The effect of adenylic acid is peculiar in that it not only increases the oxidative removal of pyruvate but makes its oxidation more complete, as shown by the higher ratio of oxygen consumed to pyruvate removed (71). In the absence of added adenylic acid, py-

[2] Annau and Erdös (72) reported an activation by Mg^{++} of the dehydrogenation of pyruvic acid in washed muscle.

ruvic acid seems to be only slowly decarboxylated and dehydrogenated to acetic acid and carbon dioxide. The necessity of adenylic acid or adenosine polyphosphate for pyruvate oxidation strongly suggested that a cycle of phosphorylation was involved.

It was found by Lipmann (29, 75, 76, 77, 62) in an analysis of the pyruvic acid oxidation system of *L. delbrückii*, that, in addition to the enzyme protein, the following are components: (*a*) diphosphothiamine; (*b*) inorganic phosphate[3] or arsenate; (*c*) magnesium, manganese, or cobalt ions; and (*d*) alloxazine-adenine dinucleotide.[4] We have seen that the first three are components of the pyruvate oxidation system of brain as well; alloxazine-adenine dinucleotide is also probably essential in brain, but this has not yet been demonstrated. There are, however, marked differences between the bacterial and the brain systems. The principal differences are the following: (*a*) The bacterial system catalyzes the oxidative decarboxylation of pyruvic acid to acetic acid and carbon dioxide, whereas oxidation of pyruvate in animal tissues is more complete. (*b*) In the *L. delbrückii* system electrons are transferred to molecular oxygen through the mediation of its autoxidizable flavin component, whereas in animal tissues (and in some bacteria [80]) reaction with molecular oxygen is mediated by the cytochrome-cytochrome oxidase system (*c*) Neither a C_4-dicarboxylic acid nor "adenine nucleotide" is a component of the *L. delbrückii* system. (*d*) The concentration of inorganic phosphate required for optimum activity is about 0.01 M in *L. delbrückii* (29, 62) and as high as 0.1 M in brain (71). And (*e*) the lower value for brain of the dissociation constant of the enzyme-prosthetic group complex.

In brain preparations pyruvic acid and other α-ketoacids can also be broken down, to some extent, by dehydrogenation to carbon dioxide and the next lower fatty acid; and, in fact, this is the only change that α-ketobutyric acid undergoes (81). Pyruvic acid probably reacts in this way only when adenylic acid is absent. Long (82) has observed that oxidation of α-ketobutyric acid by dialyzed brain

[3] Inorganic phosphate is not required for the action of yeast carboxylase (62) but seems to be necessary for the breakdown of pyruvic acid to acetylmethylcarbinol and carbon dioxide in *Aerobacter* (78).

[4] Still (79) has recently described the existence of a probably identical system in *Bacillus coli*.

dispersions requires inorganic phosphate (or arsenate) but needs neither C_4-dicarboxylic acids nor adenylic acid. Thus, there seems to be a system present in brain which is similar, if not identical, to that of *L. delbrückii*. Whether this system is an independent one or a part of the system of complete oxidation remains undecided (83). Long (36) has shown that about 20 per cent of the pyruvate removed by oxidation in brain brei can be accounted for as acetic acid.

TABLE 3

EFFECT OF DIPHOSPHOTHIAMINE ON PYRUVIC ACID OXIDATION AND ON THE ESTERIFICATION OF INORGANIC PHOSPHATE WITH HEXOSE MONOPHOSPHATE AND GLUCOSE IN DIALYZED DISPERSIONS OF BRAIN FROM THIAMINE-DEFICIENT PIGEONS

The samples contained brain dispersion, Mg^{++}, phosphate, adenylic acid, fumarate, pyruvate, 0.02 M sodium fluoride, and phosphate acceptor. Incubation time, 30 minutes; air, 38°. (From Ochoa, J. Biol. Chem., **138**, 751, 1941.)

Oxidation of pyruvic acid causes a phosphorylation of hexose monophosphate or of glucose to hexose diphosphate.

Phosphate Acceptor	Micrograms of Diphosphothiamine Added	Cubic Millimeters of Oxygen Uptake	Milligrams of Pyruvic Acid Removed	Milligrams of Phosphorus Esterified
Hexose monophosphate (Embden ester)	0	115	0.42	0.33
	2	191	.86	.53
	0	137	.52	.38
	2	212	0.94	.65
Glucose	0	66	....	.25
	2	188	....	0.76

The enzymatic oxidation of pyruvic acid is coupled, both in *L. delbrückii* (75, 62) and in animal tissues, with a phosphorylation of adenylic acid to adenosine polyphosphate, followed by a transfer of the labile phosphate groups of the latter to various acceptors (84). In muscle preparations aerobic phosphorylation of glucose occurs only upon addition of hexokinase (85), an enzyme which catalyzes the transfer of phosphate from adenosine triphosphate to hexoses (86, 87). The relation of phosphorylation to oxidation of pyruvic acid in animal tissues was independently observed by Belitzer and Tsibakowa (88), by Colowick, Welch, and Cori (89), and by Ochoa (84). Diphosphothiamine is, of course, essential for this phosphorylation (Table 3).

With brain dispersions it has been found (84) that optimally four molecules of phosphate are esterified for each molecule of oxygen consumed. Half of this esterification is coupled with the primary dehydrogenation of pyruvate; the rest seems to be connected with the transfer of the electron pair mediated by C_4-dicarboxylic acids (84, 88). Oxidation of succinic to fumaric acid in tissues is known to be coupled with phosphorylation (73).

The connection of phosphorylation with dehydrogenation of pyruvate is interpreted by Lipmann (62, 90), in analogy with the coupling between phosphorylation and dehydrogenation of triose phosphate (60, 91), as due to addition of inorganic phosphate to the carbonyl group of pyruvic acid and oxidation of this compound to acetylphosphate (92). Further reaction involves transfer of phosphate from acetylphosphate to adenylic acid (77), forming acetic acid and adenosine polyphosphate. The phosphorylated intermediate in animal tissues is apparently not acetylphosphate (93), but there is little doubt that an analogous mechanism is in operation. The nature of the phosphorylation connected with oxidation of succinic acid, and possibly with the catalytic action of C_4-dicarboxylic acids during pyruvate oxidation, has not been elucidated.

METABOLIC FUNCTIONS OF DIPHOSPHOTHIAMINE

We may first inquire: "What is the primary function of diphosphothiamine?" We have seen that diphosphothiamine is essential for decarboxylation of pyruvic acid in yeast and for its oxidation in animal tissues and certain bacteria, a process which also involves decarboxylation. Through the agency of diphosphothiamine is probably evolved all the carbon dioxide of alcoholic fermentation and a large part of the carbon dioxide of respiration. Decarboxylation of other α-ketoacids by yeast, such as α-ketobutyric and α-ketovaleric acids, also requires diphosphothiamine (81). It would seem that diphosphothiamine is primarily concerned with the decarboxylation of α-ketonic acids in all living cells.[5]

[5] D. E Green (94) has recently reported that diphosphothiamine is involved in the enzymic condensation of two molecules of acetaldehyde to acetylmethylcarbinol, as well as in a reaction between pyruvic acid and acetaldehyde yielding carbon dioxide and acetylmethylcarbinol, both of which reactions occur in some tissue preparations. He believes that diphosphothiamine may primarily catalyze a (ketol) condensation of α-keto-acids to form unstable compounds which would undergo spontaneous decarboxylation.

There is now little support for the view that diphosphothiamine acts as a hydrogen carrier in biological systems through alternate oxidation and reduction of the quaternary thiazole nitrogen atom. Reduction of thiamine or diphosphothiamine with various agents, such as hydrogen activated with platinum or palladium, or hydrosulfite, has been shown by Lipmann (95, 96) and by Stern and Melnick (97) to yield a biologically inactive product. Barron and his associates (98) have observed that diphosphothiamine is more resistant than thiamine to reduction and reoxidation. Not only is the rate of reduction of diphosphothiamine, with either hydrosulfite or platinum and hydrogen, much slower than that of thiamine, but reduction of the two compounds is considerably slower than that of diphosphopyridine nucleotide (100). Whether or not thiamine can act in oxidation-reduction systems through its disulfide, as suggested by the recent work of Zima and Williams (101) and of Zima, Ritsert, and Moll (102), cannot yet be decided.

In different types of cells pyruvic acid is either decarboyxlated prior to its oxidation (or reduction) or decarboxylated and oxidized simultaneously. It has been shown (Gordon *et al.* [103]) that aldehyde oxidase is a flavoprotein with alloxazine-adenine dinucleotide as the prosthetic group, and also that this nucleotide is a component of the pyruvate dehydrogenase of *L. delbrückii* (76). The simultaneous occurrence of dehydrogenation and decarboxylation might be ascribed to the fact that such a reaction may be catalyzed by an enzyme consisting of a single protein with two prosthetic groups: diphosphothiamine and alloxazine-adenine dinucleotide, concerned with decarboxylation and dehydrogenation, respectively. This would explain the differences in pyruvate breakdown in various types of cells without ascribing more than a single function to diphosphothiamine.

The dismutation between two molecules of pyruvic acid to yield one molecule each of carbon dioxide, acetic acid, and lactic acid is a linked reaction involving the action of both pyruvic and lactic dehydrogenases. The flavin reduced by one molecule of pyruvic acid is reoxidized by a second pyruvic acid molecule instead of by molecular oxygen or by cytochrome. It is unknown whether diphosphopyridine nucleotide is involved in the primary dehydrogenation of pyruvic acid

Intermediary reactions in which diphosphothiamine is involved.—With one possible exception diphosphothiamine is known to participate in the reactions shown in Table 4. Reaction 1 occurs in brain brei and is activated by thiamine (81). A participation of diphosphothiamine in reaction 2, the synthesis of citric acid from pyruvic and oxaloacetic acids (104, 105), is supported by evidence from experiments both *in vitro* and with the intact animal. Sober, Lipton,

TABLE 4

SOME REACTIONS IN WHICH DIPHOSPHOTHIAMINE PARTICIPATES

	Reaction	Reference
1......	$CH_3\cdot CH_2\cdot CO\cdot COOH+O=CH_3\cdot CH_2\cdot COOH+CO_2$	Long and Peters (81)
2......	$\begin{array}{l}CH_2\cdot COOH\\ \vert\\ CO\cdot COOH\end{array}+O+CH_3\cdot CO\cdot COOH=\begin{array}{l}CH_2\cdot COOH\\ \vert\;\;OH\\ C\\ \vert\;\;COOH\\ CH_2\cdot COOH\end{array}+CO_2$	Sober, Lipton, and Elvehjem (106); Barron *et al.* (98, 99)
3......	$COOH\cdot CH_2\cdot CH_2\cdot CO\cdot COOH+O=\begin{array}{l}CH_2\cdot COOH\\ \vert\\ CH_2\cdot COOH\end{array}+CO_2$	Simola (110); Barron *et al.* (109)
4......	$2CH_3\cdot CO\cdot COOH+O_2=\begin{array}{l}CO\cdot CH_3\\ \vert\\ CH_2\cdot COOH\end{array}+2\ CO_2+H_2O$	Barron *et al.* (99)
5......	$CO_2+CH_3\cdot CO\cdot COOH=COOH\cdot CH_2\cdot CO\cdot COOH$ (?)	Krebs and Eggleston (113); Smyth (115)
6......	$CH_3\cdot COOH+2O_2=2CO_2+2H_2O$	Quastel and Webley (117)

and Elvehjem (106) reported that the urinary excretion of citric acid is low in thiamine-deficient rats and is greatly increased by administration of thiamine, and Barron and his associates (98, 99) observed that thiamine increased the synthesis of citric acid *in vitro* by tissues of avitaminotic rats.[6] They also reported (99, 109) an *in vitro* effect

[6] Barron and his co-workers (99) have also reported an activation by thiamine of the synthesis of α-ketoglutaric (107, 108) and succinic acids in rat-liver slices. This may be a consequence of the increased formation of citric acids or of other C_6 acids, but the mechanism of formation of α-ketoglutaric acid from pyruvic acid is not yet well understood.

of thiamine on reactions 3 and 4. Simola (110) had reported earlier that increased amounts of α-ketoglutaric acid are excreted in the urine of thiamine-deficient rats.

Reactions 1 and 3 are oxidative decarboxylations of an α-ketoacid; and oxidative decarboxylation of pyruvic acid is certainly involved in reactions 2 and 4, although the exact mechanisms are unknown. Reaction 4 may involve a condensation to acetopyruvic acid, followed by oxidative decarboxylation to acetoacetic acid. Reactions 2 and 3 constitute individual reactions of the "citric acid cycle" of Krebs (105, 111, 112).

Krebs and Eggleston (113) have recently suggested that the Wood and Werkman reaction (114), i.e., the carboxylation of pyruvate to oxaloacetate (Table 4, reaction 5), may be the only reaction of pyruvic acid in which diphosphothiamine participates. This suggestion was based on theoretical considerations and on the observation that thiamine accelerated the utilization of pyruvate by liver but not by muscle of thiamine-deficient pigeons.[7] The contention that this occurred because "the vitamin takes part in a reaction which occurs in liver but is of no major importance in muscle" overlooked the possibility that the diphosphothiamine content of muscle of beriberic pigeons might still be above the saturation level. This possibility is supported by the work of Ochoa and Peters (25), who found that, in thiamine deficiency in pigeons, diphosphothiamine decreased in muscle from a normal average value of 3.81 to 1.04 μg. per gram, as compared with a decrease from 3.00 to 0.40 μg. in brain and from 4.33 to 0.48 μg. in liver.

Smyth (115), working in Krebs's laboratory, found that dismutation of pyruvate by thiamine-deficient staphylococci was stimulated either by thiamine or by oxaloacetate or fumarate. This was interpreted as indicating that oxaloacetate is needed as a carrier for the dismutation and that the vitamin catalyzed its formation from pyruvate and carbon dioxide. According to this view, diphosphothiamine would merely be needed to secure a formation of the dicarboxylic acids that are required for pyruvate oxidation. This, however, is certainly not the case in animal tissues, since both diphos-

[7] However, Barron *et al.* (99) have recently reported that thiamine increases the oxidative utilization of pyruvate by diaphragm from thiamine-deficient rats.

phothiamine and a C_4-dicarboxylic acid are needed for the oxidation of pyruvate in the brain of thiamine-deficient animals (71, 99).[8]

Quastel and Webley (117) have shown that the oxidation of acetic acid to carbon dioxide and water (Table 4, reaction 6) by propionic acid bacteria is greatly accelerated by thiamine, although pyruvic acid does not seem to be an intermediate. This important finding is difficult to interpret until more is known of the mechanism and the chemical reactions involved in the oxidation of acetic acid.

Diphosphothiamine and carbohydrate metabolism.—Through its effect on pyruvic acid oxidation, diphosphothiamine may influence various phases of carbohydrate metabolism, since pyruvate oxidation causes the storage of a large amount of energy as adenosine triphosphate (84, 118). Thus, diphosphothiamine may be indirectly involved in the synthesis of glycogen from glucose (119) and in the conversion of fructose to glucose (120), reactions which require a preliminary phosphorylation of the sugar molecule. It is possible that an analogous mechanism is active in the intestinal absorption of sugars and in glucose resorption from the kidney tubules.

For similar reasons diphosphothiamine must also be essential for the synthesis of carbohydrate from lactic or pyruvic acid. This synthesis is probably a reversal of the glycolytic process in which all reactions but one, the dephosphorylation of phospho(enol)pyruvic acid (121), are reversible (122, 123). We do not know exactly how phosphopyruvic acid is formed in the synthetic reaction; its formation seems to be connected with oxidation of a dicarboxylic acid (124). Solomon *et al.* (125) have recently shown that when bicarbonate, containing the radioactive carbon isotope C^{11}, is given to rats along with nonradioactive lactate, the glycogen deposited in the liver contains radioactive carbon. They suggest that the isotope

[8] Krampitz and Werkman (116) have recently obtained a crude bacterial enzyme which catalyzes the reaction $COOH \cdot CH_2 \cdot CO \cdot COOH \rightarrow CO_2 + CH_3 \cdot CO \cdot COOH$; the enzyme requires Mg^{++} but no diphosphothiamine. The same preparation can oxidize pyruvic acid (to acetic acid $+CO_2$) in the presence of both diphosphothiamine and Mg^{++}; but, unlike Smyth, they find that oxaloacetate cannot replace diphosphothiamine. They point out that the synthesis of oxaloacetate from CO_2+pyruvate is probably catalyzed by the same enzyme that is active in the reverse reaction; but, as the ΔF of the fixation reaction is positive, an energy-yielding reaction may be required to bring it about, and diphosphothiamine might be necessary for the latter.

is first incorporated by the Wood and Werkman reaction into oxalo-acetate, which, after reduction to fumarate, might form phospho-pyruvate (as suggested by Lipmann [90]), some of which would con-

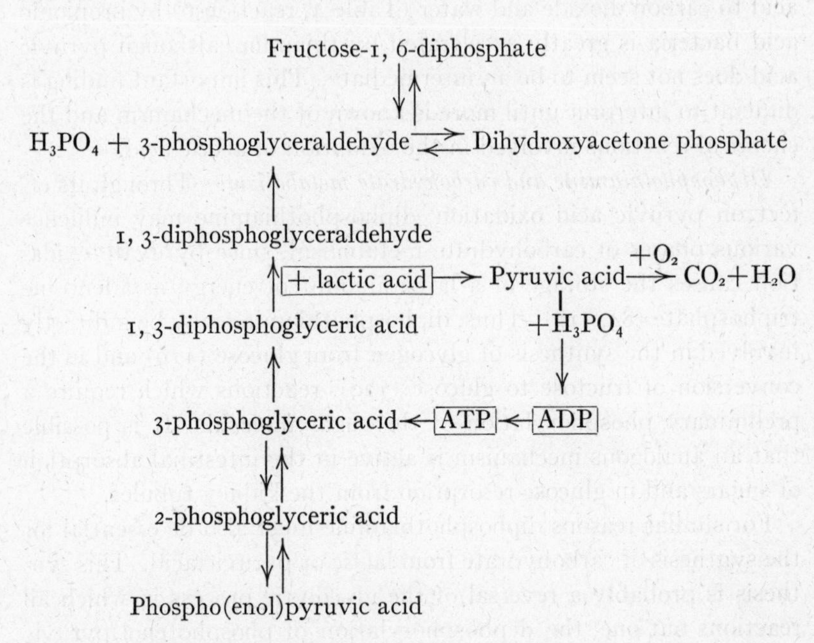

FIG. 6.—Diagrammatic representation of the oxido-reduction of glycolysis (3-phosphoglyceraldehyde + pyruvic acid + adenosine diphosphate + H_3PO_4 $\rightleftarrows$ 3-phosphoglyceric acid+lactic acid+adenosine triphosphate) as proceeding from right to left. The reaction starts by phosphorylation of 3-phosphoglyceric acid to 1, 3-diphosphoglyceric acid by adenosine triphosphate (adenosine triphosphate+3-phosphoglyceric acid $\rightleftarrows$ adenosine diphosphate+1, 3-diphosphoglyeric acid). Under aerobic conditions the pyruvic acid formed in the dismutation is oxidized, thereby rephosphorylating the adenosine diphosphate. Removal of adenosine diphosphate (ADP) and inorganic phosphate by phosphorylation to adenosine triphosphate (ATP), of pyruvic acid by oxidation, and of 3-glyceraldehyde phosphate, by the isomerase (formation of dihydroxacetone phosphate) and aldolase (condensation of glyceraldehyde phosphate+dihydroxacetone phosphate to hexose diphosphate) reactions, keeps the dismutation going to the left if an excess of 3-phosphoglyceric and lactic acids is present.

tain radioactive carbon in the carboxyl group. Thus, diphosphothiamine, if a catalyst for the Wood and Werkman reaction, might be directly involved in the synthesis of carbohydrate from pyruvic acid in the liver. Whether this is so or not, diphosphothiamine will take an indirect part in the synthesis, because reversion of the oxido-reduction between triose phosphate and pyruvate (122, 123, 60) is driven by energy-rich phosphate from adenosine triphosphate (123, 60), and the latter must be mainly regenerated by pyruvate oxidation. A diagrammatic representation of this is shown in Figure 6. Barron *et al.* (98, 99) have shown that the synthesis of carbohydrate from pyruvate is decreased in kidney slices of thiamine-deficient rats and restored to normal by the addition of thiamine.

Except for the well-established facts that lactic and pyruvic acids accumulate in the blood and tissues and that pyruvic acid and other α-keto acids are excreted in increased amounts in the urine during thiamine deficiency (126, 127, 128, 110, 129, 130), observations on the effect of thiamine on carbohydrate metabolism *in vivo* are of a rather conflicting nature (131). Reports on liver glycogen and blood sugar as affected by thiamine deficiency or thiamine administration have been contradictory, and very often no change from normal conditions has been indicated. There are a number of complicating factors in research of this nature, such as the inanition that accompanies thiamine deficiency and the possibility that, in some cases, deficiencies of other factors of the B complex may also be involved (131). It will often be difficult to obtain a degree of thiamine deficiency causing sufficient depression in pyruvate oxidation to produce deviations from normal liver glycogen or blood sugar values. Moreover, factors such as intestinal absorption of sugar and its storage as liver glycogen, which are probably affected in the same direction by a decreased oxidation of pyruvate, will affect the blood sugar level in different directions.

Since diphosphothiamine is a catalyst for the oxidation of pyruvic acid and can thus indirectly enhance carbohydrate utilization and storage, its effects on carbohydrate metabolism will somewhat parallel those of insulin. In this connection it may be of interest to note that Nitzescu and Ioanid (132) have recently reported a large increase of blood sugar in thiamine-deficient chickens and a decrease to normal a few hours after thiamine administration. When thiamine was given to normal chickens along with glucose (132), the rise in blood sugar was smaller and the return to normal values was more rapid than when glucose alone was given. There have also been reports that thiamine reinforces the effect of insulin on blood sugar (133). A decrease in brain and muscle glycogen has been reported in thiamine-deficient rats (134).

Other metabolic processes affected by diphosphothiamine.—McHenry and his associates (135, 136, 137) have shown, in nutritional experiments with rats and pigeons, that thiamine is necessary for the synthesis of fatty acids from carbohydrate; this action is probably secondary to its effect on pyruvate oxidation.

Diphosphothiamine is also indirectly involved in the synthesis of acetylcholine, which is known to be connected with pyruvate oxidation (138). Mann and Quastel (139) have demonstrated that the synthesis of acetylcholine by pigeon-brain slices, respiring in a pyruvate-containing medium, is decreased in thiamine deficiency and restored to normal by addition of thiamine. In a similar way, diphosphothiamine may be involved in other biological acetylations (90).

REFERENCES

1. Neuberg, C., and Karczag, L., Biochem. Ztschr., **36**:68, 76, 1911.
2. Neuberg, C., and Karczag, L., *ibid.*, **37**:170, 1911.
3. Neuberg, C., and Peterson, W. H., Biochem. Ztschr., **67**:32, 1914.
4. Auhagen, E., Ztschr. f. physiol. Chem., **204**:149, 1932; **209**, 20, 1932.
5. Auhagen, E., Biochem. Ztschr., **258**:330, 1933.
6. Simola, P. E., Biochem. Ztschr., **254**:229, 1932.
7. Lohmann, K., and Schuster, P., Biochem. Ztschr., **294**:188, 1937.
8. Kinnersley, H. W., and Peters, R. A., Biochem. J., **22**:419, 1928.
9. Kinnersley, H. W., and Peters, R. A., Chem. and Ind., **56**:447, 1937.
10. Stern, K. G., and Hofer, J. W., Enzymologia, **3**:82, 1937.
11. Weijlard, J., J. Am. Chem. Soc., **63**:1160, 1941.
12. Weijlard, J., and Tauber, H., J. Am. Chem. Soc., **60**:2263, 1938.
13. Stern, K. G., and Melnick, J. L., J. Biol. Chem., **131**:597, 1939.
14. Weil-Malherbe, H., Biochem. J., **34**:980, 1940.
15. Green, D. E.; Herbert, D.; and Subrahmanyan, V., J. Biol. Chem., **138**:327, 1941.
16. Kubowitz, F., and Lüttgens, W., Biochem. Ztschr., **307**:170, 1941.
17. Weil-Malherbe, H., Biochem. J., **33**:1997, 1939.
18. Buchman, E. R.; Heegaard, E.; and Bonner, J., Proc. Nat. Acad. Sc., **26**:561, 1940.
19. Weil-Malherbe, H., Nature, **145**:106, 1940.
20. Langenbeck, W., Ergebn. d. Enzymforsch., **2**:314, 1933.
21. Ochoa, S., Nature, **141**:831, 1938.

22. Westenbrink, H. G. K., and Van Dorp, D. A., Nature, **145**:465, 1940.
23. Westenbrink, H. G. K.; Van Dorp, D. A.; Gruber, M.; and Veldman, H., Enzymologia, **9**:73, 1940.
24. Lipton, M. A., and Elvehjem, C. A., J. Biol. Chem., **136**:637, 1940.
25. Ochoa, S., and Peters, R. A., Biochem. J., **32**:1501, 1938.
26. Peters, R. A., Lancet, **230**:1161, 1936.
27. Peters, R. A., Chem. Weekblad, **34**:442, 1937.
28. Sherman, W. C., and Elvehjem, C. A., Am. J. Physiol., **117**:142, 1936.
29. Lipmann, F., Enzymologia, **4**:65, 1937.
30. Barron, E. S. G., and Lyman, C. M., J. Biol. Chem., **127**:143, 1939.
31. Krebs, H. A., Biochem. J., **31**:661, 1937.
32. Krebs, H. A., and Johnson, W. A., Biochem. J., **31**:645, 1937.
33. Lipmann, F., Skandinav. Arch. f. Physiol., **76**:255, 1937.
34. Weil-Malherbe, H., Biochem. J., **31**:2202, 1937.
35. McGowan, G. K., Biochem. J., **31**:1627, 1937.
36. Long, C., Biochem. J., **32**:1711, 1938.
37. Green, D. E.; Westerfeld, W. W.; Vennesland, B.; and Knox, W. E., J. Biol. Chem., **140**:683, 1941.
38. Banga, I.; Ochoa, S.; and Peters, R. A., Biochem. J., **33**:1109, 1939.
39. Westenbrink, H. G. K., and Goudsmit, J., Enzymologia, **5**:307, 1938.
40. Ochoa, S., and Peters, R. A., Nature, **142**:356, 1938.
41. Ochoa, S., and Rossiter, R. J., J. Physiol., **97**:1P, 1940.
42. Hennessy, D. J., and Cerecedo, L. R., J. Am. Chem. Soc., **61**:179, 1939.
43. Ritsert, K., Klin. Wchnschr., **18**:1370, 1939.
44. Widenbauer, F., Klin. Wchnschr., **18**:1613, 1939.
45. Cedrangolo, F., Arch. di sc. biol. (Napoli), **26**:89, 1940.
46. Caro, L. de, and Butturini, L., Boll. d. Soc. ital. biol. sper., **15**:210 1940.
47. Pyke, M., Biochem. J., **34**:1341, 1940.
48. Goodhart, R. S., and Sinclair, H. M., Biochem. J., **33**:1099, 1939.
49. Sinclair, H. M., Biochem. J., **33**:1816, 1939.
50. Säker, G., Klin. Wchnschr., **19**:99, 1940.
51. Tauber, H., Enzymologia, **2**:171, 1937.
52. Euler, H. von, and Vestin, R., Naturwissenschaften, **25**:416, 1937.
53. Peters, R. A., Biochem, J., **31**:2240, 1937.
54. Lipschitz, M. A.; Potter, V. R.; and Elvehjem, C. A., J. Biol. Chem., **124**:147, 1938.
55. Ochoa, S., Biochem. J., **33**:1262, 1939.
56. Silverman, M., and Werkman, C. H., Enzymologia, **5**:385, 1939.
57. Ferrebee, J. W., J. Biol. Chem., **136**:719, 1940.
58. Laszt, L., Verhandl. fr. schweiz. Physiol., January, 1938.
59. Lipton, M. A., and Elvehjem, C. A., Cold Spring Harbor Symp. Quant. Biol., **7**:184, 1939.

60. Warburg, O., and Christian, W., Biochem. Ztschr., **303**:40, 1939.
61. Lineweaver, H., and Burk, D., J. Am. Chem. Soc., **56**:658, 1934.
62. Lipmann, F., Cold Spring Harbor Symp. Quant. Biol., **7**:248, 1939.
63. Tauber, H., J. Biol. Chem., **123**:499, 1938.
64. Melnick, D., and Field, H., Jr., J. Biol. Chem., **130**:97, 1939.
65. Westenbrink, H. G. K., and Goudsmit, J., Arch. néerl. de physiol., **24**:305, 1939.
66. Borsook, H.; Buchman, E. R.; Hatcher, J. B.; Yost, D. M.; and McMillan, E., Proc. Nat. Acad. Sc., **26**:412, 1940.
67. Drill, V. A., Am. J. Physiol., **122**:486, 1938.
68. Peters, R. A., and Rossiter, R. J., Biochem. J., **33**:1140, 1939.
69. Mouriquand, G.; Morin, G.; and Czerszchowska, R., Compt. rend. Soc. de biol., **131**:1070, 1939.
70. Abderhalden, E., and Abderhalden, R., Pflügers Arch. f. d. ges. Physiol., **242**:508, 1939; **243**:85, 1940.
71. Banga, I.; Ochoa, S.; and Peters, R. A., Biochem. J., **33**:1980, 1939.
72. Annau, E., and Erdös, T., Ztschr. f. physiol. Chem., **257**:111, 1939.
73. Colowick, S. P.; Welch, M. S.; and Cori, C. F., J. Biol. Chem., **133**: 359, 1940.
74. Ochoa, S., Nature, **144**:834, 1939.
75. Lipmann, F., Nature, **143**:281, 1939.
76. Lipmann, F., *ibid.*, **143**:436, 1939.
77. Lipmann, F., *ibid.*, **144**:381, 1939.
78. Silverman, M., and Werkman, C. H., Proc. Soc. Exper. Biol. & Med., **43**:777, 1940.
79. Still, J. L., Biochem. J., **35**:380, 1941.
80. Barron, E. S. G., and Friedemann, T. E., J. Biol. Chem., **137**:593, 1941.
81. Long, C., and Peters, R. A., Biochem. J., **33**:759, 1939.
82. Long, C., personal communication.
83. Peters, R. A., Nature, **146**:387, 1940.
84. Ochoa, S., Nature, **145**:747; **146**:267, 1940; J. Biol. Chem., **138**:751, 1941.
85. Belitzer, V. A., and Golovskaya, K. S., Science, **92**:536, 1940.
86. Meyerhof, O., Naturwissenschaften, **23**:850, 1935.
87. Colowick, S. P., and Kalckar, H. M., J. Biol. Chem., **137**:789, 1941.
88. Belitzer, V. A., and Tsibakowa, E. T., Biokhimiya, **4**:516, 1939.
89. Colowick, S. P.; Welch, M. S.; and Cori, C. F., J. Biol. Chem., **133**: 641, 1940.
90. Lipmann, F., Advances in Enzymology, **1**:99, 1941.
91. Negelein, E., and Brömel, H., Biochem. Ztschr., **303**:132, 1939.
92. Lipmann, F., J. Biol. Chem., **134**:463, 1940; Proc. Fed. Am. Soc. Exper. Biol., **1**, 122, 1942.
93. Ochoa, S.; Peters, R. A.; and Stocken, L. A., Nature, **144**:750, 1939.

94. GREEN, D. E., Proceedings of the twenty-ninth annual meeting of the Federation of American Societies for Experimental Biology. Boston, 1942.
95. LIPMANN, F., Nature, **138**:1097, 1936.
96. LIPMANN, F., and PERLMANN, G., J. Am. Chem. Soc., **60**:2574, 1938.
97. STERN, K. G., and MELNICK, J. L., J. Biol. Chem., **135**:365, 1940.
98. BARRON, E. S. G., and LYMAN, C. M., Science, **92**:337, 1940; J. Biol. Chem., **141**:951, 1941.
99. BARRON, E. S. G.; LYMAN, C. M.; LIPTON, M. A.; and GOLDINGER, J. M., J. Biol. Chem., **141**:957, 1941.
100. OCHOA, S., unpublished observations.
101. ZIMA, O., and WILLIAMS, R. R., Ber. d. deutsch. chem. Gesellsch., **73**:941, 1940.
102. ZIMA, O.; RITSERT, K.; and MOLL, TH., Ztschr. f. physiol. Chem., **267**:210, 1941.
103. GORDON, A. H.; GREEN, D. E.; and SUBRAHMANYAN, V., Biochem. J., **34**:764, 1940.
104. KNOOP, F., and MARTIUS, C., Ztschr. f. physiol. Chem., **242**:204, 1936.
105. KREBS, H. A., and JOHNSON, W. A., Enzymologia, **4**:148, 1937.
106. SOBER, H. A.; LIPTON, M. A.; and ELVEHJEM, C. A., J. Biol. Chem., **134**: 605, 1940.
107. EVANS, E. A., JR., Biochem. J., **34**:829, 1940.
108. EVANS, E. A., JR., and SLOTIN, L., J. Biol. Chem., **136**:301, 1940.
109. BARRON, E. S. G.; GOLDINGER, J. M.; LIPTON, M. A.; and LYMAN, C.M., J. Biol. Chem., **141**:975, 1941.
110. SIMOLA, P. E., Biochem. Ztschr., **302**:84, 1939.
111. KREBS, H. A., Biochem. J., **34**:460, 775, 1940.
112. KREBS, H. A., and EGGLESTON, L. V., Biochem. J., **34**:442, 1940.
113. KREBS, H. A., and EGGLESTON, L. V., *ibid.*, **34**:1383, 1940.
114. WOOD, H. G.; WERKMAN, C. H.; HEMINGWAY, A.; and NIER, A. O., J. Biol. Chem., **135**:789, 1940.
115. SMYTH, D. H., Biochem. J., **34**:1598, 1940.
116. KRAMPITZ, L. O., and WERKMAN, C. H., Biochem. J., **35**:595, 1941.
117. QUASTEL, J. H., and WEBLEY, D. M., Nature, **144**:633, 1939; Biochem. J., **35**:192, 1941.
118. COLOWICK, S. P.; KALCKAR, H. M.; and CORI, C. F., J. Biol. Chem., **137**: 343, 1941.
119. SUTHERLAND, E. W.; COLOWICK, S. P.; and CORI, C. F., J. Biol. Chem. **140**:309, 1941.
120. OCHOA, S.; CORI, G. T.; and CORI, C. F., unpublished observations.
121. MEYERHOF, O.; OHLMEYER, P.; GENTNER, W.; and MAIER-LEIBNITZ, H., Biochem. Ztschr., **298**:396, 1938.

122. GREEN, D. E.; NEEDHAM, D. M.; and DEWAN, J. G., Biochem. J., **31**:2327, 1937.
123. MEYERHOF, O.; OHLMEYER, P.; and MÖHLE, W., Biochem. Ztschr., **297**: 113, 1938.
124. KALCKAR, H., Biochem. J., **33**:631, 1939.
125. SOLOMON, A. K.; VENNESLAND, B.; KLEMPERER, F. W.; BUCHANAN, J. M.; and HASTINGS, A. B., J. Biol. Chem., **140**:171, 1941.
126. LU, G. D., Biochem. J., **33**:774, 1939.
127. BOLLMAN, J. L., and FLOCK, E. V., J. Biol. Chem., **130**:565, 1939.
128. FORNAROLI, P., and BONI, I., Boll. Soc. ital. biol. sper., **15**:218, 1940.
129. BANERJI, G. G., and HARRIS, L. J., Biochem. J., **33**:1346, 1939.
130. SHILS, M.; DAY, H. G.; and MCCOLLUM, E. V., Science, **91**:341, 1940; J. Biol. Chem., **139**:145, 1941.
131. WILLIAMS, R. R., and SPIES, T. D., Vitamin B_1 (thiamin) and its use in medicine. New York: Macmillan Co., 1939.
132. NITZESCU, I. I., and IOANID, V., Compt. rend. Soc. de biol., **133**:490, 492, 1940.
133. WILSON, A., Ztschr. f. klin. Med., **136**:77, 1939.
134. FORNAROLI, P., and BONI, I., Boll. d. Soc. ital. biol. sper., **15**:515, 1940.
135. LONGENECKER, H. E.; GAVIN, G.; and MCHENRY, E. W., J. Biol. Chem., **134**:693, 1940.
136. MCHENRY, E. W., Science, **86**:200, 1937.
137. MCHENRY, E. W., and GAVIN, G., J. Biol. Chem., **128**:45, 1939.
138. MANN, P. J. G.; TENNENBAUM, M.; and QUASTEL, J. H., Biochem. J., **32**:243, 1938.
139. MANN, P. J. G., and QUASTEL, J. H., Nature, **145**:856, 1940.

VITAMIN B_1: CLINICAL ASPECTS

NORMAN JOLLIFFE
College of Medicine, New York University

A NUTRITIONAL inadequacy begins the instant that adequate amounts of an essential nutrient fail to reach the internal environment. This results, after varying periods, in malnutrition, the successive stages of which are represented by (*a*) tissue depletion; (*b*) biochemical "lesions" (1); (*c*) altered function; and, finally, by (*d*) anatomical lesions (2). The clinical recognition of these stages of malnutrition, as a rule, follows the reverse order—i.e., anatomical lesions, altered function, biochemical "lesions," and tissue replenishment. This order of events has been followed in the development of our clinical knowledge of vitamin-B_1 deficiency.

THE KNOWN ANATOMICAL LESIONS

The known anatomical lesions are polyneuropathy, the ophthalmoplegia of Wernicke's syndrome, and circulatory disturbances.

Polyneuropathy.—As late as 1936 it was thought that vitamin-B_1 deficiency was rare in the Western world (3). At that time, however, criteria for the diagnosis of vitamin-B_1 deficiency required the presence of classical beriberi in a subject who gave no history of an etiologic factor that could possibly account for the findings, other than a grossly inadequate diet. Identical clinical pictures occurring in subjects having increased requirements, impaired absorption or utilization, altered vitamin/caloric ratios (due to increased consumption of vitamin-free or -poor food), or hastened excretion were designated as a "polyneuropathy." This diagnosis was then qualified by a label descriptive of the supposed etiology. Thus we had such terms as "infectious," "toxic," "cachetic," "alcoholic," "diabetic," "metabolic," and "gestational" polyneuropathy. We now know that these labels were often applicable only in so far as they designated the conditioning factor by which the essential nutrient failed to reach the internal environment in an amount sufficient to prevent nutritional failure under the existing condition designated by the qualifying label (4–19).

The inclusion of these polyneuropathies under "beriberi" increased manyfold the recognized prevalence of nutritional failure. The true prevalence of this anatomic lesion is still underestimated because of failure to look for early changes. The average neurologic examination, as conducted by the general practitioner, internist, or surgeon, consists of pupillary reflexes, knee jerks, the plantar response, and, if the patient is ambulatory, the Rhomberg test. By this type of examination mild polyneuropathies are almost invariably missed because bilateral calf-muscle tenderness, plantar dysesthesia and other sensory changes, and absence of the ankle jerks are not looked for.

The clinical picture of thiamine-deficiency polyneuropathy begins, as far as objective signs are concerned, with plantar dysesthesia and calf-muscle tenderness. The plantar dysesthesia is not the common ordinary tickling sensation usually elicited by scratching the plantar surface of the foot, but definite hyperesthetic pain, which is manifest and unmistakable in the facial expression. A healthy calf muscle, if squeezed from behind, so as not to include the tibia in the grip, can stand considerable pressure; this is not so in the presence of mild polyneuropathy. At about this time the vibratory sensation in the toes becomes diminished. These signs are suggestive. When, however, in addition to these signs, the ankle jerks become absent, a diagnosis of polyneuropathy can be made. By this time the plantar dysesthesia may have extended so that there is sock dysesthesia. The vibratory sensation is usually absent in the toes and occasionally may be absent in the malleoli or even in the tibiae. Position sensation in the toes is, as a rule, intact, though a few mistakes may be made in very small changes in position.

As the deficiency progresses to that of moderate polyneuropathy, the knee jerks disappear, but the signs are still limited to the lower extremities. Definite impairment of position sensation in the toes can now be generally demonstrated, and vibratory sensation is lost over a greater extent, even on occasion up to and including the pelvis. Some atrophy of the calf muscles may be evident. Calf tenderness and sock dysesthesia continue. Occasionally a "delayed" plantar dysesthesia (20, 21) now becomes evident. The gait may be natural, but often a definite abnormality is noted. The burning soles of the feet, with some loss of position sense, make these patients walk carefully, as though barefoot on a floor scattered with carpet tacks. Toe and foot drop are not usually present at this time. At this stage the signs are limited to the lower extremities.

If the deficiency continues, the upper extremities become involved, so that the biceps and triceps jerks disappear. Glove dysesthesia and loss of finger dexterity rapidly develop. Calf-muscle atrophy is now usually marked; toe and foot drop are usually plainly evident; and wrist drop soon appears. The gait, if the patient is able to walk, is by now that of the steppage type. However, walking is, as a rule, difficult or impossible because of the central nervous or circulatory involvement.

The neurologic manifestations of vitamin-B_1 deficiency, whether in a mild or severe form, are bilateral and symmetrical and characteristically involve first and predominantly the lower extremities. Peripheral neuritis that involves a single nerve, or that is not bilateral and symmetrical, or that does not involve first and predominantly the lower extremities, is not, in my experience, due to vitamin-B_1 deficiency. Exceptions that prove the rule can probably be found for each of these dicta. For example, a man crippled by hip-joint disease was confined to a wheel chair, which he propelled with his arms. Polyneuropathy occurred first and predominantly in his upper extremities.

Ophthalmoplegia of Wernicke's syndrome.—A portion of Wernicke's syndrome is now recognized as thiamine deficiency (22–25). This syndrome is clinically characterized by varying degrees of ophthalmoplegia, clouding of consciousness, ataxia, and polyneuropathy. The essential pathology is confined to the periventricular gray matter and is characterized by small foci of degeneration and varicose deformities of the blood vessels. The clinical picture, as well as the essential pathology, was first described by Wernicke in 1881. Wernicke's first case occurred in a patient with intractable vomiting, following a suicidal attempt with sulfuric acid. His other two cases occurred in alcoholic patients admitted in delirium. He did not indict alcohol as the causative agent but suggested that various toxins, including alcohol, might produce the syndrome. Nevertheless, alcohol gradually came to be accepted as the etiologic basis of this condition, in spite of the fact that the literature contains some forty cases described in non-alcoholic individuals, most of whom had some gastrointestinal disturbances, accompanied by vomiting and cachexia. In 1938 Alexander (23) and his co-workers were able to reproduce the pathologic lesions in pigeons fed on a thiamine-deficient diet. They could not reproduce the disease in pigeons fed thiamine, even though they were deprived of all other vitamins or of any one other vitamin for a period of over six months. In 1940 Alexander showed conclusively that the lesions of Wernicke's syndrome occurring in man and the disease he produced experimentally in pigeons deficient in vitamin B_1 were identical in their topographic distribution and in their morphologic and histologic characteristics.

Jolliffe, Wartis, and Fein (24) have recently reported the clinical findings in 27 cases. Of the total, 3 occurred in non-alcoholic patients (2 depressed patients who refused to eat, and 1 case of pulmonary tuberculosis with associated vomiting). The other 24 occurred in alcoholics. Our results (26) may be summarized as follows:

The syndrome as originally described by Wernicke is probably a combination of several nutritional deficiencies, any one of which may be predominant. Delirium, with its marked increase in psychomotor activity and hence in total metabolism, usually precedes the development of this syndrome. It is believed that this increases certain of the vitamin requirements of the individual and tends to aggravate any latent deficiency state which may be present. Other deficiency syndromes, such as pellagra, nicotinic acid deficiency encephalopathy, ariboflavinosis, and scurvy, may and do superimpose themselves upon or accompany the Wernicke syndrome. These require specific treatment. The ophthalmoplegia responds to thiamine therapy but not to the administration of nicotinic acid, riboflavin, or pyridoxine. The ophthalmoplegia is invariably preceded or accompanied by an acute peripheral symmetrical polyneuropathy. Since the latter is almost always associated with thiamine deficiency, this finding supports Alexander's thesis that both have a common etiology and that the polioencephalopathic changes represent a more complete deficiency of thiamine. The clouding of consciousness responds in most cases to thiamine therapy; but in other cases it may be related to any other factor which interferes with proper brain metabolism, such as lack of carbohydrate, oxygen, nicotinic acid, riboflavin, and possibly to a lack of other substances. The ataxia is difficult to evaluate, both as to its genesis and its response to therapy. All cases that received adequate vitamin therapy recovered unless a complicating condition was present which in itself was sufficient cause for death. We have now had 14 consecutive recoveries in cases so treated. In the recovered cases, the succession of a Korsakoff syndrome is the rule. The latter does not show a consistent response to thiamine therapy, as has frequently been claimed.

Circulatory disturbances.—After the recognition of the common etiology of beriberi and many varieties of polyneuropathy occurring in this country, attention was naturally directed to circulatory manifestations so frequently described in the Orient. Weiss and Wilkins (27) were among the first to recognize these circulatory disturbances and placed their frequency as 1 in each 160 admissions to two medical services at Boston City Hospital. Jolliffe and Goodhart (8, 28) were able to find clinical evidence of cardiovascular disturbances in one-third of their subjects having thiamine-deficiency polyneuropathy.

Clinically, the circulatory manifestations can be divided into three groups, as follows: (1) edema (and serous effusions) occurring without enlargement of the heart or other signs of congestive heart failure; (2) edema and serous effusions occurring with supporting signs and symptoms of congestive heart failure, usually with definite roentgenographic evidence of cardiac enlargement; and (3) sudden circulatory collapse.

Edema without enlargement of heart, or other signs of congestive heart failure, is the type of circulatory disturbance most frequently seen. The edema is dependent; it may be mild and limited to pitting at the ankles, or it may be anasarca. The edema cannot be attributed to a failing heart, as there are no other signs of heart failure, such as an elevated venous pressure, prolonged circulation time, dilated cervical veins, or enlarged heart. In these subjects the plasma proteins are above the critical level of edema; though many subjects have edema due to low plasma proteins, these cases are not included in this group. There is no evidence of renal disease. Also, the edema in many of these patients responds to bed rest alone, and in many subjects the response is dramatic. The novice is often bewildered by seeing a patient with marked edema, possibly so extensive as to be anasarca, only to find the following day that the anasarca now consists of moderate, or even mild, pitting of the ankles. Similarly, mild or moderate degrees of edema frequently disappear with 24–48 hours of bed rest.

The diagnosis of the cardiac form of beriberi should be made, in the absence of definite heart enlargement, only when there is evidence of congestive heart failure other than edema and serous effusions. If this rule is followed, the cardiac form of beriberi will, as a rule, manifest signs of both right and left heart failure, though the signs attributed to failure of the right heart usually predominate. Consequently, a patient with the cardiac form of beriberi usually shows, in addition to edema and possibly serous effusions, dilated cervical veins, a palpable liver, dyspnea, and orthopnea and will usually complain of palpitation, breathlessness, particularly after exertion, and often of precordial pain. Pulmonary congestion is common; most patients develop pulmonary edema before exitus. The pulse is rapid and bounding, and often there is a high pulse pressure with pistol-shot sounds heard over the great arteries. Cyanosis is not frequent, but generalized arteriolar dilatation is common. The velocity of the blood flow is usually normal or increased, and there is a low arteriovenous oxygen difference. As noted by Weiss, epinephrine exaggerates the symptoms, while pitressin brings about temporary improvement. Teleoroentgenographic examination shows enlargement of the heart, attributed chiefly to enlargement of the right ventricle and auricle; and, frequently, increase in the size of the pulmonary artery is noted. The left auricle and ventricle often contribute to the enlargement of the cardiac shadow but, as a rule, to a lesser extent than their mates on the right. Although few patients present normal electrocardiographic tracings, the alterations found are not usually characteristic so as to be diagnostic.

Circulatory collapse and sudden death are described as common in all studies of beriberi in the Orient. Some resemble shock, with rapid, thready pulse and low or unobtainable blood pressure; others resemble the syndrome produced by a hyperactive carotid-sinus reflex of the vagotonic type. These manifestations may occur without previous warning or only after other circulatory manifestations are well established. They occur most frequently in ambulatory patients and particularly in those engaged in physical labor.

DISTURBANCES IN FUNCTION

We now come to disturbances in function. These may, of course, have an anatomic basis—but, if so, this has not been detected by our present technique. Disturbances in function due to thiamine deficiency are probably and logically much more common than the recognized anatomic lesions. Since these symptoms are often found only in patients "in whom nothing organic can be found," they have heretofore been included in the diagnostic grab bag of "neurasthenia" (29–34). This syndrome consists of tension and irritable-weakness states. It is manifested in complaints of fatigability, weakness, and exhaustibility, head pressures, poor sleep, irritability, feeling of tenseness, various aches and pains, subjectively poor memory, and difficulty in concentration. Additional complaints referable to the bowels, heart, skin, and genitourinary apparatus are not uncommon. The genesis of this neurasthenic syndrome is not clear; but the author has suggested that anorexia, fatigability, and disturbances of sleep are the fundamental symptoms, which may occur from a variety of causes. These symptoms, if not soon corrected in a susceptible individual, lead to the development of the complete picture. Various etiologies have been suggested, but none satisfactorily explains the picture. Freud himself felt that neurasthenia was the result of physical factors and not psychogenic. As the various hormones were isolated, each in turn was held responsible. In this vitamin era, similar indictments are being made. McLester (35) noted that many of the pellagra patients seen at the Hillman Hospital in Birmingham were considered neurasthenics before the objective signs of pellagra became manifest. It is now well recognized that in most pellagrins there is a coexisting deficiency of thiamine. He suggested that many of the nervous and mental symptoms of pellagra depend primarily on a lack of sufficient thiamine in the dietary regimen.

With a diet poor in vitamin B_1, Jolliffe (31) and his co-workers were able to produce a neurasthenic syndrome in 4 out of 5 experimental subjects. The subjects (internes) complained at fatigue, lassitude, anorexia, precordial pain, burning of the feet, dyspnea on exertion, muscle cramps, and palpitation. The objective signs observed were skin dysesthesia in a sock distribution, changes in the electrocardiogram, and calf-muscle tenderness. Symptoms were observed as early as the fourth day, and objective signs as early as the fifth day, although 1 subject developed no definite symptoms or objective signs in 30 days with a diet estimated to contain only 62 per cent of his vitamin-B_1 requirement.

The addition of thiamine alone to the experimental diet caused all symptoms to disappear within 3 days, and the objective signs within 6 days.

For several years I have been cognizant of this group of symptoms in my patients having anatomic signs of a thiamine deficiency. In spite of the experimental work in our own clinic in producing a neurasthenia by an isolated thiamine deficiency, and in spite of Freud's belief in its physical basis, I usually attributed it to an abnormal psyche, which, leading to further dietary restrictions, in turn led to the development of objective signs. Adequate treatment for the deficiency was followed (31) not only by disappearance of the anatomic signs but also, as a rule, of the neurasthenic syndrome. I then applied to subjects having the neurasthenic syndrome without anatomic signs of vitamin deficiency the treatment regimen of dietary correction, vitamin supplements rich in the entire B complex, and thiamine chloride. Many, though not all, of these patients were helped. The improvement was attributed to better nutrition plus the psychotherapy of this dietary regimen. Not until Williams, Mason, Wilder, and Smith (30, 31), in a well-controlled experiment with human subjects, reproduced this characteristic neurasthenic syndrome by inducing an isolated thiamine deficiency, have I been willing to include this syndrome as a manifestation of thiamine deficiency. It should not be inferred, however, that all neurasthenia is based on thiamine deficiency. Such is definitely not the case. The problem is additionally complicated by the fact that similar syndromes have been reported as cured by nicotinic acid, vitamin B_6, and vitamin E. Furthermore, it should be kept in mind that these symptoms frequently respond to psychotherapy. The need to isolate the group due to nutritional failure from the larger group of neurasthenia, and each of the types of nutritive failure from each other, is obvious.

BIOCHEMICAL LESIONS

It is now possible to detect clinically certain of the biochemical lesions of thiamine deficiency. Evidence has been presented that pyruvic acid is a normal intermediary in the metabolism of carbohydrate *in vitro* and *in vivo*. Banga, Ochoa, and Peters (36) demonstrated that thiamine pyrophosphate is necessary for the proper catabolism of pyruvic acid in experimental animals; and others have shown that pyruvic acid accumulates in body fluids in oriental beriberi, a disease known to include thiamine deficiency. It is therefore logical to expect pyruvemia in human thiamine-deficient subjects in this country.

Following the development by Bueding and Wortis (37) of an accurate method for the determination of blood pyruvic acid, using iodoacetate as a stabilizer, we (38) have investigated the pyruvic acid blood levels in normal subjects and in a variety of illnesses associated and unassociated with thiamine deficiency. These subjects have been investigated under basal conditions and following metabolic strain produced by the oral ingestion of 1.75 gm. of dextrose per kilogram of body weight (39). In 87 normal subjects the fasting blood pyruvic acid averaged 1.0 mg. per cent, with a variation of from 0.77 to 1.16 mg. per cent. Three times the standard deviation would place the upper limits of normal at 1.30 mg. per cent. In 27 normal subjects the pyruvemia was determined for 5 hours following glucose ingestion. The maximum rise, varying from 0.14 to 0.93 mg. and averaging 0.43 mg. above the fasting level, occurred at the end of 1 hour in every case but one, in which case the peak was reached in 30 minutes. Following the peak, the pyruvic acid level fell, reaching the fasting level at or before the third hour in all but one subject; in the latter instance it returned to the fasting level at the fourth hour.

In two subjects the pyruvemia, after returning to a fasting level, again showed an elevation in the fourth hour. In both subjects this secondary rise was associated with hypoglycemia, which was demonstrable both clinically and chemically.

In thiamine-deficient subjects, as evidenced by an acute bilateral peripheral neuropathy and in Wernicke's disease, the fasting blood pyruvic acid was elevated in 45 of 48 subjects. Of greater significance, however, is the fact that, when these thiamine-deficient subjects were subjected to the additional stress of metabolizing ingested dextrose, the pyruvemia was not only greater than normal but the maximum rise occurred after 1 hour and did not return to normal within 4 or 5 hours.

Tissue depletion, as evidenced by blood levels of thiamine, is now under active investigation in more than one clinic; and soon we may expect correlation of anatomical, functional, and biochemical alterations.

BIBLIOGRAPHY

1. PETERS, R. A., Lancet, **230**:1161, 1936.
2. JOLLIFFE, N., J.A.M.A., **117**:1496, 1941.
3. JOLLIFFE, N., New Internat. Clin., 4:46, 1938.
4. SPIES, T. D., and ARING, C. D., J.A.M.A., **110**:1081, 1938.
5. JOLLIFFE, N.; COLBERT, C. N.; and JOFFE, P. M., Am. J. M. Sc., N.S., **191**:515, 1936.
6. JOLLIFFE, N., and COLBERT, C. N., J.A.M.A., **107**:642, 1936.
7. GOODHART, R., and JOLLIFFE, N., J.A.M.A., **110**:414, 1938.
8. JOLLIFFE, N., and GOODHART, R., J.A.M.A., **111**:380, 1938.
9. JOLLIFFE, N., and ROSENBLUM, L. A., M. Clin. North America, **23**:759, 1939.
10. JOLLIFFE, N., New York Acad. Med., 2d ser., **15**:469, 1939.
11. JOLLIFFE, N., M. Clin. North America, **24**:733, 1940.
12. FEIN, H. D.; RALLI, E. P.; and JOLLIFFE, N., J.A.M.A., **115**:1973, 1940
13. WECHSLER, I. S., M. J. & Rec., **131**:441, 1930.
14. WECHSLER, I. S., Arch. Neurol. & Psychiat., **29**:813, 1933.
15. VORHAUS, M. G.; WILLIAMS, R. R.; and WATERMAN, R. E., J.A.M.A., **105**:1580, 1935.
16. BORSON, H. J., Ann. Int. Med., **14**:1, 1940.
17. FANTUS, B. (ed.), with TRAUT, E. F., and GREENBAUM, R. S., J.A.M.A., **115**:450, 1940.
18. MEIKLEJOHN, A. P., New England J. Med., **223**:265, 1940.
19. BROWN, M. R., J.A.M.A., **116**:1615, 1941.

20. WORTIS, H.; STEIN, M. H.; and JOLLIFFE, N., Arch. Int. Med., **69**:222, 1942.
21. STEIN, M. H.; WORTIS, H.; and JOLLIFFE, N., Arch. Neurol. & Psychiat., **46**:464, 1941.
22. CAMPBELL, A. C. P., and BIGGART, J. H., J. Path. & Bact., **48**:245, 1939.
23. ALEXANDER, L., Arch. Neurol. & Psychiat., **42**:1172, 1939.
24. JOLLIFFE, N.; WORTIS, H.; and FEIN, H. D., J. Nerv. & Ment. Dis., **93**:214, 1941; Arch. Neurol. & Psychiat., **46**:569, 1941.
25. JOLLIFFE, N., New York Acad. Med., **17**:195, 1941.
26. WORTIS, H.; BUEDING, E.; STEIN, M. H.; and JOLLIFFE, N., Arch. Neurol. & Psychiat. **47**:215, 1942.
27. WEISS, S., and WILKINS, R. W., J.A.M.A., **109**:786, 1937.
28. GOODHART, R., and JOLLIFFE, N., Am. Heart J., **15**:569, 1938.
29. WILLIAMS, R. D.; MASON, H. L.; and SMITH, B. F., Proc. Staff Meet. Mayo Clin., **14**:787, 1939.
30. WILLIAMS, R. D.; MASON, H. L.; WILDER, R. M.; and SMITH, B. F., Arch. Int. Med., **66**:785, 1940.
31. JOLLIFFE, N.; GOODHART, R.; GENNIS, J.; and CLINE, J. K., Am. J. M. Sc., **198**:198, 1939.
32. JOLLIFFE, N., Quart. J. Studies on Alcohol., **1**:517, 1940.
33. JOLLIFFE, N., J. Am. Diet. A., **17**:5, 1941.
34. JOLLIFFE, N., Bull. New York Acad. Med., **17**:195, 1941.
35. MCLESTER, J. S., J.A.M.A., **112**:2110, 1939.
36. BANGA, I.; OCHOA, S.; and PETERS, R. A., Biochem. J., **33**:1109, 1939.
37. BUEDING, E., and WORTIS, H., J. Biol. Chem., **133**:585, 1940.
38. BUEDING, E.; WORTIS, H.; STEIN, M. H.; and JOLLIFFE, N., J. Clin. Inv., **20**:441, 1941.
39. BUEDING, E.; STEIN, M. H.; WORTIS, H., J. Biol. Chem., **140**:697, 1941.

RIBOFLAVIN

PAUL GYÖRGY
Babies and Childrens Hospital, and the Department of Pediatrics
School of Medicine, Western Reserve University

RIBOFLAVIN is distinguished by two important and historically interesting characteristics: (1) It was the first vitamin to be recognized, on its isolation, as a pro-enzyme; in other words, in historical perspective it was the first representative of a rather large group of vitamins or vitamin-like substances that form part of definite enzymatic systems. (2) It was the first member of the vitamin B_2 complex to be isolated and biologically and chemically identified (1, 2)—an achievement that gave stimulus to the speedy unraveling of the multiple vitamin B_2 complex.

By the end of 1932 only two separate components of the vitamin B complex had been distinguished, as needed by the rat: (*a*) vitamin B_1, the antineuritic factor; and (*b*) vitamin B_2 (vitamin G in American nomenclature), the antipellagra factor. The separate existence of a third factor, called vitamin B_4, absence of which was said (3) to be associated with symptoms of nerve lesions, such as disturbance of co-ordination and ataxia, had not been generally accepted (4). Even less credit had been given to the claim that there were two more special factors, B_3 and B_5, as needed by pigeons (5). Chick and Copping (6) had postulated the existence of a separate growth-promoting water-soluble factor, but neither its specific biological effect nor its relation to the vitamin B complex had been investigated.

The British Committee on Accessory Food Factors (7) in 1927 defined vitamin B_2 as

> the more heat-stable, water-soluble dietary factor, recently described and named P-P ("pellagra-preventive") factor by Goldberger, Wheeler, Lillie and Rogers (1926) and found necessary for maintenance of growth and health and prevention of characteristic skin lesions in rats, and considered by the latter workers to be concerned in the prevention of human pellagra.

Sure (8), Thatcher (9), and Gurin (10), and their associates, even before 1932, had expressed the opinion that vitamin B_2 is a complex of two factors, one being predominantly growth promoting, the other the factor that prevents development of pellagra. None of the supporters of this theory, however, had been able to bring forward convincing proof for their views. Roscoe (11), as late as 1933, stated that in her extensive studies made on rats "no support was found for the theory postulating the existence of separate dietary factors responsible respectively for preventing and curing dermatitis and for promoting growth."

My own studies of vitamin B_2 were prompted by a special interest which I took in pathological changes of the skin produced in rats by dietary means. I considered that egg-white injury and the so-called "rat pellagra" were the two most prominent conditions calling for investigation. The work on the factor protective against egg-white injury, vitamin H (12), now known as "biotin" (13), started in 1929, and that on vitamin B_2 (1) in 1931. The chemical experiments in both investigations were done with the collaboration of Professor Richard Kuhn and members of his staff. Those on biotin (vitamin H) were continued and concluded in collaboration with Professor Vincent du Vigneaud and his co-workers.

Research concerning vitamin B_2 has made rapid progress. It was found that the weight curves of young rats kept on the ration originally devised by Bourquin and Sherman (14), and at that time generally used for the production of B_2 deficiency in rats, soon flattened out or showed decline (15). It was noted, moreover, that all the concentrates which proved to be active in promotion of the growth of these rats were colored with an intensity in direct proportion to their biological effect. The color of these concentrates was green-yellow, and fluorescence was distinctly visible in those prepared in neutral solutions or in solutions not strongly acid or alkaline. Colored, clear concentrates, such as those prepared from heart muscle, were exposed to complementary wave-lengths of visible light for from 6 to 24 hours. By the use of special filters care was taken to exclude the ultra-violet spectrum. It was thus definitely established (16; see also 1) that exposure to visible light destroyed the vitamin-B_2 activity of these concentrates, which, when they were not irradiated, were highly effective (Fig. 1).

In view of the fact that the biological activity of concentrates which were nonfluorescent as a result of their preparation in strongly acid or alkaline solution was also destroyed by visible light, it was thought that the inactivation was due probably to light absorption by the colored, dyelike vitamin itself rather than to photosensitiza-

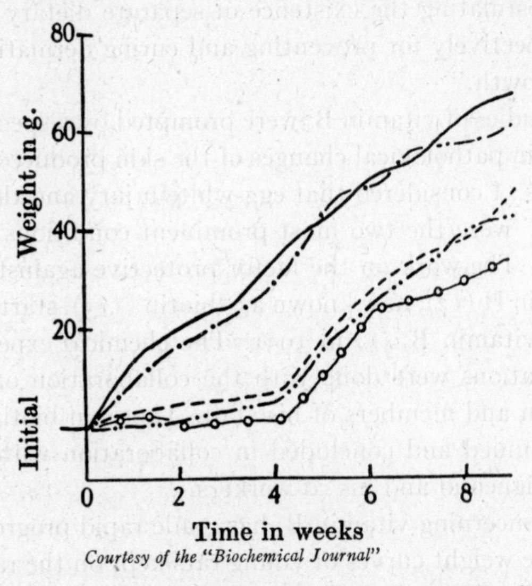

Courtesy of the "Biochemical Journal"

Fig. 1.—Weight curves of 5 rats which were given vitamin B_1 and liver concentrate irradiated at neutral (o—o), at alkaline (—··—), and at acid (---) reactions, and nonirradiated liver concentrate at neutral (——) and at alkaline (—·—) reactions. Riboflavin (10 µg. daily) was added at the end of the fourth week. (From György [16].)

tion. Such a working hypothesis, which identified vitamin B_2 with a yellow-green pigment, soon met serious difficulties, when concentrates that were further purified and more highly colored proved to be biologically inactive. By supplementing the diet, however, with a yeast concentrate from which all colored material had been removed by adsorption, the biological activity of the colored preparation was restored. Thus it was proved (17; see also 1, 15) that vitamin B_2 is, in fact, not a single substance but that it may be separated into two components, one of which was characteristically a pigment.

By this approach, which can now be considered the first successful attack on the biological analysis of the vitamin B_2 complex, isolation and identification of the colored component of the B_2 complex were readily achieved. The isolation was accomplished early in 1933 in collaboration with Kuhn and Wagner-Jauregg (1, 2). It soon became apparent that this substance, first obtained in pure form from milk and hence called "lactoflavin," corresponded to the colored component of the "yellow oxidation enzyme" of Warburg and Christian (18). One product resulting from the irradiation of this colored component was isolated in pure form by Warburg and Christian at the end of 1932 and is now known as "lumiflavin." Lumiflavin is biologically inactive.

Working independently, Ellinger and Koschara (19) had also called attention to the presence of this fluorescent substance in various tissues and tissue fluids. They, too, prepared purified concentrates of the substance, the vitamin-like quality of which, however, completely escaped their observation.

The final experiment (1, 15) proving the growth-promoting activity of lactoflavin was carried out with the pure substance. The Bourquin-Sherman diet was replaced by a synthetic diet devoid of vitamin B and supplemented with crystalline vitamin B_1 in place of the alcoholic wheat extract employed in the diet of Bourquin and Sherman. The weight curve of rats failing to grow on this diet showed no response when pure lactoflavin was added to the diet. The further addition of a yeast preparation free from lactoflavin, such as may be obtained, according to Peters and his collaborators (20), by adsorption of yeast concentrates on charcoal and subsequent elution with alcohol acidified with hydrochloric acid, resulted in rapid growth of the rats. Peters' eluate was completely inactive in the absence of lactoflavin. Thus the close interrelationship between pure lactoflavin and other factors of the vitamin B_2 complex was clearly demonstrated (Fig. 2). This experiment has been discussed at length because both its biological and its practical medical significance have apparently still not been generally appreciated.

The supplementary effect of such flavin-free concentrates as Peters' eluate was attributed at first to vitamin B_4, which Reader (3) in Peters' laboratory claimed at that time to be a member of the vitamin B_2 complex. Actually, Peters' eluate had been devised as a potent concentrate of B_1 and B_4. A purified preparation of B_4, kindly placed at our disposal by Professor Peters, also proved to be effective in supplementing lactoflavin. Later, however, it became evident that this supplementary factor was a new member of the vitamin B_2 complex, a factor in which the so-called "B_4" concentrates were rich. I then called it "vitamin B_6" (17, 21).

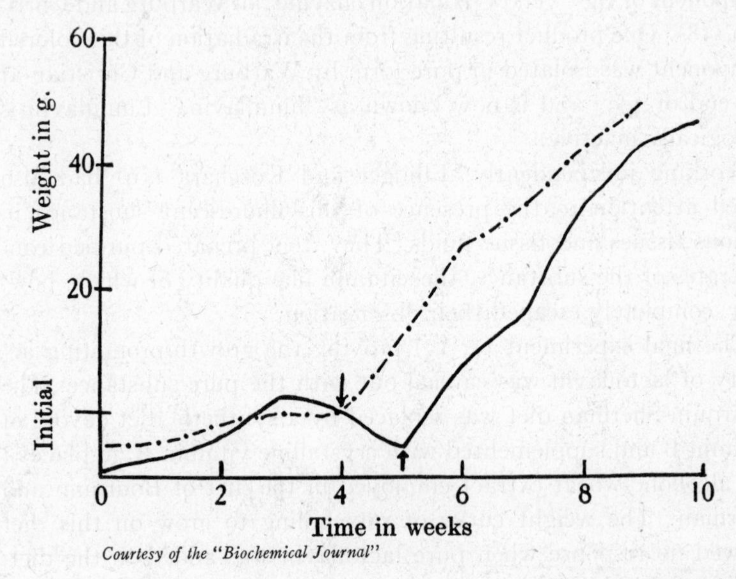

Courtesy of the "Biochemical Journal"

FIG. 2.—Weight curves of 2 rats which were given, in addition to the basal diet, 3 pigeon doeses of vitamin B_1 daily. Animal —— was given a daily supplement of 10μg. of riboflavin, and at the end of the fourth week 1 ml. of Peters' eluate daily was also added; animal -·-·- was given a daily supplement of 1 ml. of Peters' eluate, and at the end of the third week 10 μg. of riboflavin daily was also added. An increase of weight was produced only by the combined administration of vitamin B_1 + riboflavin + Peters' eluate. (From György [15].)

The work of Warburg and Christian (18) on the "yellow oxidation enzyme" and my own studies on vitamin B_2, carried out in collaboration with Kuhn and the members of his staff (1, 2), started from completely different points of view. One can even now distinguish between those aspects of the problem pertaining to cell oxidation and inaugurated by Warburg, and in part before him by Szent-Györgyi (22) and their collaborators, and those which constitute more particularly a dietary problem. In the last analysis this distinction is, of course, artificial.

Shortly after the isolation of the flavin from milk (23, 2), crystalline flavin preparations were obtained from egg white (2). One of these concentrates was found to be biologically inactive. In the light of such differences the suggestion was made that the term "flavin" be reserved for the whole group of these yellow fluorescent water-soluble pigments and that a prefix be attached to indicate their origin. Accordingly, the term "ovoflavin" was introduced to designate the flavin isolated from egg white; "hepatoflavin," the flavin from liver; and so forth.

Parallel to this preparatory work, the chemical identification of the flavins was being attacked successfully in different laboratories. Karrer (24), Kuhn (25), and Stern (26) and their respective collaborators laid the groundwork for the structural analysis. The synthesis was performed in 1935 independently by Kuhn and by Karrer and their collaborators.

The first conclusion drawn from the chemical analysis was that all biologically active flavins are chemically identical. The biologically active flavin is a derivative of isoalloxazine with two methyl groups and a sugar (pentose) radical attached. Since in lactoflavin the sugar radical is ribose, the term "lactoflavin" has been changed to riboflavin, a designation which in 1937 was adopted (27) by the Council on Pharmacy and Chemistry of the American Medical Association and is now in general use. The terms "lactoflavin," "ovoflavin," and "hepatoflavin" have been discarded.

Riboflavin ($C_{17}H_{20}N_4O_6$) is 6, 7-dimethyl-9-(*d*, 1′-ribityl)-isoalloxazine. The structural formula is shown in Figure 3. Riboflavin forms clusters of fine orange-yellow crystals which melt with decomposition at about 275° C. It is sparingly soluble in water, showing an intense greenish-yellow fluorescence visible optimally between pH 3 and 9. Irradiation of alkaline solutions causes the formation of biologically inactive, chloroform-soluble lumiflavin, whereas irradiation of acid or neutral solutions brings about the formation of the blue-fluorescent, biologically inactive degradation product, lumichrome, together with varying amounts of lumiflavin.

In cells and cell products, such as milk, riboflavin exists in the free state or is bound with protein, when it is called "flavoprotein" (28). These flavoproteins form part of various enzymatic systems. Six representatives of the group of flavoproteins prepared from yeast, heart, kidney, milk, and liver are, at the present time, fairly well characterized as to their prosthetic group, the position of the adsorption bands, and the substrate on which they act.

The first step that leads from free riboflavin to flavoprotein is apparently the phosphorylation of the riboflavin molecule. Laszt and Verzár (29) claimed that this phosphorylation is regulated by the adrenal glands and that dysfunction of phosphorylation mechanisms

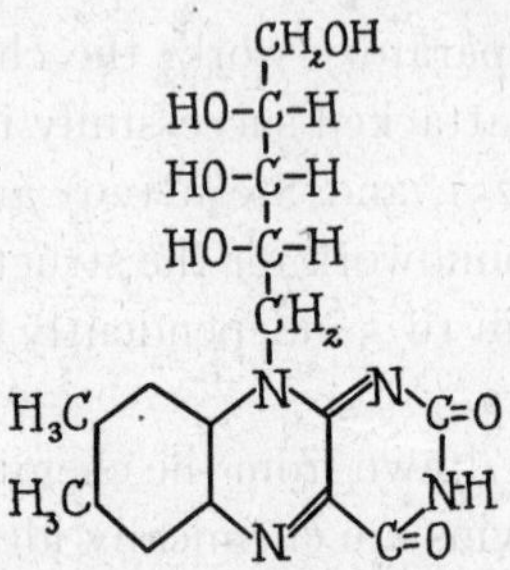

CH_2OH
HO-C-H
HO-C-H
HO-C-H
CH_2
H_3C N N C=O
NH
H_3C N C=O

FIG. 3.—Structural formula of riboflavin

produces a spruelike condition. These claims have been refuted and their foundation disproved (30).

Deficiency of riboflavin must naturally lead to a disruption of all cellular reactions that are linked with enzymatic processes in which flavoproteins participate. From the nutritional point of view, one should, however, bear in mind the important fact that, in addition to lack of flavoproteins, lack of the substrate will have an equal effect on cell metabolism and therefore also in respect to pathological manifestations. This conclusion is clearly illustrated by recent studies on carcinoma of the liver in rats fed a diet containing "butter yellow" (paradimethylaminoazobenzene). It has been shown by Rhoads and his collaborators (31) that the presence of riboflavin is essential in order to prevent the production of injury of the liver following the ingestion of "butter yellow," provided that casein is incorporated simultaneously in the diet. It has been shown by work in our laboratory (32) that casein can be replaced in the diet by a combination of cystine and choline. It can be assumed, therefore, that riboflavin as part of the enzymatic system, together with cystine plus choline, or rather that the product (perhaps methionine) built up by the interaction of these substances, is responsible for the prevention of liver injury in rats fed a diet containing "butter yellow."

Riboflavin is needed apparently by all animals—by man and even by a large number of bacteria. In ruminants—for instance, in sheep—riboflavin is synthesized in the rumen by bacteria (33).

Lack of riboflavin manifests itself first by retardation and later by complete cessation of growth. The more specific symptoms vary to some extent from one species to another. In rats riboflavin deficiency is characterized mainly by a specific involvement of the ectodermal organs, such as the skin and the eyes, as well as by suspended growth. The skin manifestations in riboflavin deficiency in rats are not so characteristic and striking as they are in the so-called "rat pellagra," now known as "rat acrodynia" (21), resulting from a deficiency of vitamin B_6. They are, rather, of a more trivial nature, with very definite seborrheic qualities. Progressive alopecia is the leading symptom. It is localized in certain areas, such as the back between the shoulders, the lines joining the eyes and ears (leaving a median comb of hair in between), and, finally, the chest. In many cases there may be observed minute, almost punctate, whitish yellow scales on the uninflamed skin in the midst of the scanty patches of fur. The fur may also appear moist and matted (Fig. 4). In advanced cases the eyes are sometimes surrounded by a spectacle-like loss of hair, while the eyelids are often stuck together with a serous, reddish fluid (15). In black and piebald rats whose diet was deficient in riboflavin, graying of the fur was noticed by Hunt (34), despite the presence of all other known members of the B_2 complex.

If treatment, i.e., addition of riboflavin to the diet, is not begun in time, the animals succumb to general exhaustion. The end is usually ushered in by meteorism, dyspnea, and blue discoloration of the extremities. Continuous administration of riboflavin at the appropriate time will avert this end, and gradually all pathological manifestations will regress until they have completely disappeared.

Chronic riboflavin deficiency in rats has been found, in our own investigations, to be often accompanied by pediculosis (35). At first, pediculosis was regarded as a purely accidental and unspecific occurrence, related possibly to a generally diminished vitality in these rats because they were unable to keep themselves clean in the efficient manner of normal animals. The majority of the rats with pediculosis, however, were by no means weakened and inactive. Moreover, pediculosis has never been observed in rats receiving a

Courtesy of the "Biochemical Journal"

FIG 4.—Deficiency syndrome in rat fed a diet deficient in riboflavin

vitamin-B–free diet supplemented with vitamin B_1 and riboflavin, even when they were moribund from acrodynia (B_6 deficiency). In rats suffering from riboflavin deficiency and also from pediculosis, therapeutic administration of riboflavin was followed by complete disappearance of the pediculi, which was often accompanied by replacement of the diseased patches by new fur. That it is possible to cure pediculosis in rats by nutritional means is in itself a significant finding and adds further weight to the conclusion that pediculosis and riboflavin deficiency in rats, at least under the conditions chosen, are interrelated. The practical implications of these findings with special reference to skin parasites in man have not yet been investigated.

Another ectodermal organ, the eye, plays a prominent and perhaps the most specific role in riboflavin deficiency in rats. The ocular changes involve the cornea and, to a limited extent, the lens.

Attention to these lesions was called first by Day and his associates (36). According to these authors, cataract developed after from 4 to 12 weeks in a very high percentage of rats kept on a synthetic diet which had been carefully freed from riboflavin and supplemented with other members of the vitamin B_2 complex, whereas rats that received riboflavin in their diet showed no lenticular changes. In its initial stages cataract, they found, could be stopped from spreading by timely administration of riboflavin. Other investigators, such as Bessey and Wolbach (37), myself (38), and Eckardt and Johnson (39), have been unable to obtain so high an incidence of cataract. In the few cases of cataract seen in rats by Eckardt and Johnson the opacity started from the fetal nucleus and then extended in rapid progression over the whole lens. The discrepancy between the observations on cataract made by Day and his collaborators and those of other workers has not yet been explained. In contrast to the apparently irregular formation of cataract, corneal vascularization has been found generally to be the most consistent ocular change in riboflavin-deficient rats (Fig. 5). The vascularization starts as "a marked radial ingrowth of capillaries into the cornea from the vessels of the limbus. . . . . The first capillaries to be seen lie just beneath the corneal epithelium, close to the limbus" (Bessey and Wolbach [37]). They "often form intertwined loops" and "may extend far toward the center of the cornea before leucocytes appear outside of the vessels" (37). Keratitis may precede the vascularization; but, as a rule, it is a late and probably a secondary complication, appearing together with necrosis and ulceration. When it is present, the ulcer lies centrally from the capillary loops; and in this respect, as well as in others, the picture closely resembles that of so-called "rosacea keratitis" in man. Administration of riboflavin in proper doses prevents and cures the corneal changes due to riboflavin deficiency.

It should be emphasized that, even from a strictly dietary point of view, neither pediculosis nor the lesions of the cornea, such as vascularization, keratitis, and ulceration, are limited to riboflavin deficiency. Pediculosis has also been observed (40) in rats fed supplements of vitamin B_1, riboflavin, and vitamin B_6, in addition to the

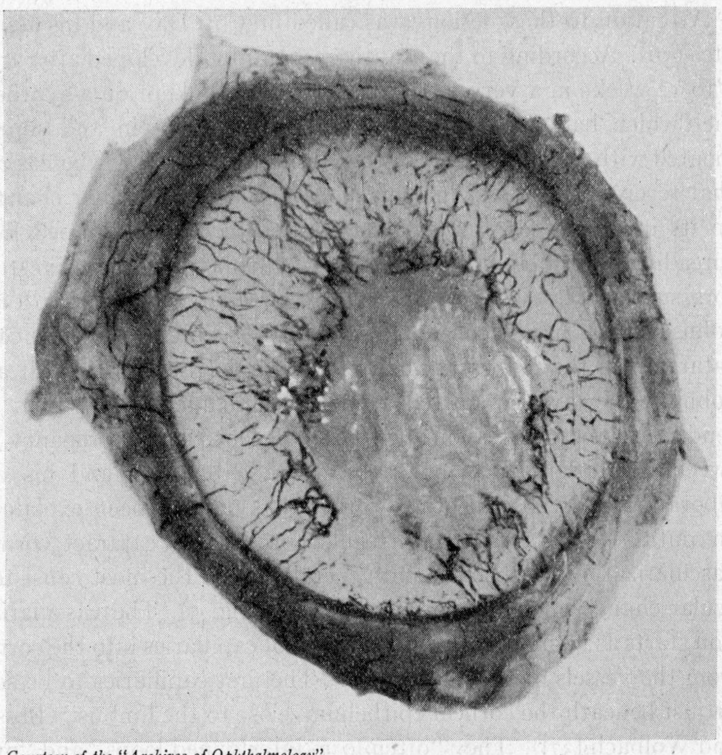

Courtesy of the "Archives of Ophthalmology"

FIG. 5.—Vascularized cornea of rat fed a diet deficient in riboflavin. India ink was injected into the heart before complete corneal section. The iris was removed, and the cornea was fixed to preserve its normal curve. (From Eckardt and Johnson [39].)

usual vitamin-B–free diet. It was then cured or prevented from recurring by the further supplement of pantothenic acid (41). Rats kept on the simple diet for producing acrodynia, consisting of a vitamin-B–free ration plus vitamin B_1 and riboflavin, were, as already mentioned, free from pediculosis.

Keratitis and vascularization of the cornea were frequently encountered in rats that received vitamin B_1, riboflavin, vitamin B_6, and pantothenic acid as supplements to their vitamin-B-free diet (41). In rats with simple acrodynia (those fed a diet lacking vitamin B_6) corneal changes were not seen (41).

All these experimental observations need further amplification and analysis. Even now, however, one can see in them ample proof of the complicated interaction of several dietary factors, most of which pertain to the vitamin B_2 complex.

Riboflavin deficiency has been studied most intensively in rats, but data are also available on the effect of the lack of riboflavin in other animals. Chicks are apparently very sensitive to an insufficient supply of riboflavin. In addition to stunted growth, the most common effect in chicks is the so-called "curled toe paralysis" (42), which has been correlated with nervous changes found on histological examination of the corresponding peripheral nerves.

Egg production and hatchability (43) of eggs are intimately related to the riboflavin content of the diet and consequently to the riboflavin content of the egg. The latter can be increased by the diet to a maximum content of 2.9 μg. per gram of the egg white and of 3.9 μg. per gram of the yolk. The skin and feathers of chicks kept on a diet deficient in riboflavin remain intact; feather production in turkey poults, however, is definitely impaired (44).

Dogs (45), and apparently also pigs (46), that have reached a severe stage of riboflavin deficiency often exhibit a syndrome of sudden fatal collapse with signs of vagotonia and drop in body temperature; at autopsy a "yellow," fatty liver is revealed. This syndrome, first described by Sebrell and his associates (45), is probably only the last stage of degenerative changes that take place in the peripheral nerves and in the posterior columns of the spinal cord. Corneal changes, as well as scaly dermatoses similar to those encountered in rats, are also seen in dogs and pigs.

The skin, the eye, the eye lens, and the nervous system are all made up of ectodermal tissue and are evidently especially susceptible to riboflavin deficiency. Other tissues, however, are by no means resistant to lack of riboflavin. In collaboration with Whipple and Robscheit-Robbins (47) we were able to show that administration of riboflavin to dogs with posthemorrhagic anemia was followed by a distinct increase in production of hemoglobin, in contrast to control animals fed a special diet poor in riboflavin.

The Bourquin-Sherman unit of riboflavin is the rat-day dose which maintains growth in rats for 8 weeks with an average weekly gain in weight of 3 gm. It corresponds to about 2.5 μg. of riboflavin. Chick *et al.* (48) and I (15), on the other hand, have advocated as the unit of riboflavin the rat-day dose which for 4 weeks would permit a gain of 10 gm. a week on a riboflavin-free diet supplemented with a riboflavin-free concentrate of the vitamin B_2 complex. This unit varies within limits, according to the nature of the supplement used. When Peters' yeast eluate is employed, the unit has been found to be about 7 μg. of riboflavin.

For the quantitative analysis of riboflavin in food products and in concentrates various methods have been devised.

I am indebted to my collaborator, Dr. Robert E. Eckardt, for the data collected with regard to these assay procedures and for tabulation of the results concerning distribution of riboflavin in food products.

There are, in general, two chief types of assay at the disposal of the investigator—those which take advantage of the physicochemical properties of riboflavin, and those which take advantage of its biological properties.

Assays dealing with the physicochemical properties of riboflavin may be subdivided into three groups: (1) those which measure the yellow color of the riboflavin (colorimetric determination) (49, 50); (2) those which measure the yellow-green fluorescence of riboflavin in blue or ultra-violet light (fluorimetric determination) (51, 52); and (3) those which depend on the conversion of riboflavin in alkaline solution by visible light into the chloroform-soluble photoderivative, lumiflavin, and the subsequent determination of the lumiflavin either colorimetrically or fluorimetrically (53, 54).

In both the colorimetric and the fluorimetric determination of riboflavin in foodstuffs or in biological materials, riboflavin must be extracted; and, furthermore, any pigments other than riboflavin which might interfere with the determination must be removed. An attempt was made to achieve the latter objective by the use of potassium permanganate, sodium hyposulfite, or hydrogen peroxide.

These methods have, in general, been found unreliable (55), mainly for two reasons: because the removal of interfering pigments is incomplete, and the riboflavin values found are, accordingly, excessively high, and because riboflavin may be also partly destroyed, yielding values that are lower than is actually the case.

The method involving lumiflavin takes advantage of the fact that riboflavin is converted to the photoderivative lumiflavin by irradiation in an alkaline solution. The lumiflavin can be extracted from acid solutions by chloroform and can therefore be separated easily from the other, interfering water-soluble pigments present in the material to be tested. Lumiflavin, moreover, has a yellow color and fluoresces yellow-green when it is exposed to ultra-violet light, so that it can be estimated either colorimetrically or fluorimetrically. Here, again, the extraction of lumiflavin is often incomplete, the colorimetric and fluorimetric determinations are inaccurate, and, finally, the conversion of riboflavin to lumiflavin is accompanied by inconstant and unpredictable losses constituting as much as 60 per cent of the content of riboflavin (54, 56).

In view of these possible errors, the conclusion appears to be warranted that the only acceptable determination of riboflavin is the biological one (55), using either the higher animals, such as rats and chicks, or bacteria as test subjects. The animal experiments are naturally long and cumbersome and have a limited degree of accuracy, but the results obtained are directly correlated with the biologically active flavins.

In these biological tests on animals the basal diet should be deficient in riboflavin and in riboflavin only. For this reason it is difficult to evaluate assays of riboflavin that were made by the usual rat-growth methods before the other components of the vitamin B_2 complex had been recognized. With regard to basal diets to be used in the assay of riboflavin by the rat-growth method, the ideal diet would be one deficient in the vitamin B complex and supplemented with adequate and known amounts of thiamine, pyridoxine, pantothenic acid, choline, and other factors, except riboflavin, known to be essential for the growth of rats. An ideal diet of this kind cannot, as yet, be prepared; and, until it is, we can accept as only tentative the values for riboflavin determined by the rat-growth method. The most complete diet with regard to all the necessary food constituents except riboflavin is apparently a basal diet devoid of the vitamin B complex and supplemented with all the known pure vitamins and a riboflavin-free liver extract, such as has been used by El Sadr and Macrae (57) and by Elvehjem (58) and their respective collaborators.

Snell and Strong (59) have worked out a quantitative estimation of riboflavin, using bacteria. They found that within certain limits the formation of acid by *Lactobacillus casei* ε is proportional to the amount of riboflavin present in the medium. Their basal medium was adequate for the growth of this organism in all respects except riboflavin. This method is known as the "microbiological method."

This simple and quick method has been used with different modifications by various investigators. Blood appears to contain a substance different from riboflavin that enhances the effect of riboflavin on *Lactobacillus casei* ε. Thus the microbiological method, at least without further modification, is not applicable to the determination of riboflavin in blood. Urine and a large number of food products seem to be devoid of the specific interfering substance present in blood.

The results obtained by various investigators by each of the two biological methods of estimation of riboflavin content in foodstuffs have been collected by my collaborator, Dr. Eckardt, in Table 1 for comparison. It is apparent that discrepancies exist between the values determined by the two different methods. When necessary to do so, the conversion factor 1 Bourquin-Sherman unit = 2.19 μg. of riboflavin was used (59).

Disregarding differences in the methods, a review of the collected data reveals a somewhat surprising scarcity of riboflavin in the food products in common use. With the exception of milk, liver, kidney, and eggs, all common foodstuffs are rather poor sources of riboflavin. In this connection it is interesting to note that even whole cereals are by no means rich in riboflavin, in contrast to their high content of thiamine, pyridoxine, and pantothenic acid.

For these data to have practical implications the riboflavin requirement of the human organism should be established.

I believe, however, that I stand on sufficiently solid ground to

TABLE 1

Occurrence of Riboflavin in Natural Foodstuffs in Decreasing Order of Potency*

(Micrograms per Gram of Fresh Weight, except When Otherwise Indicated)

Substance	Rat-Growth Method	Micro-biological Method
Ox-liver meal, dry	45 (50) 68 (60)	72 (52) 50 (59)
Yeast, dry	61.5 (58) 73 (60)	62.5 (58) 36–52 (52)
Liver, pig	37 (50) 23 (62)	25.4–29 (59) 18–21 (63)
Liver, beef	16–25 (61†) 23 (62)	21–25 (63) 44 (59)
Liver, calves	17–21 (61)	20–27 (63)
Kidney, beef	16–20 (61) 18–22 (61)	18–20 (63) ....
Kidney, calves	16–20 (61)	
Milk powder	20 (59)	17–20 (52) 17 (59)
Alfalfa meal, dry	20 (58)	13–15 (52)
Cheese, American	8 (61)	
Eggs, yolk	3.4–4.2 (61)	7.6 (59)
Heart, beef	....	7.6 (63)
Wheat germ	7 (38)	....
Liver, cod	6.5 (50)	....
Cheese, Swiss	6 (61)	....
Cod roe	6 (50)	....
Plums, dried	5.2–6.2 (61)	....
Heart, pig	....	5 (63)
Peanuts	4.7 (60)	....
Cheese, Cheddar	4–5 (61)	....
Soybean oil meal	....	4 (52)
Sardines	3.5 (50)	....
Herring	3.5 (60)	....
Egg white	1.6–2.2 (61) 2.0–2.5 (61)	3.1 (59) ....
Soybean meal	8.5 (60)	3 (59)
Peas, dried	2.0–3.13 (61)	....
Brain, beef	....	2.5 (63)
Oats, ground	2.5 (65)	....
Veal	3.0–3.75 (61)	2.4 (63)
Tongue, beef	....	2 (63)
Pig loin	2.19 (62)	2.0–2.7 (63)
Kippers	2 (50)	....
Muscle, beef	....	1.9 (63)
Milk, whole (per cc.)	1.76–2.55 (61) 2.4 (50) 1.0–1.88 (61) 0.6–2.25 (61)	1.5–2.5 (59) ....
Eggs, whole	2.2–2.75 (61)	1.9–2.3 (64)
Wheat, whole	1.75 (65) about 1 (65)	....
Corn, yellow	1.5 (65)	....
Rice polishings	about 1.5 (38)	....
Cheese, cream	1.4 (61)	....
Cauliflower	1.0–1.25 (61) 1.2–1.5 (61)	....
Carrots	1.0–1.25 (61)	....
Beets, red	1.0–1.25 (61)	....
Cabbage	1.0–2.5 (61) 0.5–1.5 (61)	....
Peas, green	1.0–1.25 (61) 1.8 (50)	....
Spinach	2.5–3.13 (61)	....
Pears	1.0–1.25 (61)	....
Molasses, cane	about 1 (38)	....
Bread, wheat	0.76 (61)	....
Bananas	0.7–0.88 (61)	....
Beans	0.5–0.63 (61)	....
Potatoes	0.5–0.63 (61) 0.4–0.75 (61)	....
Apples	0.4–0.63 (61)	....
Tomatoes	0.24–0.3 (61) 0.32–0.4 (61)	....

* As determined by the microbiological method when the two methods showed varying results. Numbers in parentheses refer to references in the bibliography at the end of the chapter.

† Our attention has been called by Dr. Hazel E. Munsell to the fact that the values given by Emmerie (61) were partly converted values taken from the 1933 edition of H. C. Sherman, *Chemistry of Food and Nutrition*, or from E. P. Daniel and H. E. Munsell, *The Vitamin Content of Foods* . . . . (U.S. Dept. Agric. Misc. Pub. 275 [June, 1937]). A conversion factor of from 2 to 2.5 was used in changing the biological units to milligrams. Both of these publications have been superseded by more recent ones—Dr. Sherman's by a new edition, and Dr. Munsell's by a table in "Vitamins and Their Occurrence in Foods," *Milbank Fund Quarterly*, October, 1940.

credit riboflavin, as a food constituent, with special importance, on the basis of its physiological role in a large and increasing number of cellular reactions, as well as on the basis of its distribution in food products.

BIBLIOGRAPHY

1. György, P.; Kuhn, R.; and Wagner-Jauregg, T., Naturwissenschaften, **21**:560, 1933; Klin. Wchnschr., **12**:1241, 1933.
2. Kuhn, R.; György, P.; and Wagner-Jauregg, T., Ber. d. deutsch. chem. Gesellsch., **66**:317, 576, 1933.
3. Reader, V., Biochem. J., **23**:689, 1929; **24**:77, 1827, 1930.
4. Harris, L. J., Ann. Rev. Biochem., **4**:331, 1935; Kinnersley, H. W.; O'Brien, J. R.; and Peters, R. A., Biochem. J., **29**:701, 1935.
5. Harris, L. J., Ann. Rev. Biochem., **1**:337, 1932.
6. Chick, H., and Copping, A. M., Biochem. J., **24**:1764, 1930.
7. The Biochemical Society, meeting of November 14, 1927.
8. Sure, B.; Kik, M. C.; and Smith, M. E., Proc. Soc. Exper. Biol. & Med., **28**:498, 1930–31.
9. Thatcher, H. S.; Sure, B.; and Walker, D. J., Arch. Path., **11**:425, 1931.
10. Gurin, S. S.; Eddy, W. H.; Denton, J.; and Ammerman, M., J. Exper. Med., **54**:421, 1931.
11. Roscoe, M. H., Biochem. J., **27**:1537, 1933.
12. György, P., J. Biol. Chem., **131**:733, 1939, and see Bibliography.
13. György, P.; Melville, D. B.; Burk, D.; and du Vigneaud, V., Science, **91**:243, 1940; du Vigneaud, V.; Melville, D. B.; György, P.; and Rose, C. S., Science, **92**:62, 1940; György, P.; Rose, C. S.; Hofmann, K.; Melville, D. B.; and du Vigneaud, V.; Science, **92**:609, 1940; du Vigneaud, V.; Hofmann, K.; Melville, D. B.; and György, P., J. Biol. Chem., **140**:643, 1941.
14. Bourquin, A., and Sherman, H. C., J. Am. Chem. Soc., **53**:3501, 1931.
15. György, P., Biochem. J., **29**:741, 1935.
16. György, P., *ibid.*, p. 767.
17. György, P., Nature, **133**:498, 1934.
18. Warburg, O., and Christian, W., Biochem. Ztschr., **254**:438, 1932; Naturwissenschaften, **20**:980, 1932; Biochem. Ztschr., **266**:377, 1933.
19. Ellinger, P., and Koschara, W., Ber. d. deutsch. chem. Gesellsch., **66**:315, 1933; Nature, **133**:553, 1934.
20. Kinnersley, H. W.; O'Brien, J. R.; Peters, R. A.; and Reader, V., Biochem. J., **27**:225, 1933.
21. Birch, T. W.; György, P.; and Harris, L. J., Biochem J., **29**:2830, 1935; Birch, T. W., and György, P., Biochem. J., **30**:304, 1936; György, P.; Sullivan, M.; and Karsner, H. T., Proc. Soc. Exper. Biol. & Med., **37**:313, 1937–38.

22. BANGA, I.; SZENT-GYÖRGYI, A.; and VARGHA, L., Ztschr. f. physiol. Chem., **210**:228, 1932.
23. KUHN, R.; GYÖRGY, P., and WAGNER-JAUREGG, T., Ber. d. deutsch. chem. Gesellsch., **66**:1034, 1933.
24. KARRER, P.; BECKER, B.; BENZ, F.; FREI, P.; SALOMON, H.; and SCHÖPP, K., Helvet. chim. acta, **18**:1435, 1935.
25. KUHN, R.; REINEMUND, K.; WEYGAND, F.; and STRÖBELE, R., Ber. d. deutsch. chem. Gesellsch., **68**:1765, 1935.
26. STERN, K. G., and HOLIDAY, E. R., Ber. d. deutsch. chem. Gesellsch., **67**: 1442, 1934.
27. J.A.M.A., **108**:1340, 1937; **109**:507, 1937.
28. GYÖRGY, P.; KUHN, R.; and WAGNER-JAUREGG, T., Ztschr. f. physiol. Chem., **223**:241, 1934.
29. LASZT, L., and VERZÁR, F., Arch. f. d. ges. Physiol. (Pflügers), **236**:693, 1935; **237**:483, 1936; **239**:136, 1937; VERZÁR, F.; HÜBNER, H.; and LASZT, L., Biochem. Ztschr., **292**:152, 1937.
30. FERREBEE, J. W., J. Biol. Chem., **136**:719, 1940.
31. KENSLER, C. J.; SUGIURA, K.; YOUNG, N. F.; HALTER, C. R.; and RHOADS, C. P., Science, **93**:308, 1941.
32. GYÖRGY, P.; POLING, E. C.; and GOLDBLATT, H., Proc. Soc. Exper. Biol. & Med., **47**:41, 1941.
33. MCELROY, L. W., and GOSS, H., J. Nutrition, **20**:527, 1940.
34. HUNT, C. H., unpublished paper given at Gibson Island Research Conference, Chemistry Section on Vitamins, American Association for the Advancement of Science, July, 1940.
35. GYÖRGY, P., Proc. Soc. Exper. Biol. & Med., **38**:383, 1938.
36. DAY, P. L.; LANGSTON, W. C.; and O'BRIEN, C. S., Am. J. Ophth., 3d ser., **14**:1005, 1931; DAY, P. L.; DARBY, W. J.; and LANGSTON, W. C., J. Nutrition, **13**:389, 1937; DAY, P. L.; DARBY, W. J.; and COSGROVE, K. W., J. Nutrition, **15**:83, 1938.
37. BESSEY, O. A., and WOLBACH, S. B., J. Exper. Med., **69**:1, 1939.
38. GYÖRGY, P., unpublished data.
39. ECKARDT, R. E., and JOHNSON, L. V., Arch. Ophth. (Chicago), N.S., **21**:315, 1939.
40. GYÖRGY, P., and ECKARDT, R. E., Biochem. J., **34**:1143, 1940.
41. GYÖRGY, P.; JOHNSON, L. V.; and ECKARDT, R. E., unpublished data.
42. ENGEL, R. W., and PHILLIPS, P. H., J. Nutrition, **16**:585, 1938; PHILLIPS, P. H., and ENGEL, R. W., J. Nutrition, **18**:227, 1939.
43. NORRIS, L. C.; WILGUS, H. S., JR.; RINGROSE, A. T.; HEIMAN, V.; and HEUSER, G. F., Cornell Agric. Exper. Sta. Bull. 660 (1936); HUNT, C. H.; WINTER, A. R.; and BETHKE, R. M., Poultry Sc., **18**:330, 1939.
44. LEPKOVSKY, S., and JUKES, T. H., J. Nutrition, **12**:515, 1936.

45. SEBRELL, W. H.; ONSTOTT, R. H.; and HUNT, D. J., Pub. Health Rep., 52:427, 1937; SEBRELL, W. H., and ONSTOTT, R. H., Pub. Health Rep., 53:83, 1938; AXELROD, A. E.; LIPTON, M. A.; and ELVEHJEM, C. A., Am. J. Physiol., 133:555, 1941.
46. HUGHES, E. H., J. Nutrition, 17:527, 1939; 20:233, 1940; PATEK, A. J., JR.; POST, J.; and VICTOR, J., Am. J. Physiol., 133:47, 1941.
47. GYÖRGY, P.; ROBSCHEIT-ROBBINS, F. S.; and WHIPPLE, G. H., Am. J. Physiol., 122:154, 1938.
48. CHICK, H.; COPPING, A. M.; and EDGAR, C. E., Biochem. J., 29:722, 1935.
49. WARBURG, O., and CHRISTIAN, W., Biochem. Ztschr., 257:492, 1933.
50. LUNDE, G.; KRINGSTAD, H.; and OLSEN, A., Ztschr. f. physiol. Chem., 260: 141, 1939.
51. EULER, H. VON, and ADLER, E., Ztschr. f. physiol. Chem., 223:105, 1934.
52. HODSON, A. Z., and NORRIS, L. C., J. Biol. Chem., 131:621, 1939.
53. EULER, H. VON; ADLER, E.; and SCHLÖTZER, A., Ztschr. f. physiol. Chem., 226:87, 1934.
54. KUHN, R.; WAGNER-JAUREGG, T.; and KALTSCHMITT, H., Ber. d. deutsch. chem. Gesellsch., 67:1452, 1934.
55. ELLINGER, P., Biochem. J., 32:376, 1938.
56. EEKELEN, M. VAN, and EMMERIE, A., Acta brev. Neerland., 5:77, 1935.
57. EL SADR, M. M.; MACRAE, T. F.; and WORK, C. E., Biochem J., 34:601, 1940.
58. WAGNER, J. R.; AXELROD, A. E.; LIPTON, M. A.; and ELVEHJEM, C. A., J. Biol. Chem., 136:357, 1940.
59. SNELL, E. E., and STRONG, F. M., Indust. & Engin. Chem. (Anal. ed.), 11:346, 1939.
60. SUPPLEE, G. C.; BENDER, R. C.; and JENSEN, O. G., Indust. & Engin. Chem. (Anal. ed.), 11:495, 1939.
61. EMMERIE, A., Ztschr. f. Vitaminforsch., 7:244, 1938.
62. DARBY, W. J., and DAY, P. L., J. Nutrition, 10:209, 1938.
63. MICKELSEN, O.; WAISMAN, H. A.; and ELVEHJEM, C. A., J. Nutrition, 18:517, 1939.
64. SNELL, E. E., and QUARLES, E., J. Nutrition, 22:483, 1941.
65. GYÖRGY, P., Biochem. J., 29:760, 1935.

HUMAN RIBOFLAVIN DEFICIENCY (ARIBOFLAVINOSIS)

W. H. SEBRELL
Division of Chemotherapy, National Institute of Health
U.S. Public Health Service, Bethesda, Maryland

THE identification of human riboflavin deficiency, or ariboflavinosis, necessarily awaited the isolation of riboflavin, as well as the identification of nicotinic acid as a pellagra-curative substance. With these two materials available in pure form, Sebrell and Butler (1, 2) in 1938 and 1939 observed a group of patients on a diet low in both riboflavin and nicotinic acid and studied the symptomatology which developed and failed to respond to nicotinic acid but did respond to riboflavin.

These observations clarified, to some extent, a confused clinical picture which had been recognized by the earliest writers on pellagra. Strambio (1794) and Roussel (1845) and a number of the other earlier writers recognized a form of pellagra without skin lesions, which they called "pellagra sine pellagra." It is possible that at least some of these cases may have been riboflavin deficiency, although it must be remembered that many of these could also have been nicotinic acid deficiency without skin lesions. However, in 1918 Goldberger, Wheeler, and Edgar Sydenstricker (3) first made the suggestion that two separate dietary factors may have been concerned in the production of clinical pellagra; and they stated: "It is suggested that . . . . pellagra includes at least two commonly associated, etiologically distinct, though closely related, syndromes." Goldberger and Tanner (4) in 1925, in some experiments with a casein diet, described a syndrome under the title of "pellagra sine pellagra," which now appears to have been riboflavin deficiency. The latter state:

> . . . . there developed . . . . a dry, glazed, vermilion border of one (usually the lower) or both lips with or without scaling or exfoliation; erosions of the skin at the angles of the mouth with or without fissuring of the commissures; perlèche; reddening of one or both lips, alone or associated with stomatitis; slight

seborrhoea about the nose. . . . . In addition there appeared in several of the patients a peculiar, to us unfamiliar and heretofore undescribed, lesion (a more or less marked accumulation of a pasty, caseous material on a linear reddening of the skin) in the groove at the angles of the nose and in the transverse groove below the nasal septum; in some there developed a conjunctivitis with a secretion that tended to accumulate and dry at the inner canthus of the eyes or on the lids along the palpebral margin.

Some of these symptoms are similar to those seen by Stannus (5) in association with pellagra in Nyasaland in 1912.

Goldberger and Tanner then go on to say that the lesions about the nose and the conjunctivitis were entirely new in their experience with pellagra. In the light of our knowledge today there is little doubt that Goldberger and Tanner were describing riboflavin deficiency, and their work recalls Goldberger's earlier suggestion that the condition characterized by these symptoms may be distinct from pellagra as characterized by the typical dermatitis. This possibility was discussed at some length by Wheeler (6) in 1933. At about the same time, many reports were appearing from various parts of the world describing clinical syndromes in many respects similar to this and attributed to a nutritional defect of some kind. Thus, Wright (7) in 1930 had described in Sierra Leone skin lesions at the mucocutaneous junctions, together with disorders of the nervous system cured by the use of cod-liver oil and yeast.

Fitzgerald (8) in 1932 reported an outbreak of ulceration at the angles of the mouth and gastrointestinal symptoms in an Assam prison and found 1 ounce of yeast daily of benefit. Moore (9) in 1934 described a syndrome of photophobia, sore mouth, white patches at the edges of the lips, dry, scaly, itchy scrotum, and nervous manifestations in Nigeria; and he later reported (10) that the condition was benefited by yeast.

Landor and Pallister (11) from Singapore and Johore, Cicely D. Williams (12) from the Gold Coast, and Aykroyd and Krishnan (13) from India have described clinical syndromes with lesions in the angles of the mouth which appeared to be nutritional in origin and which in some instances responded to treatment with yeast.

It still has not been clarified whether all or any of these conditions are due to riboflavin deficiency. It is quite possible that some of them are multiple deficiencies and that riboflavin deficiency may be involved in the production of some of the lesions. In the meantime, in the course of studies on experimental pellagra, or blacktongue, in dogs, Sebrell (14) reported a fatty degeneration of the liver, which he stated was probably associated in some manner with the diet; and in 1933 (15) he reported an extensive series of experiments to show that this condition, then designated "yellow liver," was probably due to a deficiency of a hitherto unrecognized dietary factor for dogs.

Zimmerman and Burack (16) in 1934 observed lesions in the central nervous system in dogs on diets deficient in vitamin G (B_2), and Zimmerman, Cowgill, and Fox (17) in 1937 extended these observations; while Sebrell, Onstott, and Hunt (18) presented evidence that the "yellow liver" previously described by them was due to riboflavin deficiency. In 1938 Sebrell and Onstott (19) described riboflavin deficiency in the dog, and this was confirmed by Street and Cowgill (20) in 1939. Street, Cowgill, and Zimmerman (21) recently have extended their studies to include chronic riboflavin deficiency in the dog.

Thus, in 1938 it was evident that riboflavin deficiency occurred in the dog sometimes in connection with experimental pellagra diets, and there were a number of reports in the literature of a clinical syndrome in man different from typical pellagra but frequently associated with pellagra; and Sebrell (22) again discussed the possibility of clinical pellagra being a multiple deficiency and mentioned that riboflavin deficiency might occur in man. Thus, with nicotinic acid and riboflavin available, Sebrell and Butler were able to separate the symptoms of riboflavin deficiency from those of nicotinic acid deficiency and to show that symptoms similar to those formerly described by Goldberger as pellagra sine pellagra were due to riboflavin deficiency. The changes as observed by Sebrell and Butler (1, 2) consisted of lesions on the lips, which began with pallor of the mucosa in the angles of the mouth. This pallor was soon followed by maceration; and within a few days superficial linear fissures, usually bilateral, appeared exactly in the angle of the mouth. These fissures showed very little inflammatory reaction, remained moist, and became covered with a superficial yellowish crust, which could be scraped off without bleeding. In some instances these linear fissures showed a tendency to extend onto the skin of the face but did not extend into the mouth. At the time the fissures were developing, the lips became abnormally red, shiny, and superficially denuded along the line of closure. These lesions of the lips were designated "cheilosis."

In addition to the cheilosis, there was also a scaly, slightly greasy desquamative lesion on a mildly erythematous base in the nasolabial folds, on the alae nasi, in the vestibule of the nose, and occasionally on the ears and around the eyelids, especially at the inner and outer canthi.

It was demonstrated that these lesions occurred on a riboflavin deficient diet, disappeared on administration of riboflavin, recurred on withdrawal of riboflavin, failed to respond to treatment with nicotinic acid, and occurred even though sufficient nicotinic acid was given to cure pellagra.

Following this, Vilter, Vilter, and Spies (23) noted clinical improvement in cases of pellagra following the administration of riboflavin; and Oden, Oden, and Sebrell (24) observed 3 cases of ariboflavinosis which responded to riboflavin administration. These 3 cases were the first of this deficiency disease to be recognized and reported in a practitioner's private practice.

Spies, Bean, and Ashe (25) report patients having such lesions who responded to riboflavin, and noted the occurrence of comedones giving a "sharkskin" appearance in the region of the nose and eyes and occasionally of the ears and malar prominences. Spies (26) reports two cases successfully treated with the phosphoric ester of riboflavin. Spies, Bean, and Ashe also noted that some of these patients gave a history of visual disturbances. Spies, Vilter, and Ashe (27) mention the symptoms of riboflavin deficiency seen in their patients and describe an eye lesion, characterized by conjunctivitis, lacrimation, burning of the eyes, and failing vision, which in some instances responded to riboflavin.

Jolliffe, Fein, and Rosenblum (28) then recognized the condition as one which they had been observing in patients in New York, and they reported 15 cases recognizing additional facial lesions, which consisted of filiform excrescences of a seborrheic nature located especially in the nasolabial folds and alae nasi, and occasionally on the bridge of the nose. Because of the frequency with which they have seen the condition, they express the opinion that it may not be uncommon in the northeastern states. V. P. Sydenstricker, Geeslin, Templeton, and Weaver (29) reported 6 cases from Georgia and noted in 2 cases the presence of conjunctivitis, which responded to riboflavin therapy.

In 1940 Kruse, Sydenstricker, Sebrell, and Cleckley (30) called especial attention to changes in the tongue associated with riboflavin deficiency. A specific type of glossitis was recognized in which the tongue is clean, the papillae flattened or mushroom-shaped rather than atrophic, and the color definitely magenta or purplish-red, in contrast to the scarlet-red tongue of nicotinic-acid deficiency. These authors also report 9 cases, and later Sydenstricker, Sebrell, Cleckley, and Kruse (31) report a total of 47 cases, of riboflavin deficiency in which ocular lesions were present as a result of interstitial keratitis. Johnson and Eckardt (32) reported similar findings under the designation of "rosacea keratitis."

It is to be noted that Spies, Bean, and Ashe (25) and Spies, Vilter, and Ashe (27) were the first to report instances in which ocular lesions responded to treatment with riboflavin, although they did not report the symptoms as being due to the presence of keratitis.

Pock-Steen (33) reported that photophobia, dimness of vision, mydriasis, and keratitis in 109 patients with sprue were cured by riboflavin.

The occurrence of eye lesions in experimental animals with riboflavin deficiency has been noted by many observers. The most detailed study of corneal vascularization in rats on a riboflavin-deficient diet is that of Bessey and Wolbach (34), who stated that vascularization of the cornea was an early and constant finding in riboflavin-deficient rats. Eckardt and Johnson (35) also noted keratitis or vascularization of the cornea in rats on a riboflavin-deficient diet.

It is of interest to recall, in this connection, that eye symptoms of various kinds have been described in association with pellagra from the very earliest literature on the subject, being mentioned as early as 1791 by Soler, and in this country especially by Clark (36) and Whaley (37) in 1909. It now appears likely that some of these eye lesions were due to riboflavin deficiency, since the eye symptoms reported are so similar to those seen with the corneal vascularization and keratitis of riboflavin deficiency. The principal eye symptoms are severe photophobia, circumcorneal injection and a burning sensation of the eyeball, dimness of vision and intense injection of the vessels of the fornix, and sclera which superficially resembles conjunctivitis. Some cases show corneal opacities, mydriasis, and iritis. In many early cases of riboflavin deficiency beginning vascularization of the cornea can be seen with the slit lamp long before gross lesions can be detected, indicating that the eye lesions in man are similar to those seen in experimental animals.

From the point of view of distress and disability, the eye lesions are the most important symptoms of riboflavin deficiency. They do not appear to be present invariably in riboflavin deficiency, nor can all cases of keratitis be said to be due to riboflavin deficiency.

Last year Spies, Bean, Vilter, and Huff (38) made a special study of endemic riboflavin deficiency in infants and children. They report 241 cases with the characteristic lesions, and they state that they are convinced that it is the most common clinical deficiency disease among infants and children in a section of Alabama.

To summarize the clinical picture of ariboflavinosis, the usual lesions are: (1) ocular lesions, consisting usually of a vascularizing keratitis with photophobia, dimness of vision, severe injection of the vessels of the fornix and sclera, burning of the eyes, lacrimation, and, in severe cases, opacities of the cornea; (2) oral lesions, consisting usually of linear fissures in the angles of the mouth, a reddened, shiny, denuded appearance of the lower lip, and a flattening of the papillae of the tongue, which becomes magenta red in color; and (3) dermal lesions, consisting usually of seborrheic accumulations in the folds of the skin, especially in the nasolabial folds, around the eyelids, on the ears, and in some cases comedones and a sharkskin-appearing lesion on the nose and over the malar eminences. In some cases the seborrheic dermal lesions may be extensive and may involve other regions of the body.

In the treatment of ariboflavinosis we have found a daily dose of 5–10 mg. to be sufficient to bring about rapid improvement in most cases. A few cases seem to require more than this amount. It must be kept in mind that, if there is a complicating disease of the gastro-intestinal tract which may interfere with absorption or utilization, it may be necessary to give the material parenterally. Because of the rapid elimination of riboflavin in the urine, it is preferable to give it in small amounts at frequent intervals, instead of just one daily dose.

Since ariboflavinosis seems to be so prevalent in this country, it is of considerable interest to determine the human requirement for riboflavin. Several investigators have studied the urinary excretion of riboflavin. Among the more important of these studies are the observations of Emmerie (39, 40, 41), who found a daily urinary excretion in men of 819 to 1,250 µg. He observed an increase in excretion on increased intake, and in one individual on a restricted intake the daily excretion dropped from 650 µg. to 300–400 µg. Hogan (42) estimated the human riboflavin requirement at 2–3 mg. a day on the basis of Emmerie's data. Ferrebee (43) found that riboflavin excretion depended on riboflavin intake and that the daily excretion in 5 normal subjects eating their usual diet varied from 700 to 1,700 µg. per day.

Strong, Feeney, Moore, and Parsons (44), in a study of the riboflavin content of blood and urine, found human blood to contain around 0.5 µg. per gram except in 3 subjects on a restricted riboflavin intake. Five hundred to 800 µg. per day were excreted in the urine by normal adults on an unrestricted diet. In 4 normal women this decreased to from 50 to 150 µg. on a daily intake of 1–2 mg. of riboflavin. They believe, therefore, that an intake of this quantity is perhaps insufficient to supply the daily requirement.

Sebrell, Butler, Wooley, and Isbell (45), in a long-continued balance study on 10 women taking a diet containing approximately 0.5 mg. of riboflavin per 2,400 cal., found a daily average excretion of only 77 µg., as compared with a daily average excretion of 357 µg. in women on an institution diet; while 11 normal men on their usual diets excreted from 234 to 1,740 µg. a day. The 10 women on the restricted riboflavin intake were given varying amounts of riboflavin, and the urinary excretion again estimated. An effort was made to estimate the human daily requirement for riboflavin on the basis of these data.

The amount of riboflavin unaccounted for by urinary excretion in each subject at the various levels of riboflavin dosage is shown in Figure 1. This chart shows a significant increase in the riboflavin unaccounted for on an intake between 0.085 and 0.11 mg. per kilogram of body weight. Thus, when two subjects were receiving 0.085 mg. of riboflavin per kilogram of body weight daily, the amount unaccounted for by urinary excretion was 40.5 and 53.0 μg. per kilo-

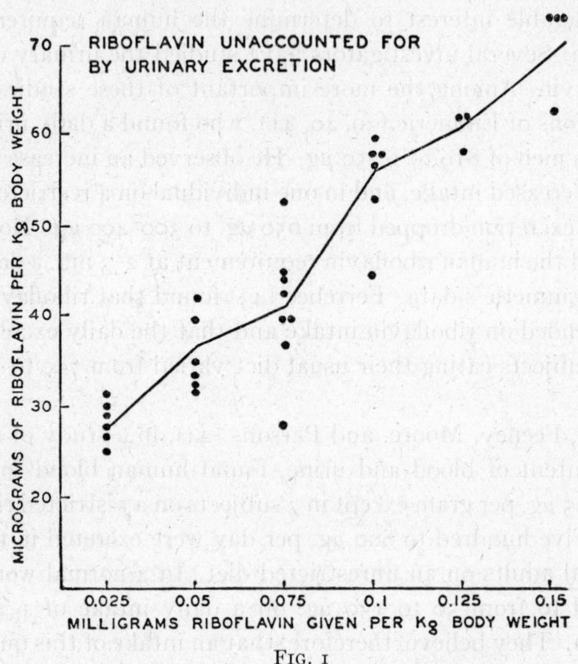

FIG. 1

gram of body weight per day. On increasing the daily intake to 0.11 mg. per kilogram of body weight, the amount unaccounted for by urinary excretion became 58.5 and 73.0 μg. per kilogram of body weight, respectively. This suggests that with the larger doses a greater amount of riboflavin is either being destroyed or is not absorbed, and that 0.085 mg. per kilogram of body weight is probably an intake greater than that needed for riboflavin saturation.

On an intake of 0.035 mg. of riboflavin per kilogram of body weight, the average urinary excretion ranged from 140 to 186 μg. per day. These figures are lower than the average for the women on the institution diet (357 μg.). On an intake of 0.06 mg. per kilogram of body weight, the average urinary excretion varied from 793 to 1,265 μg. per day, which is higher than the average amount excreted by the women on the institution diet and is within the normal range for men.

Because of the exceptionally large increase in daily urinary excretion which occurred on the 0.06 mg. per kilogram intake, it appears that this amount is probably above the normal requirement, while the 0.035 mg. per kilogram amount is marginal or below the normal requirement.

Sebrell and Butler (1, 2) also noted that a supplement of 0.025 mg. per kilogram of body weight was an insufficient amount in the treatment of some cases of ariboflavinosis.

The above lines of evidence indicate that 0.035 mg. of riboflavin per kilogram of body weight is not quite enough to meet the adult requirement and that 0.06 mg. per kilogram of body weight is slightly above the required amount. On this basis, the daily requirement of an adult would be approximately 3 mg.

It appears to be difficult to obtain this amount of riboflavin in the usual adult American diet unless a considerable amount of milk is included, and it has been suggested that the estimated daily requirement is too high and perhaps represents an amount of riboflavin necessary for saturation rather than a maintenance requirement. However, the very widespread occurrence of ariboflavinosis suggests that the American diet may actually be deficient in riboflavin, and the rapid fall in urinary excretion of riboflavin when the daily intake is reduced to 2 mg. suggests that these estimated requirements, if too high, are not very much above the daily requirement. The National Research Council Committee on Food and Nutrition has recommended a daily allowance of 2.7 mg. for a moderately active man.

In conclusion, then, although riboflavin deficiency as such has been recognized in humans only for about two and a half years, the prominent clinical features have been established, suitable dosage for treatment has been determined, and a reasonable approximation of the human daily requirement for riboflavin has been obtained. However, we still know nothing of the underlying biochemical changes responsible for these symptoms, and the question of why these symptoms develop is yet to be answered.

BIBLIOGRAPHY

1. SEBRELL, W. H., and BUTLER, R. E., Pub. Health Rep., **53**:2282, 1938.
2. SEBRELL, W. H., and BUTLER, R. E., *ibid.*, **54**:2121, 1939.
3. GOLDBERGER, JOSEPH; WHEELER, G. A.; and SYDENSTRICKER, EDGAR J.A.M.A., **71**:944, 1918.
4. GOLDBERGER, JOSEPH, and TANNER, W. F., Pub. Health Rep., **40**:54, 1925
5. STANNUS, H. S., Tr. Soc. Trop. Med. & Hyg., **5**:112, 1912.
6. WHEELER, G. A., Pub. Health Rep., **48**:67, 1933.
7. WRIGHT, E. JENNER, Dietetics in warm climates, p. 367. J. Neil Leitch. London: Harrison & Sons, Ltd., 1930.
8. FITZGERALD, G. H., Indian M. Gaz., **67**:556, 1932.
9. MOORE, D. G. F., Ann. Trop. Med., **28**:295, 1934.
10. MOORE, D. FITZGERALD, Lancet, **232**:1225, 1937.
11. LANDOR, J. V., and PALLISTER, R. A., Tr. Roy. Soc. Trop. Med. & Hyg., **29**:121, 1935.
12. WILLIAMS, CICELY D., Lancet, **229**:1151, 1935.
13. AYKROYD, W. R., and KRISHNAN, B. G., Indian J. M. Res., **24**:411, 1936.
14. SEBRELL, W. H., Pub. Health Rep., **44**: 2697, 1929.
15. SEBRELL, W. H., Nat. Inst. Health Bull. 162, p. 23, 1933.
16. ZIMMERMAN, H. M., and BURACK, E., J. Exper. Med., **59**:21, 1934.
17. ZIMMERMAN, H. M.; COWGILL, G. R.; and FOX, J. C., JR., Arch. Neurol. & Psychiat., **37**:286, 1937.
18. SEBRELL, W. H.; ONSTOTT, R. H.; and HUNT, D. J., Pub. Health Rep., **52**:427, 1937.
19. SEBRELL, W. H., and ONSTOTT, R. H., Pub. Health Rep., **53**:83, 1938.
20. STREET, H. R., and COWGILL, G. R., Am. J. Physiol., **125**:323, 1939.
21. STREET, H. R.; COWGILL, G. R.; and ZIMMERMAN, H. M., J. Nutrition, **22**:7, 1941.
22. SEBRELL, W. H., J.A.M.A., **110**:1665, 1938.
23. VILTER, R. W.; VILTER, S. P.; and SPIES, T. D., J.A.M.A., **112**:420, 1939.
24. ODEN, J. W.; ODEN, L. H., JR., and SEBRELL, W. H., Pub. Health Rep., **54**:790, 1939.
25. SPIES, T. D.; BEAN, W. B.; and ASHE, W. F., Ann. Int. Med., **12**:1830, 1939.
26. SPIES, T. D., South. M. J., **32**:618, 1939.
27. SPIES, T. D.; VILTER, R. W.; and ASHE, W. F., J.A.M.A., **113**:931, 1939.
28. JOLLIFFE, N.; FEIN, H. D.; and ROSENBLUM, L. A., New England Med., **221**:921, 1939.
29. SYDENSTRICKER, V. P.; GEESLIN, L. E.; TEMPLETON, C. M.; and WEAVER, J. W., J.A.M.A., **113**:1697, 1939.
30. KRUSE, H. D.; SYDENSTRICKER, V. P.; SEBRELL, W. H.; and CLECKLEY, H. M., Pub. Health Rep., **55**:157, 1940.

31. SYDENSTRICKER, V. P.; SEBRELL, W. H.; CLECKLEY, H. M.; and KRUSE, H. D., J.A.M.A., **114**:2437, 1940.
32. JOHNSON, L. V., and ECKARDT, R. E., Arch. Ophth., N.S., **23**:899, 1940.
33. POCK-STEEN, P. H., Geneesk. tijdschr. v. Nederl.-Indië, **79**:1986, 1939. Abstr., J.A.M.A., **113**:2102, 1939.
34. BESSEY, O. A., and WOLBACH, S. B., J. Exper. Med., **69**:1, 1939.
35. ECKARDT, R. E., and JOHNSON, L. V., Arch. Ophth., N.S., **21**:315, 1939.
36. CLARK, A. B., Tr. Nat. Conf. on Pellagra, Columbia, S.C., 1910, p. 275.
37. WHALEY, A. M., *ibid.*, p. 279.
38. SPIES, T. D.; BEAN, W. B.; VILTER, R. W.; and HUFF, N. E., Am. J. M. Sc., N.S., **200**:697, 1940.
39. EMMERIE, A., Nature, **138**:164, 1936.
40. EMMERIE, A., Acta brev. Neerland., **6**:108, 1936.
41. EMMERIE, A., *ibid.*, **7**:71, 1937.
42. HOGAN, A. G., The vitamins, p. 271. Chicago: American Medical Assoc., 1939.
43. FERREBEE, J. W., J. Clin. Investigation, **19**:251, 1940.
44. STRONG, F. M.; FEENEY, R. E.; MOORE, B.; and PARSONS, H. T., J. Biol. Chem., **137**:363, 1941.
45. SEBRELL, W. H.; BUTLER, R. E.; WOOLEY, J. G., and ISBELL, H.; Pub. Health Rep., **56**:510, 1941.

THE STORY OF PELLAGRA AND ITS TREATMENT WITH NICOTINIC ACID

DAVID T. SMITH
Departments of Bacteriology and Medicine, Duke University School of Medicine

IN THE original descriptions of pellagra by Casal in 1735 and Thiéry in 1755 both the dietary and the photosensitization theories are vaguely suggested (1). There is a statement that the disease is most prevalent at the season of the spring equinox and an insistence that the skin lesions must be located on the exposed surfaces of the hands or feet to justify the diagnosis of mal de la rosa (pellagra). The importance of diet is suggested in the following sentence: "The malady has never been described as far as I know, and does not exist perhaps elsewhere with as much violence as in *Asturians*, especially those of *Oviedo:* for the Asturians of *Santillana* are more healthy by nature of the soil, by the quality of the air, & *of the* food."[1]

The studies of Francesco Frapolli of Italy in 1771 led to the use of our modern name "pellagra" (*pelle agro*, "rough skin"). Frapolli was the first student of the disease to insist that the lesions were precipitated by exposure to sunlight (2).

The prevalence of pellagra in Spain, Italy, Rumania, and France in areas where maize formed a considerable portion of the diet suggested to the early students of the disease the presence of some toxic substance in the maize. This theory was supported by the absence of pellagra in Bulgaria, where little maize was consumed, and by its disappearance in France when the planting of maize was forbidden.

Raubitschek in 1912 attempted to explain by his photosensitization theory the observed effects of sunlight in areas where maize was consumed (3). He assumed that maize and possibly other cereals contained a photosensitizing substance which sensitized the body tissues and that subsequent exposure to sunlight precipitated the lesions.

[1] The italics are the author's.

With the explosive outbreak of pellagra in the southern part of the United States between 1905 and 1910 the disease became a national problem. Southern physicians were about equally divided in their adherence to the "poison-corn" theory and the "infection" theory. Their conclusions were not so absurd as they appear to us today because the onset of the disease was frequently sudden and violent and of epidemic proportions, death following often after only a few days or weeks. The Illinois Pellagra Commission of 1910 concluded that pellagra was "due to infection with some living micro-organism." The Thompson-McFadden Pellagra Commission of 1912 and 1916 decided that pellagra was an alimentary canal infection, and Joseph Goldberger was assigned the problem of isolating the infecting organism. After a most thorough and exhausting study Goldberger concluded that pellagra was due not to an infection but to a dietary deficiency. The final proof of the dietary origin of the disease was given in 1915, when Goldberger and Wheeler produced pellagra in 6 of 11 convicts who had volunteered to eat the "pellagra-producing diet" (4).

The significance of a good diet in the prevention and cure of pellagra was implied by Casal and emphasized by many later Italian and French investigators. As early as 1912 both Funk (5, 6) and Sandwith (7) independently suggested that pellagra was a dietary deficiency disease analogous to beriberi. In no instance, however, was the suggestion followed by concrete demonstration until Goldberger and his associates carried out their important and time-consuming experiments which offered convincing proof of the dietary origin of the disease.

Strange as it seems to us today, Goldberger's prison-farm experiment did not convince the majority of the students of pellagra. Harris has compiled an imposing list of contemporary pellagra specialists who questioned the results on the ground that Goldberger did not produce the typical explosive endemic disease. Even more confusing were the later human experiments of Wheeler on hospitalized patients, where a general debility was produced without typical skin lesions. These cases were classified as "pellagra sine pellagra," or pellagra without typical skin lesions (8). The explanation of the failure to produce explosive pellagra with typical skin lesions probably lies in the fact that Goldberger and his associates chose to ignore the other factor in producing the pattern of clinical pellagra, namely, the effect of sunlight on the skin of the deficient patient. In Wheeler's study the subjects were confined to hospital beds, where they were protected from direct sunlight; and in the original prison-farm experiment, where mild but definite skin lesions were produced, the exposure to sunlight was only incidental and sporadic.

Goldberger's preventive work was magnificent and was readily accepted. His separation of the heat-labile vitamin B_1 from the B complex by means of autoclaving released that factor from all implication in the etiology of pellagra, thus opening up another whole field of vitamin research. Goldberger's observation that canine blacktongue was the analogue of human pellagra indicated an experimental animal and mode of study which led ultimately to the discovery of the specific protective vitamin, nicotinic acid.

By 1930 the problem of preventing and curing pellagra was solved in theory. It was agreed that a well-balanced diet containing an abundance of milk, eggs, fresh vegetables, and muscle meats would prevent the disease. But a considerable part of the population in the South, either through ignorance, poverty, or wilfulness, would not eat this diet, and pellagra continued a scourge. Yeast alone would prevent the disease and would cure the mild cases, but it was not adequate to cure the severely ill patients.

CLINICAL METHODS OF STUDY

Between 1930 and 1937 more critical clinical methods of evaluating the curative effect of hypothetical "pellagra-curative materials" were developed, and so it was possible to obtain quickly in 1937 and 1938 conclusive proof that Elvehjem's nicotinic acid was the pellagra-curative vitamin.

Goldberger having shown that a well-rounded diet containing muscle meat, milk, eggs, and fresh fruits or vegetables not only would prevent pellagra but would cure the milder cases, it was obvious that such a diet was not suitable for the assay of curative materials. In a series of pellagra cases studied by Blackford (9) of the University of Virginia there was little, if any, difference in mortality, or the duration, of the disease in one group receiving the usual hospital diet and another given a daily supplement of yeast. Sydenstricker (10) of the University of Georgia Medical School found a mortality of 33.7 per cent in a group of 92 pellagrins treated with the usual hospital diet and a mortality of 25.56 per cent in 356 pellagrins treated with a daily supplement of 90 gm. of dried brewers' yeast. These observations did not prove that yeast had no pellagra-curative value but proved that there was about as much pellagra-curative substances in the hospital diet as in the yeast

TABLE 1

STANDARD BASIC DIET NO. 1

Article	Quantity (Gm.)	Protein (Gm.)	Fat (Gm.)	Carbohydrate (Gm.)	Minerals (Gm.)			Vitamins					Calories
					Calcium	Phosphorus	Iron	A	B	C	D	G	
Corn meal	92	8.3	2.0	69.0	0.0110	0.1225	0.0006	.....	±	.....	.....	±	
Cane syrup	105	.....	.....	89.2	.....	.....	.....	.....	+	.....	.....	+	
Flour	111	12.5	1.2	83.4	.0220	.1030	0.0010	.....	+	.....	.....	−	
Lard	81	.....	81.0	.....	.....	.....	.....	.....	.....	.....	.....	.....	
Rice	25	2.0	0.1	19.6	.0023	.0240	0.0002	.....	.....	.....	.....	.....	2,890.0
Field peas	90	19.2	1.4	54.6	.0756	.0760	0.0052	+	+	.....	.....	+	
Hominy grits	51	4.3	0.3	40.6	.0056	.0734	0.0005	+	+	.....	.....	+	
Fat salt pork	60	1.1	51.3	0.0	.0011	.0115	0.0001	.....	.....	.....	.....	.....	
Cod-liver oil	90 cc.	.....	90.0	.....	.....	.0117	.....	+++	.....	.....	+++	+	810.0
Tomato juice	45 cc.	0.4	0.1	2.0	.0050	.....	0.0002	+	+	+++	.....	+	10.3
Iron ammonium citrate	6	.....	.....	.....	.....	.....	1.0200	.....	.....	.....	.....	.....	.....
Calcium gluconate	6	.....	.....	.....	.5580	.....	.....						
Cheese	60	17.4	21.6	.....	0.5586	0.4098	0.0007	+	+	.....	.....	.....	264.0
Total	.....	65.2	249.0	358.4	1.2392	0.8319	1.0285	+++	++	+++	+++	+	3,974.3

supplement. It was obvious, then, that a standard basic deficient diet must be used before the curative effects of the supplement could be evaluated.

In 1931, controlled clinical studies with a standard deficient diet were introduced independently by Spies and his associates in Cleveland (11, 12) and by our group at Duke (13, 14). Later similar studies, using controlled diets, were reported by Fouts (15, 16), Sydenstricker (17), Jolliffe (18), Sebrell (19, 20), and many other investigators. Spies used very restricted diets made up from (*a*) lactose and cornstarch or from (*b*) corn-meal mush, corn-meal muffins, pork fat, maple syrup, polished rice, cornstarch pudding, coffee, and sugar, which were almost completely deficient in all vitamins and mineral elements. In contrast to this, we (13) devised a "Standard Basic Diet" (Table 1) which was thought to contain all the known elements essential to nutrition except Goldberger's pellagra-preventive factor. It was known at the time that the diet contained more than traces of the pellagra-preventive factor and that it would be necessary to have a preliminary period of observation on each patient to see that they were not making a spontaneous recovery before adding the material which was being tested.

After synthetic vitamin C became available, this was substituted for the tomato juice in the original diet, and the modified diet was designated "Standard Basic Diet No. 2." When the curative tests with nicotinic acid were begun, the diet was restricted by eliminating cod-liver oil, ascorbic acid, and the iron and calcium, to see what effect would be obtained by nicotinic acid alone. This modification was called "Standard Basic Diet No. 3."

EFFECT OF SUNLIGHT ON THE CLINICAL MANIFESTATIONS OF PELLAGRA

In Spies's early studies (11, 12) with the deficient diet he noted that extensive skin lesions disappeared while the patient was receiving practically no vitamins and certainly no pellagra-preventive materials. We (13, 21) noted the same phenomenon in patients confined to the hospital and fed our Standard Basic Diet No. 1. However, when our patients were exposed to sunlight, some of them had a recurrence of the skin lesions and, coincidental with this, an exaggeration of their clinical symptoms (22, 21). Bass (23) of New Orleans exposed pellagrins to sunlight as early as 1910 and produced skin lesions. He also noted aggravation of existing symptoms, with the development of new symptoms so alarming that the experimental exposures were discontinued. In 1935 Spies (24) reported in his study on the "Relationship of Pellagrous Dermatitis to Sunlight" that some pellagrins recovered while being exposed to sunlight and others developed rather atypical skin lesions while subsisting on the deficient diet but without exposure. These apparently conflicting observations were clarified by a careful study of the different types of skin lesions occurring in pellagrins and the effect of sunlight on their clinical manifestations (21). Ruffin and Smith (22) confined their patients to bed and fed them the standard deficient diet. After a preliminary period of observation they were divided into two groups. Those that were apparently growing worse were treated at once with some pellagra-curative material; the others, who were apparently stationary or improving slightly, were exposed to graded doses of sunlight. One arm, or one leg, was exposed to the direct rays of the sun for 30 minutes, and the time was increased by 30 minutes each day up to a maximum of 2 hours per daily exposure. Members of the staff or medical students served as controls, and in no instance was the exposure severe enough to produce sunburn in the control subjects. A definite dermatitis developed over the exposed area in 34 of 81 pellagrins tested (42 per cent). The dermatitis produced was indistinguishable from that which appears spontaneously on the exposed skin of patients with pellagra. In 32 instances the lesions were produced on a previously involved area. In 10 patients, however, the dermatitis was produced on apparently healthy skin which had been previously protected from sunlight by clothing. In 2 patients no dermatitis was induced, but constitutional symptoms appeared and the exposures were discontinued. The condition of the tongue became definitely worse in 27 of the 36 patients. Exposure was followed by an increase in diarrhea and anorexia in 21 patients. Nausea and vomiting developed in 10, and dementia[2] in 4. In all 36 patients

[2] The acute inflammation of the skin, the gastrointestinal disturbances, and the dementia which develop after a pellagrin exposes himself to direct sunlight suggest some type of acute poisoning. The symptoms are not unlike those observed in acute porphyrin intoxication, and accumulation of endogenous porphyrins in the skin and other tissues of the patient has been suggested as an explanation.

Until recently no accurate methods were available for measuring porphyrin excretion in pellagrins. The method reported by Beckh, Ellinger, and Spies (93) gives values which are obviously too high, since not only porphyrins but other colored substances in the urine are included. More accurate but much more laborious methods have been devised by Watson (94, 95, 96, 97) and by Dobriner, Strain, and Localio (98). Dobriner (99) and his associates found an increased excretion of coproporphyrin I in both the urine and feces of a pellagrin. Following treatment and clinical improvement, the values returned to normal.

This evidence of increased porphyrins in acute pellagra might be offered as an

constitutional symptoms developed after the first exposure to sunlight; yet neither cutaneous lesions nor constitutional symptoms occurred in any of these 36 patients after re-exposure to maximum doses of sunlight following adequate therapy.

The pellagra patients employed for the clinical evaluation of the effect of nicotinic acid were selected according to the criteria outlined above. We considered the pellagra active if, while subsisting upon the basic diet, the patient grew worse or if the lesions and symptoms were reactivated by experimental exposure to sunlight.

In 45 of the original 81 pellagrins exposed to sunlight no local cutaneous or generalized symptoms developed. In many instances, as reported by Spies in 1935 (24), the skin lesions healed rapidly while they were being exposed to sunlight, even though they were subsisting solely on the basic deficient diet without therapeutic supplements. Similar spontaneous recoveries have been reported by Matthews (25) and by Sydenstricker and his associates (17).

No entirely satisfactory explanation can be given for these apparently spontaneous recoveries. The following observations may afford a partial explanation for the observed facts. In a number of our cases it was learned that the patients had eaten yeast, liver, red muscle meat, or fish *after* the appearance of the skin lesions and shortly before admission to the hospital; (2) the basic diet contains an appreciable amount of nicotinic acid and, in general, is a better diet than that eaten by the patient at home; (3) the maximum period of exposure to sunlight, while in the hospital, was only 2 hours, in contrast to 8–12 hours of spontaneous exposure to which the patient was frequently subjected before the development of the original lesions; and (4) the patients were in bed, and consequently less active than before admission, and might not require as much nicotinic acid as ambulatory patients. It is obvious, in any case, that this type of nonreactive patient cannot be used for a critical assay of pellagra-curative substances.

---

explanation for the patients' increased sensitivity to sunlight if it were not well known that a similar increase occurs in lead poisoning, in certain cirrhoses of the liver (100), in arsenical dermatitis, and in poisoning with cincophen, sulfonal, and trional (96) and may therefore be a result, rather than a cause, of the disordered metabolism in pellagra.

TYPES OF SKIN LESIONS FOUND IN PELLAGRINS

The study of Smith and Ruffin (21) on the effect of sunlight in producing the lesions on the exposed surfaces of the body led to a critical study of the various types of skin lesions found in pellagrins and their response to therapy (22). The lesions may be classified under six types: (*a*) The most important lesions are those on the exposed surfaces of the body which are precipitated by exposure to sunlight (21). (*b*) The second type is a "dyssebacia," sometimes mislabeled "seborrhea," where the orifices of the sebaceous glands are plugged with dry, grayish-yellow material, which usually projects above the surface of the skin and feels like sandpaper or sharkskin (26, 27). These lesions occur usually about the alae nasi but sometimes spread over the forehead, face, and neck. The lesions are not inflammatory and are apparently confined to the face. They have no direct relation to the inflammatory lesions precipitated by exposure to sunlight, though both may occur on the face of the same patient. (*c*) There may be hyperkeratosis with increased pigmentation over the bony prominences of the body (21). (*d*) There are frequently excoriated lesions on the skin about the anus and genitalia. Lesions about the female genitalia are very common (21). (*e*) Lesions may appear on the lips, which are red and scaly, and in the corners of the mouth at the mucocutaneous junctions, as cracks or sores, associated with scaly lesions in the orifices of the nose and on the delicate skin of the ears (20). (*f*) Lesions of the external portions of the eyes may appear (28).

The first type of skin lesion is precipitated by exposure to sunlight, and there is a close relationship between its severity and time of appearance and the severity of the constitutional symptoms. The other five types of lesions bear no relation to exposure to sunlight and cannot be correlated with the severity of the constitutional symptoms. One common factor may be found in all six types of skin lesions. The resistance of the tissues to chemical, mechanical, and thermal injury has been specifically lowered.

LIVER AND LIVER EXTRACTS IN THE TREATMENT OF PELLAGRA

The use of liver and the various liver extracts in pellagra serve to connect the studies of Goldberger and his associates with the final isolation of nicotinic acid amide by Elvehjem and his collaborators.

Voegtlin (29) prepared an extract of liver for the treatment of pellagra in 1914. While reasonably good results were reported, this form of therapy was not employed widely until many years later, probably owing to the fact that liver extracts were not readily available until they were prepared commercially for the treatment of pernicious anemia. Goldberger found that liver was one of the most potent blacktongue preventive materials, and in 1930 Goldberger and Sebrell (30) showed that experimental blacktongue could be prevented and cured by a powdered extract of liver (Lilly's 343). This work of Goldberger and Sebrell formed the connecting link between the original Goldberger studies and the subsequent studies on the liver and liver fractions. Two years after the animal experiments of Goldberger and Sebrell, Boggs and Padget (31) reported a series of pellagrins who made surprisingly good recoveries from pellagra after treatment with this powdered liver extract. It should be noted, however, that their patients were fed a well-balanced diet while receiving the liver extract, so that the recovery cannot be attributed entirely to the supplementary therapy. That this powdered liver extract will cure pellagra was demonstrated by our studies at Duke in 1934 (13) and by those of Fouts and his associates (15, 16) in 1936. In these studies the patients were maintained upon a deficient diet and were studied under carefully controlled conditions.

After the introduction of the parenteral extracts of liver for the treatment of pernicious anemia Ramsdell and Magness (32) and Spies (33) cured a series of patients by injecting the liver intramuscularly. Their results were confirmed by a number of other observers (16, 34, 35, 36, 37). Spies (35) and his associates used large doses of liver extract intravenously and intramuscularly with dramatic results and reported a reduction in mortality from 32 to 6 per cent with this method of therapy. The patients, however, were receiving a hospital diet at the time they were given the parenteral liver, and the results cannot be attributed entirely to the liver extract. These parenteral extracts, when tested by our methods (38), were found to be only partly effective in curing the patients.

In contrast to the results with parenteral extracts, we found crude aqueous extracts of whole liver completely effective in curing pellagra. This work was first reported in 1932 (14), and later in more detail in 1934 (13) and in 1937 (38). In 1937 we treated patients with the parenteral fraction of whole liver[1] containing the pernicious-anemia factor, and with the residue fraction of liver after the removal of the pernicious-anemia factor, separately and in combination. The patients failed to improve while receiving daily doses of 1 cc. of the parenteral extract (derived from 100 gm. of liver) or while receiving the 24–30 cc. of the residue; but when the intramuscular extract and the residue were given simultaneously, in doses which had previously proved ineffective when administered alone, dramatic recovery occurred. This suggested the possibility of there being two or more factors in liver which were required for the cure of pellagra. Experiments with canine blacktongue were carried out simultaneously with the clinical studies on pellagra (39). The results were comparable to those obtained in patients (38). The simple aqueous extracts of the Valentine's type, which retain most of the vitamins of the B complex, were very effective in curing experimental blacktongue; the parenteral extracts were only partly effective. The residue fractions derived from an amount of liver comparable to that from which the parenteral fractions were derived were also ineffective in curing the animals; but when the two fractions were combined, the results were as dramatic as when the whole crude water extract was employed. This also indicated that there were two or more fractions needed for the cure of canine blacktongue. The later discovery by Elvehjem and his associates that nicotinic acid alone cured experimental blacktongue was apparently in conflict with this conclusion. The explanation lay in an unrecognized partial deficiency of B_1 and riboflavin in the basic diet employed for the production of blacktongue (40), which will be discussed in more detail later. Apparently, nicotinic acid was partly distributed in the parenteral fraction and partly in the

[1] The term "parenteral fraction of whole liver" is used in the medical literature to designate certain highly refined and purified fractions of liver which contain large amounts of the pernicious-anemia factor and are suitable for either intramuscular or intravenous injections.

The material which is left over after the extraction of this purified fraction is referred to as the "residue fraction."

residue fraction, while a larger part of the B_1 and riboflavin remained in the residue fraction.

Numerous studies were carried on in various laboratories on the fractions of liver with the object of obtaining the most potent possible parenteral extract for the treatment of pellagra and with the hope that the chemical substances responsible could be isolated.

THE HISTORY OF NICOTINIC ACID

Nicotinic acid was prepared in pure chemical form as early as 1867 by Huber (41). It is produced with ease by oxidizing nicotine, thus destroying the toxic effect of this alkaloid and leaving the vitamin, nicotinic acid.

In 1911 Funk (5, 6), and later Suzuki, isolated nicotinic acid from rice polishings in their search for vitamin B_1. The material was discarded when it was found to be ineffective in curing beriberi. Nicotinic acid was the first vitamin to be isolated in pure chemical form; yet its vitamin activity was not recognized until 1937. Bottles of the curative material remained on the shelves of the chemical laboratories gathering dust for over twenty-five years while millions of patients died of pellagra.

We have seen that nicotinic acid appeared first as an oxidation product of nicotine. Next it was isolated by Funk from rice polishings, a food. In 1935 it appeared again in a new role when Warburg (42) and von Euler (43) found that nicotinic acid amide is an essential part of one of the coenzyme systems. Its role in the nutrition of bacteria was discovered when Knight (44) found nicotinic acid essential for the growth of *Staphylococcus aureus* when cultivated on a synthetic medium; and Mueller (45) found it growth-promoting for diphtheria bacilli. Mueller observed that liver extracts stimulated the growth of diphtheria bacilli, and, in searching for this growth-promoting factor, isolated nicotinic acid amide and found it as effective as the whole liver extract. Elvehjem and his collaborators had been studying for years the effect of liver extracts of various types on experimental blacktongue in dogs. Their efforts finally culminated in the brilliant discovery in 1937 by Elvehjem, Madden, Strong, and Woolley (J. Am. Chem. Soc., **59**:1767, 1937) that nicotinic acid would cure canine blacktongue and that nicotinic acid amide could be isolated from the blacktongue-curative fraction of liver.

Elvehjem's discovery was soon confirmed by Dann (46, 47), by Street and Cowgill (48), by Smith, Margolis, and Margolis (49), and by Sebrell, Onstott, Fraser, and Daft (50).

ORIGINAL STUDIES ON THE USE OF NICOTINIC ACID IN HUMAN PELLAGRA

The effectiveness of nicotinic acid in the treatment of human pellagra was demonstrated independently and almost simultaneously by four different groups of workers. The first published report showing the potency of this material was by Fouts and his associates (51) in November, 1937. On December 18, 1937, there appeared two communications—one by Harris (52), the other by Smith, Ruffin, and Smith (53)—reporting the value of nicotinic acid in pellagra. Spies, Cooper, and Blankenhorn (J.A.M.A., **110**: 622, 1938) reported a series of seventeen cases in February, 1938. Since then there have been numerous reports of the effective use of nicotinic acid in the treatment of pellagra (54, 55, 56, 25, 57, 58, 59, 60, 61, 17). The most extensive clinical studies have been made by Spies and his associates, by Jolliffe and his collaborators, by Sebrell and the United States Public Health investigators, by Sydenstricker and his co-workers, and by the group at Duke.

PELLAGRA TREATED WITH NICOTINIC ACID

It has been the universal experience of investigators that treatment with nicotinic acid usually results in prompt and, in many instances, dramatic improvement. Desperately ill patients, who undoubtedly would have died before the discovery of this vitamin, have been restored to health by its use.

The first noticeable effect of the treatment is on the glossitis. Within 24 hours after treatment is started, the fiery redness of the tongue disappears, and the ulcers beneath the tongue and on the lips usually heal within 3 to 5 days. There is a striking relief of soreness and pain in the mouth, and the papillae of the tongue regenerate within 7 to 14 days.

The anorexia which is such a constant symptom in active pellagra disappears after a few days of treatment except in those patients where there are other deficiencies present, especially a deficiency of vitamin B_1. In these cases the appetite will not return until the nicotinic acid therapy has been supplemented with thiamine. Occasionally there is a marked improvement in the appetite with nicotinic acid treatment and then a recurrence of the anorexia 5 to 7 days later. The administration of thiamine chloride at this point usually results in a rapid return of the appetite.

Nausea and vomiting are striking symptoms in the very acutely ill patients and usually subside after 2–4 days' treatment with the vitamin.

Diarrhea is a variable symptom; but, when it is severe, the prognosis is grave. Diarrhea usually responds a little more slowly than the other symptoms, probably because of interference with absorption due to the damaged intestinal mucosa.

Mental symptoms are very common in pellagra. The milder symptoms of nervousness and irritability are almost constantly present. Actual psychoses with delusions and hallucinations are much less common but indicate a severe state of deficiency and a grave prognosis. With the exception of its effect upon the glossitis, the improvement in the patients' mental condition following treatment with nicotinic acid is the most spectacular and dramatic result of the therapy. Often within 4 or 5 days after treatment patients who have been completely disoriented become entirely rational. If, however, there has been irreparable damage to the cells of the central nervous system, as occurs frequently when the psychoses have persisted for a period of months and even occasionally in the early acute case, one cannot expect a cure from the nicotinic acid therapy. The first published case report demonstrating the beneficial effect of nicotinic acid in the treatment of the psychoses of pellagra came from the Duke Clinic in December, 1937 (53). The most extensive studies of the effect of nicotinic acid on this type of patient have been reported by Matthews (25), by Spies and his associates (59, 60), by Jolliffe *et al.* (18), and by Sydenstricker and his associates (17, 54).

Jolliffe, Bowman, Rosenblum, and Fein (18) reported a type of nutritional encephalopathy which responded in a dramatic fashion to treatment with nicotinic acid. This syndrome is characterized by cloudiness of consciousness, cogwheel rigidity of the extremities, and uncontrollable grasping sucking reflexes. It occurs most often in chronic alcoholics with or without pellagra. Jolliffe is of the opinion that it represents an acute total deficiency of nicotinic acid, in contrast to the partial, more chronic deficiency in typical pellagra. In a study involving 150 patients with this syndrome Jolliffe and his associates found that treatment with parenteral fluids alone or with the addition of thiamin chloride failed to prevent the death of 60 out of 62 consecutive patients. In contrast to this, the administration of nicotinic acid in doses of 100 to 200 mg. by mouth every hour for 5 doses resulted in recovery of 15 out of 22 patients.

Cleckley, Sydenstricker, and Geeslin (54) treated a series of atypical psychotic, stuporous, and malnourished patients with nicotinic acid and reported that the majority became clinically well. Some of the cases in this series corresponded to those described by Jolliffe and his associates. Others were apparently somewhat more chronic and not as acutely ill as those with typical nutritional encephalopathy. It is interesting that in 5 of these cases a remarkable improvement in hearing occurred following treatment. It is important to remember that not all psychotic patients will respond to treatment with nicotinic acid, since it is well known that patients with mental disease are characteristically difficult to feed, and secondary pellagra is relatively common. The nicotinic acid treatment may cure the symptoms of pellagra but leave untouched the basic original pyschosis.

It has been pointed out earlier in this discussion that there are six types of dermatitis seen in pellagra: (*a*) the typical dermatitis over the exposed surfaces; (*b*) sebaceous-gland changes about the face; (*c*) the thickening and pigmentation over the bony prominences; (*d*) perineal and genital lesions; (*e*) lesions of the lips and mucocutaneous surfaces at the corners of the mouth; and (*f*) changes in the superficial structures of the eye. The dermatitis over the exposed surfaces responds promptly to treatment with nicotinic acid. The thickening and pigmentation over the bony prominences respond more slowly but usually subside after 6–10 days' time. The perineal and genital lesions heal promptly in 5–10 days. The sebaceous-gland lesions respond much more slowly to nicotinic acid than when treated with crude liver extracts or autoclaved yeast. It was the opinion of Smith and her collaborators (26), who made a special study of these lesions, that the curative factor was in the B complex and that it was not primarily a deficiency of nicotinic acid or riboflavin. The curative factor was present in crude extracts of liver but not the parenteral fraction, and the lesions did not respond to treatment with vitamin A. The lesions of the lips have been studied in detail by Sebrell and his associates, who introduced the term "ariboflavinosis" (19, 20). These lesions found in cases of ariboflavinosis do not respond to nicotinic acid but are cured specifically by riboflavin. A lesion, clinically very similar, has been found to respond to treatment with B_6 (pyridoxine) (62). Still other lesions of the lips have been seen in cases of sprue where none of the vitamins were effective but where prompt recovery followed the use of parenteral liver extract. The eye lesions have been studied in detail by Sebrell (20) and by Sydenstricker and his associates (28). They find that the lesions respond specifically to riboflavin.

NATURAL SOURCES OF NICOTINIC ACID

Goldberger reported that liver, yeast, red muscle meats, kidney, fish, and wheat germ were effective, approximately in the order named, in preventing pellagra in man and experimental black-tongue in dogs. Vegetables were definitely less effective, and milk prevented pellagra only when consumed in such large quantities that it practically replaced all other foods. Fat meats and purified cereals were almost entirely devoid of the curative factors. With the development of chemical tests for nicotinic acid the exact amounts contained in various foods are being assayed. Bacharach (63) in 1941 reviewed the results of the assays up to the time of his publication. Recent extensive work by Waisman, Mickelsen, McKibbin, and Elvehjem at Wisconsin (64) and by Dann and Handler at Duke (65) has laid the foundation for an accurate evaluation of the nicotinic acid content of the common food substances. The original reports on cereals were undoubtedly too high, probably because of the contaminating substances in the extracts. Even the most potent sources, such as liver, muscle meats, and kidneys, contain only 5–20 mg. of nicotinic acid per 100 gm. wet-weight portions.

ABSORPTION AND STORAGE

Synthetic nicotinic acid is readily absorbed from the intestinal tract, and presumably it is readily absorbed in the more complex forms in which it occurs in natural foods. Sydenstricker (66, 67) has made the suggestion that patients with achlorhydria are unable to extract the nicotinic acid from the natural foods and implies that these patients would be more likely to develop pellagra if consuming a restricted diet. There have been numerous reports of pellagra developing, on an apparently good diet, in patients with ulcerative colitis, regional ileitis, carcinomas of the intestinal tract, and other intestinal conditions where absorption of the vitamin from the food was severely restricted.

This type of deficiency has been demonstrated experimentally in dogs (68). In one instance a dog receiving 10 mg. per kilogram of nicotinic acid developed severe blacktongue, which was relieved by parenteral administration of the same dose. The faulty absorption in this case was found later to be due to a secondary deficiency of other vitamins. When these were supplied, the oral therapy was adequate.

Storage of nicotinic acid occurs in most of the tissues of the body but is greatest in the liver. For a water-soluble vitamin, its storage is fairly good, since from 30 to 40 days, and occasionally even longer, is required to deplete the reserves of a dog sufficiently to allow the development of blacktongue. In the experimental studies on man by Goldberger and Wheeler (4) and by Sebrell (20) a period of months was required to produce the initial symptoms of pellagra. The experimental subjects were relatively inactive, and depletion may occur much more rapidly if the patient is working or if there is an infection present. We have observed the return of pellagra in 2 months in a child who had been saturated with yeast while in the hospital. One adult patient who was in the hospital with a chronic lung abscess was fed a good diet, including a liberal supply of red meat, milk, eggs, and vegetables for 4 months, and then discharged.

The patient began working while the lung abscess was still active, and returned to the hospital 6 weeks later with an acute attack of pellagra. Sydenstricker feels that chronic alcoholics and other patients with liver damage have difficulty in storing the vitamin (36). These patients may need larger doses of nicotinic acid for the initial treatment and a larger maintenance supply than the normal individual (67).

PHYSIOLOGICAL FUNCTIONS OF NICOTINIC ACID

It is now well established that nicotinic acid amide is present in the molecules of two coenzymes: diphosphopyridine nucleotide (cozymase, coenzyme I) and triphosphopyridine nucleotide (coenzyme II). These two coenzymes play a major role in intercellular oxidation and can be measured indirectly by their growth-promoting actions on parainfluenza bacilli. The coenzymes concentration in the red blood cells of pellagrins and normal individuals have been studied by Kohn (69, 70), by Spies (72), by Elvehjem (71), and by their associates. Kohn's method is better adapted for quantitative results than that of Spies, but both agree that ingestion of nicotinic acid results in a rapid increase in the coenzymes of the blood well above normal in both pellagrins and controls. Kohn and Klein (69) have found that human red blood cells can synthesize the coenzymes *in vitro*. The studies by Elvehjem and his associates and Kohn and his groups show that the coenzyme level is somewhat reduced in the tissues of dogs with experimental blacktongue. The largest percentage reduction was found in the liver. Elvehjem feels that a marked lowering of the coenzymes in the blood, brain, and adrenal cortex may be incompatible with life. It would be interesting to assay the coenzyme level of the brain tissues in cases of acute encephalopathy, where there is presumably a more complete deficiency of nicotinic acid than in the typical pellagrin.

A number of workers have attempted to measure nicotinic acid directly from the blood by chemical methods. Ritsert (73) reports from 3 to 3.5 μg. per cubic centimeter. Patton, Sutton, and Youmans found that the blood contained from 0.30 to 0.50 mg. per cent (74). There are colored pigments in the blood serum which may interfere with the test, and it is possible that these figures are too high.

Nicotinic acid probably has important biological functions in the living animal other than that of supplying building material for the coenzymes, but these functions have not yet been studied in detail.

EXCRETION OF NICOTINIC ACID

Nicotinic acid, when fed to dogs, is excreted in the urine as trigonelline, nicotinuric acid, and as free nicotinic acid. Considerable difficulties have been encountered in devising an accurate method for the measurement of nicotinic acid in the urine because of the presence of interfering substances. Sarett, Perlzweig, and Levy (75) found that normal human subjects excrete daily only 1–3 mg. of nicotinic acid and derivatives (amide and glycine conjugate), compared with the 30–50 mg. of trigonelline. When 100 mg. of nicotinic acid was taken by mouth, it was excreted in the urine largely as trigonelline. Later studies by Perlzweig, Levy, and Sarett (76) confirmed the daily excretion of 1–3 mg. of nicotinic acid derivatives exclusive of trigonelline. On a diet free of coffee normal subjects excrete 20–29 mg. of trigonelline per day but may excrete as much as 200 mg. when coffee is ingested. After doses of 100–200 mg. of nicotinic acid by mouth normal subjects excreted 2.5–19.4 mg. of nicotinic acid derivatives. The trigonelline excretion was appreciably increased, although the total excreted nicotinic products accounted for only about 25 per cent of the ingested nicotinic acid. Field, Melnick, Robinson, and Wilkinson (77) suggested that the measurement of trigonelline in the urine might be used as an indication of nicotinic acid nutrition. Rather complete balanced studies on the fate of nicotinic acid in the human body have been made by Sarett, Huff, and Perlzweig (78) and are now in press.

TOXICITY OF NICOTINIC ACID

Nicotinic acid is relatively nontoxic, although Chinn and his associates found that continuous treatment with 2 gm. of nicotinic acid daily produced death in dogs (79). Nicotinic acid amide and sodium nicotinate are apparently much less toxic. Unna (80) found that 2 gm. of sodium nicotinate per kilogram were well tolerated by his dogs.

Spies and his associates administered nicotinic acid in doses of 1 gm. or more to normal individuals without the development of toxic symptoms other than the flushing of the skin (81). Sydenstricker and his associates (17) have noted more severe symptoms in normal subjects with daily doses of 500 mg. In our experience (58) doses of 250 mg. given four times a day to normal subjects produced marked flushing and in some instances epigastric distress, substernal oppression, headache, and occasionally nausea and vomiting. It is our impression that normal subjects react more violently to large doses of nicotinic acid than do pellagrins. This may be explained in part by the need of the pellagra patient for the vitamin and in part by his decreased absorption from an inflamed and hypermotile intestinal tract. The flushing reactions which follow intraveneous or intramuscular doses as small as 15 mg., or oral doses as small as 50 mg., are physiological rather than pathological. There is no more pronounced or prolonged flushing following intravenous injection of 100 mg. than 15 mg. With oral therapy the flushing is materially reduced if the doses are given after meals.

Occasional sensitivity to nicotinic acid has been noted. The patients develop urticaria and itching of the skin. This may follow the initial dose or may develop during a course of treatment. Fortunately, sensitivity to the drug is apparently very rare.

THERAPEUTIC PREPARATIONS OF NICOTINIC ACID

Nicotinic acid is available commercially in tablets, in capsules, and in crystalline form. It is poorly soluble in water and in physiological saline. As a rule, it is difficult to dissolve more than 5 mg. per cubic centimeter of solution. The solution made from the crystals is probably the most economical preparation for hospital use. For oral administration the drug should be dissolved in water. For parenteral use the nicotinic acid or amide should be dissolved in physiological saline and sterilized by boiling or autoclaving. The heating (49) does not affect its potency, and the solutions can be kept for weeks without deterioration.

METHODS OF ADMINISTRATION

For critically ill patients, unable to retain food by mouth, it is important to administer the nicotinic acid intravenously or intramuscularly. Usually these patients are dehydrated and partly starved. One hundred milligrams of nicotinic acid in solution should be added to 500 cc. of 5 per cent glucose made up in physiological saline and administered slowly into a vein. The injection is almost invariably accompanied by marked flushing of the face and neck, and frequently the entire body, which fades after 15 to 20 minutes. The patient experiences, as a rule, a subjective sensation of warmth and tingling of the skin. The flushing reactions are given by nicotinic acid and sodium nicotinate but not by nicotinic acid amide or diethyl amide of nicotinic acid (coramine) (81).

Unfavorable reactions are rare, except for slight flushing, when the drug is given orally in doses of 50–100 mg. after meals. If larger amounts are indicated, it is more desirable to give 100 mg. three to four times a day rather than a single large dose.

THE USE OF RELATED PYRIDINE COMPOUNDS IN BLACKTONGUE AND PELLAGRA

Woolley, Strong, Madden, and Elvehjem (82) found nicotinic acid amide, diethyl amide of nicotinic acid (coramine), and β-picoline effective in the treatment of experimental blacktongue. Picolinic acid, isonicotinic acid, nipecotic acid, quinolinic acid, 6-methylnicotinic acid, trigonelline, pyridine, and 1-methyl-nicotinic-acid-amide-chloride were not effective in curing blacktongue.

Spies, Grant, and Huff (61) have tried a number of these new compounds on patients with pellagra. Alpha-picoline, β-picoline, trigonelline, and β-aminopyridine had no curative effect. Dinicotinic acid, 2–6-dimethyl-pyridine-3 : 5-carboxylic acid, nicotinic acid amide, sodium nicotinate, and diethyl amide of nicotinic acid (coramine) were effective in pellagra. Minimal curative doses have not been determined for any of these compounds in dogs with blacktongue or in patients with pellagra (83). With the exception of nicotinic acid amide and coramine, there is not sufficient experimental data available to justify their use on patients with pellagra.

Nicotinic acid amide, because of its failure to give the flushing reaction, is probably preferable to nicotinic acid in the treatment of pellagra (84). As much as 500 mg. has been given intraveneously to human beings without any unfavorable reactions. Diethyl amide of nicotinic acid (coramine) is also effective in curing blacktongue in dogs and pellagra in man and does not produce the flushing reaction. The experimental studies of Smith, Margolis, and Margolis (85) showed that only about 10 per cent of the drug was effective, as compared to nicotinic acid. Apparently, the extra ethyl groups must be removed by the body, thus leaving, in effect, nicotinic acid amide. The clinical results in the treatment of pellagra have been as good with coramine as with nicotinic acid or nicotinic acid amide, as shown by the reports of Spies and his associates (60, 61), by Sydenstricker (17), and by Ruffin and Smith (58, 22, 86). Coramine is curative by mouth in doses of 2–5 cc. daily. When administered parenterally, daily injections of 3 cc. have given consistently good results.

SECONDARY DEFICIENCIES IN PELLAGRA

Some difference in opinion exists as to whether pellagra is a disease of multiple etiology or whether it should be considered as a nicotinic acid deficiency. A pure vitamin deficiency in man is exceedingly rare. The patient with rickets often has a vitamin A deficiency as well as a vitamin D deficiency, and the patient with scurvy may have beriberi as a complication, as was the case in the old disease known as "ship beriberi." Pellagrins frequently have associated deficiencies of vitamins B_1, A, C, B_6, riboflavin, proteins, and mineral salts. The cardinal symptoms of pellagra are cured by nicotinic acid, and we feel very strongly that pellagra should be regarded as a nicotinic acid deficiency. The associated deficiencies should be recognized when they appear and treated accordingly.

THE USE OF NICOTINIC ACID IN OTHER DISEASES

Nicotinic acid has been used in some cases of nonspecific glossitis, trench mouth, stomatitis, lupus erythematosus, multiple sclerosis, chronic ulcerative colitis, sprue, delerium tremens, high-tone deafness, arteriosclerotic hypertensive disease, nephrosis, and for the toxic symptoms following sulfanilamide and sulfapyridine treatment, radiation sickness, and in lead poisoning, with variable results (87, 88). It has no specific value in pernicious anemia or in sprue.

Sydenstricker (67) has emphasized the importance of adding nicotinic acid to glucose in saline solutions in giving intravenous fluids to severely ill patients. The suggestion applies equally well to all of the water-soluble vitamins. The patient who is taking practically no food by mouth and who is losing fluids by vomiting or diarrhea should have the intraveneous fluids fortified by the addition of 100 mg. of nicotinic acid, 50 mg. of B_1, and 100 mg. of vitamin C. If the injections have to be continued for some days, it is possible that the other water-soluble vitamins, such as B_6, riboflavin, and pantothenic acid should also be added.

MAINTENANCE REQUIREMENTS FOR NICOTINIC ACID

The studies of Sebrell and Onstott (50, 89), of Margolis, Margolis, and Smith (40) on dogs, and of those of Sebrell and Butler (20) on patients show that the basic diets employed were partly deficient in riboflavin. Supplementing the diets with nicotinic acid alone protected from blacktongue and pellagra but eventually resulted in ariboflavinosis. Margolis, Margolis, and Smith (40) found that their blacktongue-producing diet was border line in B_1 and that, if the animals were subjected to repeated attacks of blacktongue, the B_1 deficiency became acute and the animals, because of this, failed to respond to nicotinic acid. If, however, the basic diet is supplemented by a small amount of riboflavin and vitamin B_1, the animals will survive repeated attacks of blacktongue over a period of 12 months. With the correction in the basic diet it is possible to determine accurately the curative dose and approximately the maintenance dose for dogs on a per kilogram basis. Birch (90) found that a daily dose of 0.25 mg. of nicotinic acid per kilogram of body weight was sufficient to prevent the development of blacktongue and to allow adequate gain in weight, while 0.13 mg. prevented blacktongue but resulted in a slow gain in weight. In experiments of Margolis, Margolis, and Smith (91) a total dose of 5 mg. per kilogram of body weight, administered over a 10-day period, cured their dogs in attacks of acute blacktongue and protected them from a new attack for an average time of 34 days. By calculation this gives a daily maintenance dose of 0.147 mg. per kilogram. In the same study these investigators found that 0.2 mg. per kilogram administered daily for 10 days would cure dogs with acute blacktongue, but more slowly. In a later investigation these workers found that a daily maintenance dose of 0.2 mg. per kilogram protected 2 dogs from blacktongue for as long as 744 and 785 days, respectively. Under similar conditions 0.1 mg. was inadequate. We may assume that 0.15 mg. per kilogram of body weight is approximately the daily supplement of nicotinic acid required to protect dogs from blacktongue. The actual requirement can be calculated only when the data is available to show the exact amount of nicotinic acid present in the blacktongue-producing diet of natural foods used in these studies.

All the available evidence indicates that man has approximately the same requirement of nicotinic acid per kilogram as the dog. Harvey *et al.* (39) found that the various liver fractions were curative of blacktongue in approximately the same dose per kilogram that Ruffin and Smith (38) employed for the treatment of patients with pellagra. The relatively small doses of nicotinic acid (91) or coramine (85) needed for the cure of blacktongue are in line with the results of the clinical studies of Ruffin and Smith (58), where daily doses of 100 mg. of nicotinic acid or 3 cc. of coramine were entirely effective in curing pellagra.

If there is any difference in the per kilogram requirement of man and dog of nicotinic acid, it appears that man's need may be less. Sebrell and Butler (20) found that a restricted diet of natural foodstuffs required from 76 to 362 days to produce pellagra in volunteer patients, while Ruffin and Smith (13), using an analogous diet of natural foods, produced blacktongue in dogs in from 25 to 45 days. If we accept a supplementary dose of 0.15 mg. per kilogram, then the average 70-kg. man would require approximately 10.5 mg. of nicotinic acid daily. It is interesting that Sarett, Huff, and Perlzweig (78) have found in man that there is a loss of approximately 10 mg. per day of nicotinic acid and its derivatives in the urine.

This loss is constant even under fasting conditions. Clinical studies also indicate that man's requirement for nicotinic acid is relatively low. In the records of over 500 cases of pellagra studied at the Duke Hospital there are no instances of pellagra developing in patients, free of gastrointestinal diseases, who consumed regularly one meal containing red meat, fish, or salmon twice each week.

PREVENTION OF PELLAGRA BY THE ADDITION OF NICOTINIC ACID TO BASIC FOODS

Everyone should have a well-rounded diet of natural foodstuffs which would contain not only an abundance of nicotinic acid but an abundance of all the essential vitamins and minerals in a natural state (92). Every effort should be made to see that the standard of living is raised to a point where everyone can afford such a diet and be educated to eat it. In the meantime, however, there are large sections of the population who cannot obtain or will not eat the type of diet that is described above. As a temporary expedient we are entirely justified in adding nicotinic acid, B_1, and riboflavin to specific basic foods, such as white flour, as suggested by the Committee on Food and Nutrition of the National Research Council.

BIBLIOGRAPHY

1. Casal, G., cited by Major, R. H., Classic descriptions of disease, p. 575. Springfield, Ill.: Charles C. Thomas, 1932.
2. Frapolli, F., cited by Harris, S., Clinical pellagra, p. 134. St. Louis: C. V. Mosby Co., 1941.
3. Raubitschek, H., Deutsche med. Wchnschr., **38**:2169, 1912.
4. Goldberger, J., and Wheeler, G. A., Pub. Health Rep., **30**:3336, 1915.
5. Funk, C., J. Physiol., **43**:395, 1911.
6. Funk, C., J.A.M.A., **109**:2086, 1937.
7. Sandwith, F. M., Tr. Soc. Trop. Med. & Hyg., **6**:143, 1913.
8. Wheeler, G. A., Pub. Health Rep., **48**:67, 1933.
9. Blackford, S. D., Virginia M. Monthly, **61**:140, 1934.
10. Sydenstricker, V. P., in Harris, S., and Harris, S., Jr., Clinical pellagra, p. 252. St. Louis: C. V. Mosby Co., 1941.
11. Spies, T. D., Am. J. M. Sc., **184**:837, 1932.
12. Spies, T. D., Proc. Soc. Exper. Biol. & Med., **30**:1227, 1933.
13. Ruffin, J. M., and Smith, D. T., Am. J. M. Sc., **187**:512, 1934.

14. SMITH, D. T., South. Med. & Surg., **94**:134, 1932.
15. FOUTS, P. J.; LEPKOVSKY, S.; HELMER, O. M.; and JUKES, T. H., Proc. Soc. Exper. Biol. & Med., **35**:245, 1936.
16. FOUTS, P. J., and ZERFAS, L. G., J. Indiana M. A., **27**:196, 1934.
17. SYDENSTRICKER, V. P.; SCHMIDT, H. L., JR.; FULTON, M. C.; NEW, J. S.; and GEESLIN, L. E., South. M. J., **31**:1155, 1938.
18. JOLLIFFE, N.; BOWMAN, K. M.; ROSENBLUM, L. A.; and FEIN, H. D., J.A.M.A., **114**:307, 1940.
19. SEBRELL, W. H., and BUTLER, R. E., Pub. Health Rep., **53**:2282, 1938.
20. SEBRELL, W. H., and BUTLER, R. E., *ibid.*, **54**:2121, 1939.
21. SMITH, D. T., and RUFFIN, J. M., Arch. Int. Med., **59**:631, 1937.
22. RUFFIN, J. M., and SMITH, D. T., in HARRIS, S., and HARRIS, S., JR., Clinical pellagra, p. 194. St. Louis: C. V. Mosby Co., 1941.
23. BASS, C. C., Gulf States J. Med. & Surg., **16**:1, 1910.
24. SPIES, T. D., Arch. Int. Med., **56**:920, 1935.
25. MATTHEWS, R. S., J.A.M.A., **111**:1148, 1938.
26. SMITH, S. G.; SMITH, D. T.; and CALLAWAY, J. L., J. Invest. Dermat., **4**:23, 1941.
27. SMITH, S. G., and SPRUNT, D. H., J. Nutrition, **10**:481, 1935.
28. SYDENSTRICKER, V. P.; SEBRELL, W. H.; CLECKLEY, H. M.; and KRUSE, H. D., J.A.M.A., **114**:2437, 1940.
29. VOEGTLIN, C., Pub. Health Rep., **35**:1435, 1920.
30. GOLDBERGER, J., and SEBRELL, W. H., Pub. Health Rep., **45**:3064, 1930.
31. BOGGS, T. R., and PADGET, P., Bull. Johns Hopkins Hosp., **50**:21, 1932.
32. RAMSDELL, R. L., and MAGNESS, W. H., Am. J. M. Sc., **185**:568, 1933.
33. SPIES, T. D., Proc. Soc. Exper. Biol. & Med., **31**:363, 1933.
34. HADEN, R. L., J.A.M.A., **106**:261, 1936.
35. SPIES, T. D., J.A.M.A., **104**:1377, 1935.
36. SYDENSTRICKER, V. P., and ARMSTRONG, E. S., Arch. Int. Med., **59**:883, 1937.
37. WYLIE, W. D., South. Med. & Surg., **97**:14, 1935.
38. RUFFIN, J. M., and SMITH, D. T., South. M. J., **30**:4, 1937.
39. HARVEY, H. I.; SMITH, D. T.; PERSONS, E. L.; and BURNS, M. V., J. Nutrition, **16**:153, 1938.
40. MARGOLIS, L. H.; MARGOLIS, G.; and SMITH, S. G., J. Nutrition, **17**:63, 1939.
41. HUBER, C., Ann. Chem. u. Pharm., **141**:271, 1867.
42. WARBURG, O.; CHRISTIAN, W.; and GRIESE, A., Biochem. Ztschr., **282**:157, 1935.
43. EULER, H. VON; ALBERS, H.; and SCHLENK, F., Ztschr. f. physiol. Chem., **240**:113, 1936.
44. KNIGHT, B. C. J. G., Biochem. J., **31**:731, 1937.
45. MUELLER, J. H., J. Biol. Chem., **120**:219, 1937; J. Bact., **34**:429, 1937.

46. DANN, W. J., Science, 86:616, 1937.
47. DANN, W. J., and SUBBAROW, Y., J. Nutrition, 16:183, 1938.
48. STREET, H. R., and COWGILL, G. R., Proc. Soc. Exper. Biol. & Med., 37: 547, 1937.
49. SMITH, S. G.; MARGOLIS, G.; and MARGOLIS, L. H., Proc. Soc. Exper. Biol. & Med., 38:251, 1938.
50. SEBRELL, W. H.; ONSTOTT, R. H.; FRASER, H. F.; and DAFT, F. S., J. Nutrition, 16:355, 1938.
51. FOUTS, P. J.; HELMER, O. M.; LEPKOVSKY, S.; and JUKES, T. H., Proc. Soc. Exper. Biol. & Med., 37:405, 1937.
52. HARRIS, L., and HASSAN, A., Lancet, 233:1467, 1937.
53. SMITH, D. T.; RUFFIN, J. M.; and SMITH, S. G., J.A.M.A., 109:2054, 1937.
54. CLECKLEY, H. M.; SYDENSTRICKER, V. P.; and GEESLIN, L. E., J.A.M.A., 112:2107, 1939.
55. FRANCE, R.; BATES, R. D., JR.; BARKER, W. H.; and MATTHEWS, E., Bull. Johns Hopkins Hosp., 63:46, 1938.
56. HAWKSLEY, J. C., Lancet, 234:944, 1938.
57. RACHMILEWITZ, M., and GLUECK, H. I., Brit. M. J., 2:346, 1938.
58. RUFFIN, J. M., and SMITH, D. T., South. M. J., 32:40, 1939.
59. SPIES, T. D.; ARING, C. D.; GELPERIN, J.; and BEAN, W. B., Am. J. M. Sc., 196:461, 1938.
60. SPIES, T. D.; BEAN, W. B.; and STONE, R. E., J.A.M.A., 111:584, 1938.
61. SPIES, T. D.; GRANT, H. M.; and HUFF, N. E., South. M. J., 31:901, 1938.
62. SMITH, S. G., and MARTIN, D. W., Proc. Soc. Exper. Biol. & Med., 43:660, 1940.
63. BACHARACH, A. L., Nutrition Abstr. & Rev., 10:459, 1941.
64. WAISMAN, H. A.; MICKELSEN, O.; MCKIBBIN, J. M.; and ELVEHJEM, C. A., J. Nutrition, 19:483, 1940.
65. DANN, W. J., and HANDLER, P., J. Biol. Chem., 140:201, 1941.
66. SYDENSTRICKER, V. P., Ann. Int. Med., 14:1499, 1941.
67. SYDENSTRICKER, V. P., Arch. Int. Med., 67:746, 1941.
68. SMITH, S. G., Am. J. Trop. Med., 20:593, 1940.
69. KOHN, H. I., and KLEIN, J. R., J. Biol. Chem., 130:1, 1939.
70. KOHN, H. I.; KLEIN, J. R.; and DANN, W. J., Biochem. J., 33:1432, 1939.
71. ELVEHJEM, C. A.; WAISMAN, H. A.; and AXELROD, A. E., J. Nutrition, 17, Suppl.: 11, 1939.
72. VILTER, R. W.; VILTER, S. P.; and SPIES, T. D., J.A.M.A., 112:420, 1939.
73. RITSERT, K., Klin. Wchnschr., 18:934, 1939.
74. PATTON, E. W.; SUTTON, W. R.; and YOUMANS, J. B., J. Clin. Investigation, 19:785, 1940.
75. SARETT, H. P.; PERLZWEIG, W. A.; and LEVY, E. D., J. Biol. Chem., 135: 483, 1940.
76. PERLZWEIG, W. A.; LEVY, E. D.; and SARETT, H. P., J. Biol. Chem., 136:729, 1940.

77. Field, H., Jr.; Melnick, D.; Robinson, W. D.; and Wilkinson, C. F., Jr., J. Clin. Investigation, **20**:379, 1941.
78. Sarett, H. P.; Huff, J. W.; and Perlzweig, W. A., J. Nutrition, **23**:23, 1942.
79. Chen, K. K.; Rose, C. L.; and Robbins, E. B., Proc. Soc. Exper. Biol. & Med., **38**:241, 1938.
80. Unna, K., J. Pharmacol. & Exper. Therap., **65**:95, 1939.
81. Bean, W. B., and Spies, T. D., J.A.M.A., **114**:439, 1940.
82. Woolley, D. W.; Strong, F. M.; Madden, R. J.; and Elvehjem, C. A., J. Biol. Chem., **124**:715, 1938.
83. Dann, W. J.; Kohn, H. I.; and Handler, P., J. Nutrition, **20**:477, 1940.
84. Field, H., Jr., and Robinson, W. D., Am. J. M. Sc., **199**:275, 1940.
85. Smith, D. T.; Margolis, G.; and Margolis, L. H., J. Pharmacol. & Exper. Therap., **68**:458, 1940.
86. Smith, D. T.; Ruffin, J. M.; and Smith, S. G., J. Nutrition, **19**, Suppl.: 14, 1940.
87. Manson-Bahr, P., and Ransford, O. N., Lancet, **2**:426, 1938.
88. West, R., Proc. Soc. Exper. Biol. & Med., **46**:369, 1941.
89. Sebrell, W. H.; Onstott, R. H.; and Hunt, D. J., Pub. Health Rep., **52**: 427, 1937.
90. Birch, T. W., J. Nutrition, **17**:281, 1939.
91. Margolis, G.; Margolis, L. H.; and Smith, S. G., J. Nutrition, **16**:541, 1938.
92. Sebrell, W. H., J.A.M.A., **110**:1665, 1938.
93. Beckh, W.; Ellinger, P.; and Spies, T. D., Quart. J. Med., **6**:305, 1937.
94. Watson, C. J., J. Clin. Investigation, **14**:110, 1935.
95. Watson, C. J., *ibid.*, **15**:327, 1936.
96. Watson, C. J., Oxford Med., **4**:229, 1938.
97. Watson, C. J., Proc. Soc. Exper. Biol. & Med., **39**:514, 1938.
98. Dobriner, K.; Strain, W. H.; and Localio, S. A., Proc. Soc. Exper. Biol. & Med., **36**:752, 1937.
99. Dobriner, K.; Strain, W. H.; and Localio, S. A., *ibid.*, **38**:748, 1938.
100. Brugsch, J. T., Proc. Staff Meet., Mayo Clin., **12**:609, 1937.

PYRIDOXINE

S. LEPKOVSKY
Department of Poultry Husbandry, University of California, Berkeley

HISTORICAL

PYRIDOXINE, or vitamin B_6, is the third member of the vitamin B complex to be discovered. Goldberger (1) laid the basis for this discovery by describing a dermatitis characteristic of pyridoxine deficiency. We now know that Goldberger described two kinds of skin disturbances, one characteristic of pyridoxine deficiency and one of riboflavin deficiency. Goldberger did not know, of course, that he was dealing with a multiple deficiency, though he clearly suspected the existence of more than one vitamin in his so-called "heat-stable" fraction of the water-soluble vitamin B.

Chick and Copping (2) were the first to produce good evidence for the existence of a third member of the vitamin B complex. They used the so-called "Peters eluate" (a yeast eluate from charcoal) as the source of thiamine and an extract of egg white as the source of riboflavin. These workers did not report dermatitis in their rats, but they established that the third factor in the vitamin B complex was heat stable in alkaline solution. They called the vitamin "factor Y."

The third factor of the vitamin B complex was rediscovered independently by György (3), who showed that its deficiency was accompanied by a characteristic dermatitis. The extremities were largely affected—the feet, paws, ears, and the areas around the nose, mouth, and eyes. Often the inflamed areas became edematous. He was assaying for riboflavin, which was then being concentrated, using the Bourquin-Sherman method, which employed an alcoholic extract of wheat as the source of vitamin B (thiamine). The test failed, presumably because their wheat extract containing vitamin B (thiamine) carried little of the third factor or factors; and their rats did not respond with growth when pure riboflavin or riboflavin concentrates were fed. György realized the possibility of deficiency of another factor, which at first he thought to be vitamin B_4, but later he suggested it might be similar to factor Y, of Chick and Copping. When he later used pure thiamine and riboflavin, the rats developed the so-called "specific dermatitis" characteristic of pyridoxine deficiency under these conditions. György (3) then differentiated this type of dermatitis, which he called "acrodynia" (4) from the skin disturbance resulting from riboflavin deficiency.

The third factor was found to be multiple in nature, and the terms "factor 1" and "factor 2" were introduced (5). Factor 1 consisted of an eluate from fuller's earth containing vitamin B_6; and factor 2 remained in the filtrate after the fuller's earth treatment, and has been called the "filtrate factor." Vitamin B_6 has also been referred to as "adermin" (6).

Later György (7) introduced the term "pyridoxine," which has clarified a much confused situation by replacing factor 1, vitamin B_6, adermin, antiacrodynia factor, rat antidermatitis vitamin, and factor Y. The introduction of factor 2 concentrates capable of being freed of vitamin B_6 (5) provided a diet free or nearly free of vitamin B_6 and made the vitamin-B_6 test simple and rapid when too great accuracy was not required. Under proper conditions of testing, it was often possible to obtain a fairly good assay for vitamin B_6 in less than 24 hours. Birch and György (8) reported a large number of the chemical properties of vitamin B_6, and the race for the isolation of vitamin B_6 was on. The first announcement of the crystallization of vitamin B_6 (9) appeared from the Poultry Division of the University of California. About the same time, Kerestzesy and his associates (10) announced the crystallization of vitamin B_6. But a little later György (11) reported its isolation, and his announcement was shortly followed by that of Kuhn and his co-workers (12) and by that of Ichiba and Michi (13). Within a year the investigators at the Merck laboratory (14) and those in Kuhn's laboratory (15) showed that vitamin B_6 was a pyridine derivative of the formula

CHOH
HO CHOH
CH_3
N

In another year the Merck laboratory made synthetic vitamin B_6 available for research purposes, and shortly thereafter for therapeutic use.

In this connection it is of interest to point out that Ohdahke, working in Suzuke's laboratory, isolated vitamin B_6 in 1931 (13). Its identification as a vitamin had not yet been made, nor were the means available to effect its biological recognition. There is such a thing as being ahead of the times.

PYRIDOXINE AVITAMINOSIS

Skin.—Pyridoxine deficiency in the rat has always been associated with a specific dermatitis which György (4) called "acrodynia." Experimentally this association did not always occur. Pyridoxine deficiency in the rat has not always been accompanied by acrodynia (16, 35), nor could acrodynia always be cured by pyridoxine (17).

No dermatitis has been reported for the dog and pig, although pyridoxine deficiency has been obtained with both animals. Cheilosis in man, which was thought to be characteristic of riboflavin deficiency, has in some cases been cured by pyridoxine (18). Pyridoxine deficiency has not yet been produced in the chicken or pigeon, but both of these species have been shown to respond with limited growth to pyridoxine administration under certain conditions (19). Full pyridoxine deficiency has not been established in the chicken and pigeon probably because of other limiting, but as yet unidentified, deficiencies.

The ruminant does not need pyridoxine in the food. This is synthesized by the rich microbiological flora in the spacious rumen (20) and later absorbed in the process of digestion. Addition of thiamine stimulates the activity of the microbiological flora in the ruminant, resulting in increased pyridoxine synthesis (21).

While most microörganisms synthesize pyridoxine, some do not, but require it for their growth (22). The excised roots of the tomato, at least of some varieties, require pyridoxine for normal growth (23).

Convulsions.—Chick and co-workers (24, 25) reported convulsions in pyridoxine-deficient rats and pigs resembling epileptic fits in the human. Convulsions in dogs were reported by Fouts and his associates (26). Winetrobe (27) also noted convulsions in pyridoxine-deficient pigs.

Blood stream.—Of no less interest than dermatitis and convulsions is the development of a microcytic hypochromic anemia. This has been most thoroughly worked out with the dog (28) and confirmed with the pig (24, 27). The hemoglobin and the red cells decrease progressively, the hemoglobin relatively faster than the red cells. Addition of pyridoxine causes a great reticulocyte response, with rapid increase in hemoglobin and red cells, until the normal is attained. While this has been confirmed in several laboratories and may therefore be accepted as a fact, recent work has made puzzling additions. In the work of Fouts and associates, the decline of hemoglobin and the red cells, as well as their restoration, depended on only one factor, pyridoxine, a fact substantiated with the pure material. Yet Borson and Mettier (29) have shown that, while pyridoxine will restore the hemoglobin a long way toward its normal level, it will not bring it back to normal without the addition of another factor. The factor is not pantothenic acid but is present in liver or its crude concentrates.

Presumably, pyridoxine is essential for hemoglobin formation, though just what role it plays is at present unknown. Pyridoxine seems to play a role in anemias other than pyridoxine deficiency. Pyridoxine was active in the cure of anemia resulting from the injection of typhus toxin (30), whereas riboflavin and nicotinic acid were inactive. In hemorrhagic anemia in rabbits (31) faster regeneration of hemoglobin and erythrocytes took place with pyridoxine addition than with riboflavin or nicotinic acid. The role of pyridoxine under these conditions is hard to understand, except where the pyridoxine deficiency accompanied typhus injection or hemorrhage.

Distribution.—Pyridoxine has been found in all foods assayed. Fruits, vegetables, and milk are fairly poor sources, while seeds and legumes are fairly good sources (17, 32). Wheat germ and rice polishings are good sources. Among the animal products, muscle, liver, kidney, and heart are all good sources (33). Fish liver is a good source of pyridoxine, and so is fish muscle (34). The wide spread and abundance of the distribution of pyridoxine render unlikely a deficiency in the average human diet.

Pyridoxine, dermatitis, and interrelationships.—The omission of any reference to dermatitis by Chick and Copping in factor-Y deficiency was puzzling, since so many workers could subsequently produce it regularly. Analysis of the data available seemed to indicate that acrodynia could be obtained regularly only by those workers who did not provide factor 2 or filtrate factor in the diet and therefore were working with a double deficiency. Administration of factor 2 along with thiamine and riboflavin caused irregularity in the production of acrodynia (35). Sometimes acrodynia appeared in pyridoxine-deficient animals; but often, for unexplained reasons, it did not appear, though the animals were definitely deficient, as judged by growth failure and by the spectacular response in growth and well-being which followed pyridoxine feeding.

Adequate riboflavin intake seemed of importance in this picture, since suboptimal intake of riboflavin brought on acrodynia, which could be cured by riboflavin (36). This phenomenon, however, could not be repeated at will and therefore must, for the present, remain obscure.

Factor 2 seemed also to play an irregular and unpredictable role. It now seems that pantothenic acid is definitely involved in the cure of acrodynia (37, 38).

A factor in the production of acrodynia which has received and is now receiving a great deal of attention is fat, and more especially the essential unsaturated fatty acids.

Birch, György, and Harris (4) were the first to call attention to the fact that acrodynia produced on low fat diets could be cured more readily with pyridoxine if fat was also fed. They termed this phenomenon the "sparing action of fat on pyridoxine" and called attention to the possible relationship of acrodynia with the "Burr and Burr syndrome" (39) resulting from deficiency of "essential unsaturated fatty acids" and, more specifically, of linoleic acid. The "Burr and Burr syndrome" can be characterized as a dry, scaly skin, accompanied by a disturbance of water metabolism, kidney degeneration, and reproductive disturbances. These studies were extended by Birch (40), who showed that in the presence of adequate quantities of pyridoxine acrodynia did not appear but that the scaliness and dry skin, along with kidney degeneration, were still present. In the presence of adequate fat, only acrodynia appeared. But, when either the essential fatty acids or pyridoxine were present in definite but inadequate amounts, there seemed to be some obscure interrelationship; then the acrodynia could be cured by either pyridoxine or fat. Birch advanced the idea that the essential fatty acids were necessary for the utilization of pyridoxine and that pyridoxine was required for the utilization of the essential fatty acids. These studies have been extended by Steenbock and his students (17, 37), by Salmon (38), by Richardson and Hogan (41), by Tange (42), by Emerson (43), and by others. There is no complete agreement among these workers, but most of them feel that the cure of acrodynia in rats on fat-free diets receiving thiamine and riboflavin as the only source of the vitamin B complex can be effected by the essential unsaturated fatty acids or by pyridoxine plus pantothenic acid and some other, as yet unknown, factor. The problem is still further complicated by differences in the physiological action of different essential unsaturated fatty acids. Burr and associates (44) showed that all the essential unsaturated fatty acids will cause growth in rats on fat-free diets but that linolenic acid has no great effectiveness in the cure of dermatitis (Burr and Burr syndrome), whereas linoleic and arachidonic acids are effective. Dermatitis seems to be complex, many factors playing as yet undetermined roles in its cure and production.

Whether any of the dermatoses, rashes, and eczemas afflicting the human are due in part to pyridoxine deficiency remains to be established. The possibility is by no means excluded that pyridoxine does play a role in such clinical conditions. Certain types of dermatitis observed in the clinic by Matzger (45) have been shown in preliminary observations to be more rapidly cleared up when pyridoxine was included in the therapy, especially with those dermatoses having a bilaterally symmetrical distribution and accompanied by edema.

Pyridoxine enters in other still obscure interrelationships. György (46) found that pyridoxine will aggravate cortical necrosis of kidneys in rats on low choline diets. Morgan *et al.* (47) and Lunde and Kringstad (48) have shown that pyridoxine will accelerate the graying of hair. At present these phenomena are so obscure as to render even a guess about the mechanism involved quite unprofitable.

cal entity, it would most appropriately be applied to pantothenic acid, because, of all the substances known to be stimulatory to yeast growth, pantothenic acid is effective under conditions most nearly resembling those used in the Belgian laboratories.

Before the vitamin properties of pantothenic acid were demonstrated, the broad physiological importance of the substance was clearly indicated. Its apparent occurrence in the tissues of all organisms tested, including those from many biological phyla, was itself a strong indication in this direction. Its stimulatory effect on green plants under specific conditions was another indication. Peterson and his students at Wisconsin recognized the same substance as essential for the growth of lactic acid bacteria before its effectiveness

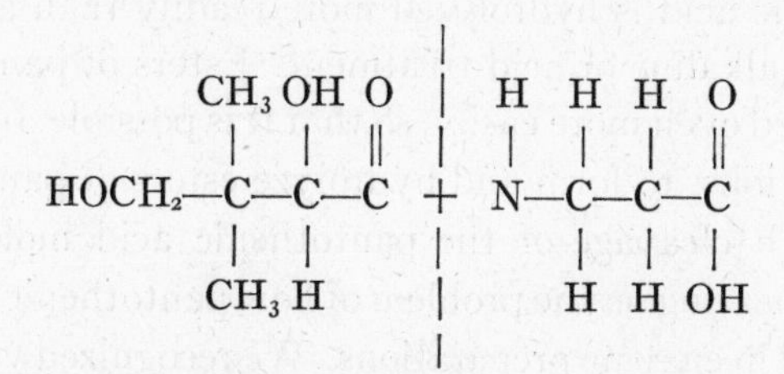

FIG. 1.—Pantothenic acid

as a vitamin was demonstrated. Mueller and co-workers found it to be effective for diphtheria organisms.

The formula for pantothenic acid is now familiar to all of you, and is given in Figure 1.

It will be interesting to review the question as to what modifications of this molecule are possible without destroying completely its physiological potency. While exhaustive research has not been carried out, we can say with considerable safety that any modification whatever of the right-hand portion (β-alanine residue) results in serious loss of physiological activity. On the left-hand portion, however, a number of changes may be made, with the result that the products possess substantial activity. For example, we may eliminate one of the methyl groups, or we may eliminate one and shift the other to the α- or γ-position, and the resulting compounds will retain some slight physiological activity toward microörganisms. Usually they are less than 1 per cent as active as pantothenic acid itself. Dr.

Mitchell prepared "hydroxy pantothenic acid" by introducing an additional hydroxyl group on one of the methyl carbon atoms. This resulted in a product which had higher, but variable, physiological activity up to 20 per cent or more of that of pantothenic acid. Hydroxy pantothenic acid appears not to be a natural-occurring substance, on the basis of the following evidence: When a natural extract is tested, using different organisms and different conditions of test, it always appears to have the same physiological potency, within limits of experimental error, as compared with pure pantothenic acid. When conditions and test organisms are varied and solutions of hydroxy pantothenic acid are subjected to similar tests, the potency of the material may vary as much as twenty-fold.

Pantothenic acid is hydrolyzed more readily than a typical peptide by mild alkaline or acid treatment. Esters of pantothenic acid are hydrolyzed even more easily, so that it is possible, by careful control of conditions, to form and hydrolyze esters of pantothenic acid without much cleavage of the pantothenic acid molecule. These facts have a bearing on the problem of how pantothenic acid is bound in tissues and in enzyme preparations. We recognized years ago that, if the liver from a freshly killed animal is extracted with hot water, very little pantothenic acid is obtained, whereas, after autolysis or merely standing at room temperature, much of the active substance is freed.

Pantothenic acid appears to require enzymatic action in order that it be freed from the bound condition. Mild acid or alkaline treatment has not been successful. This indicates that pantothenic acid probably does not occur bound through an ester linkage. β-alanine has not been successfully freed from fresh liver by mild acid or alkaline treatment; and this fact, in the light of those just mentioned, indicates that pantothenic acid in liver is not bound through the left-hand portion (Fig. 1) of the molecule. A possibility which appears probable is that it may be bound through an amide linkage on the β-alanine portion.

Recently Dr. Cheldelin and Mr. Moser have shown that pantothenic acid can be effectively released from its combination in fresh liver and in other tissues by taka-diastase and papain. This work was done with crude enzyme preparations, and nothing is known regarding the specific enzymes which may be involved.

I have stated that any alteration of the β-alanine residue in pantothenic acid results in loss of physiological activity. Dr. Snell, however, has prepared a compound, analogous to pantothenic acid, in which the carboxyl group is replaced by a sulfonic acid group. This compound has no pantothenic acid activity, but it has the very interesting property of blocking out pantothenic acid when introduced into a medium containing it. Thus, an organism requiring pantothenic acid will not grow in a medium containing pantothenic acid plus an excess of the sulfur analogue. If, however, the pantothenic acid concentration in the medium is raised to a higher level, it again becomes available and growth proceeds.

The functioning of pantothenic acid in cell metabolism has been the subject of a study by Teague at the University of Texas. He has confirmed the former finding that yeast which is deficient in pantothenic acid is stimulated in its fermentation by the addition of pantothenic acid. In cell-free systems, however, he was unable to obtain any appreciable effect. It was notable, on the other hand, that in any preparation capable of carrying on fermentation there remained an appreciable amount of pantothenic acid in bound condition and therefore not removable by dialysis.

Decarboxylation of pyruvic acid and phosphorylation of glucose could be catalyzed by cell-free preparations containing practically no free pantothenic acid, and addition of pantothenic acid failed to speed up the processes. Again, however, the preparations contained some "bound" pantothenic acid.

The effect of added pantothenic acid on the oxygen consumption of deficient chicken breast muscle gave negative results. (The breast muscle was rendered deficient by feeding the chickens on a diet low in pantothenic acid.) The anaerobic glycolysis in deficient breast and brain tissues was likewise not affected by added pantothenic acid. It was particularly interesting that the sulfur analogue of pantothenic acid likewise had no effect on anaerobic glycolysis in deficient breast muscle. This finding may be interpreted to mean that pantothenic acid is not a dissociable coenzyme necessary for this process. Of course, the tissues used contained significant amounts of bound pantothenic acid, even though they were deficient; so it is not possible to say that glycolysis can take place in the absence of this vitamin.

The question of the importance of pantothenic acid as a vitamin can well be discussed at this point. That it is essential for various

FIG. 2.—Chickens six weeks old with and without pantothenic acid in the diet

FIG. 3.—Pantothenic acid deficient pig

animals has been shown in many laboratories. Among the animals used have been rats, mice, chickens, hogs, and dogs. Others have had more experience with this work and hence are more competent to speak on this phase of the subject than I am.

Among the effects attributed to pantothenic acid deficiency are gray hair, dermatitis, ulcers in the intestinal tract, adrenal necrosis, kidney involvement, and nerve degeneration. I will not take time to discuss these except to state that on each point there is a substantial amount of evidence.

In Figure 2 are shown two chickens of the same age which were treated exactly alike except for the introduction of pantothenic acid into the diet of the better-developed specimen. From our studies and from observation it is easy to conclude that every tissue in the body is affected by pantothenic acid deficiency.

In Figure 3 we see a pantothenic acid deficient pig. Such an animal develops a "goose-stepping" syndrome which is characteristic. In Figure 4 is shown ulcers in the large intestine of such a pig. The intestinal tract is said to be ulcerated from one end to the other. I am indebted to Drs. E. H. Hughes and T. H. Jukes, of the University of California, who very kindly furnished me with the illustrations shown in Figures 3 and 4.

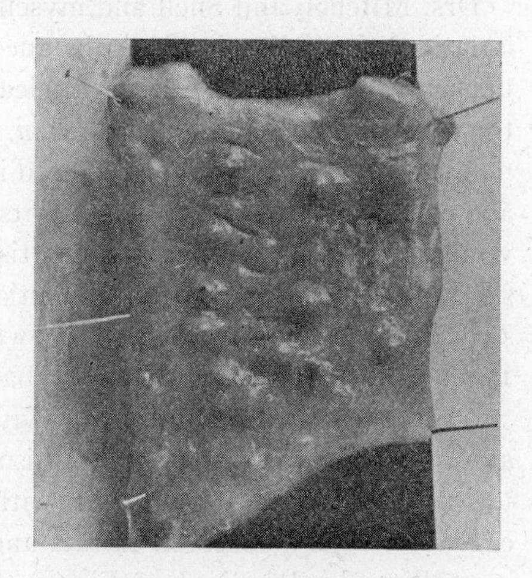

FIG. 4.—Ulcers in large intestine of pantothenic acid deficient pig.

Two facts may be cited which tend to show that natural pantothenic acid deficiencies exist. First, it has been shown that chicks fed on a diet containing 75 per cent whole corn, supplemented with casein and other vitamins, develop typical dermatitis symptoms. Evidently this grain, at least, is deficient for chickens. Second, Dr. Taylor at the University of Texas has shown that feeding extra pantothenic acid to hens already on an excellent commercial diet increased the hatchability of the eggs up to 30 per cent above the controls.

Turning to the subject of the microbiological approach, we will first consider the use of microörganisms as tools in the discovery of new vitamins and related compounds and mention some of the accomplishments made possible at the University of Texas largely through the generosity of the Clayton Foundation of Houston.

No one, I believe, will question the opinion that there are B vitamins yet to be discovered and characterized. That microörganisms will play an important part in the discovery of these seems evident. Members of the B complex in general affect microörganisms under appropriate conditions; and nutrilites for yeasts and bacteria, with a few exceptions, are vitamins for animals.

Drs. Mitchell and Snell and myself reported this summer (4) the isolation of a vitamin-like substance from spinach which is also unusually abundant in other green leaves and for which we proposed the name "folic acid" (Latin, *folium*, "leaf"). It affects yeast and a number of bacteria when introduced into media in very small doses, and even without animal experiments the indications are that it is a vitamin. It is present in all animal tissues and is released by autolysis—a fact which indicates its functional importance. There is also some evidence that it possesses growth-promoting activity for rats. It may be that it is produced by bacterial action in the intestine.

Another substance of interest to vitamin chemists is the substance avidin, which was discovered and isolated by Eakin in our laboratories. This substance combines with biotin and is responsible for egg-white injury observed in rats and chicks. It has recently been crystallized by Pennington (Fig. 5). The dissociation of the biotin-avidin complex is so slight that it is not broken down by exhaustive dialysis. Avidin appears, from analysis and from its ability to give carbohydrate tests, to be a glucoprotein.

Another important application of microörganisms to the study of vitamins consists in their use in the determination of vitamins. Various workers at Wisconsin and elsewhere, including ourselves, have developed microbiological methods for the determination of vitamins. Among the best known of these are: (1) the yeast fermentation method for thiamine of Schultz, Atkin, and Frey; (2) the Snell-Strong method for riboflavin; (3) the microbiological methods for pantothenic acid; (4) the Snell-Wright method for nicotinic acid; and (5) the yeast-growth method for biotin.

In addition, we have devised methods for pyridoxine, thiamine, inositol, and folic acid and are now publishing a bulletin (5) which will be for free distribution, describing the various methods and their application to the study of the vitamin content of normal tissue autolysates.

To express the results in graphic form, we have constructed "vitamin profiles" in which the vitamin content in gammas per gram of a whole rat carcass is taken as a unit, and every other material com-

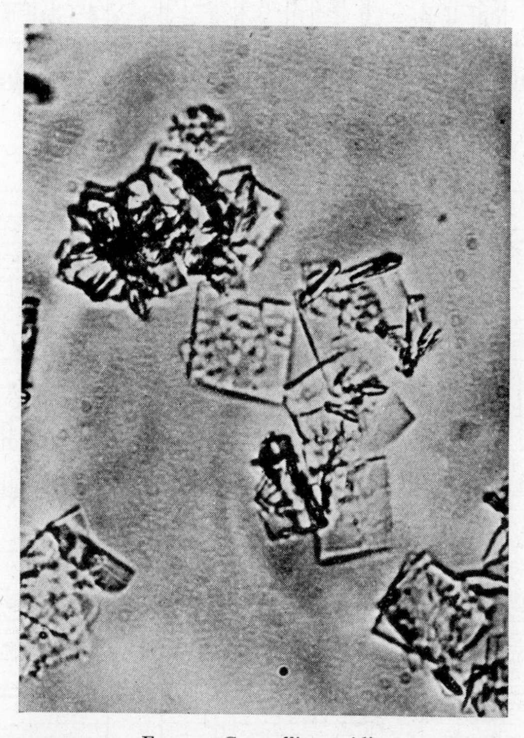

FIG. 5.—Crystalline avidin

pared to this. The vitamin profile of the rat carcass material would be represented by a series of bars, each one division high. If a bar in a profile is ten units high, this means that the tissue autolysate concerned is ten times as rich as the average tissue in a rat carcass.

In Figures 6–8 are given examples of vitamin profiles from our forthcoming bulletin. The order in which the vitamins appear (abbreviated by their initial letters) is arbitrary but is the same in all the illustrations.

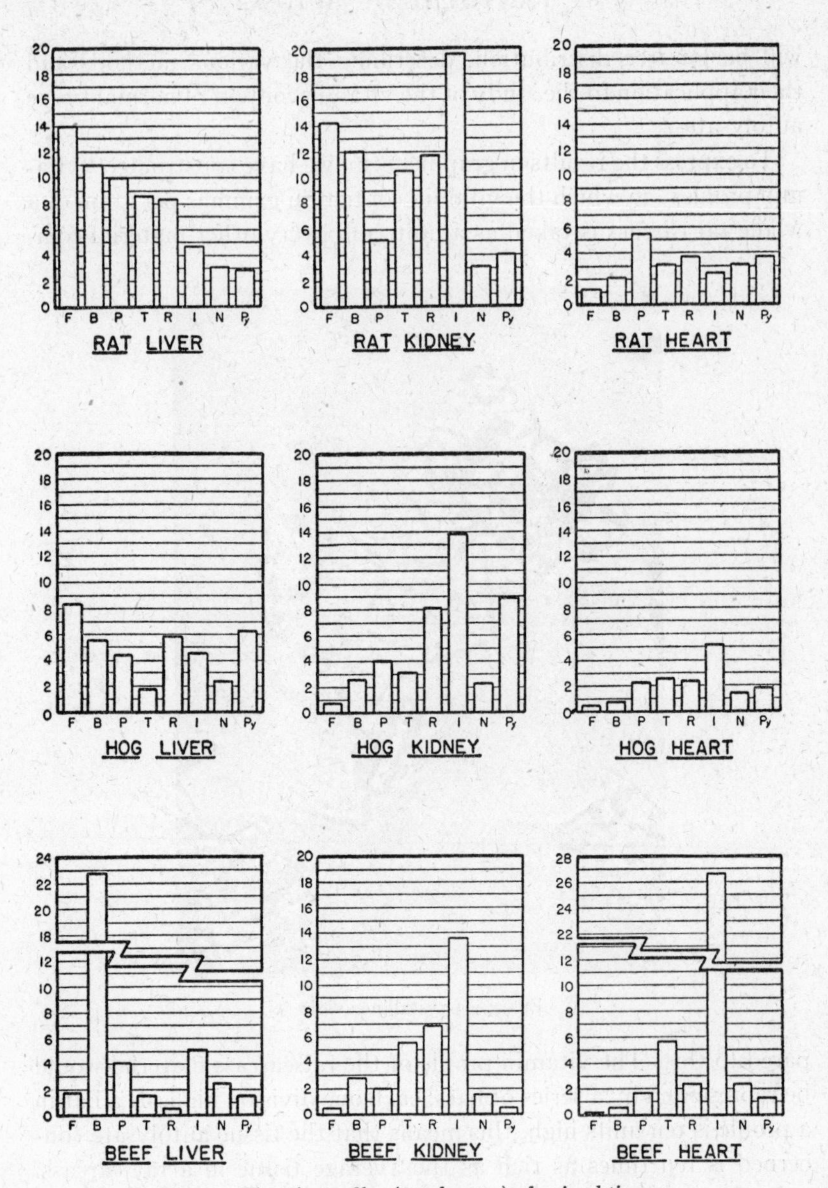

FIG. 6.—Vitamin profiles (autolysates) of animal tissues

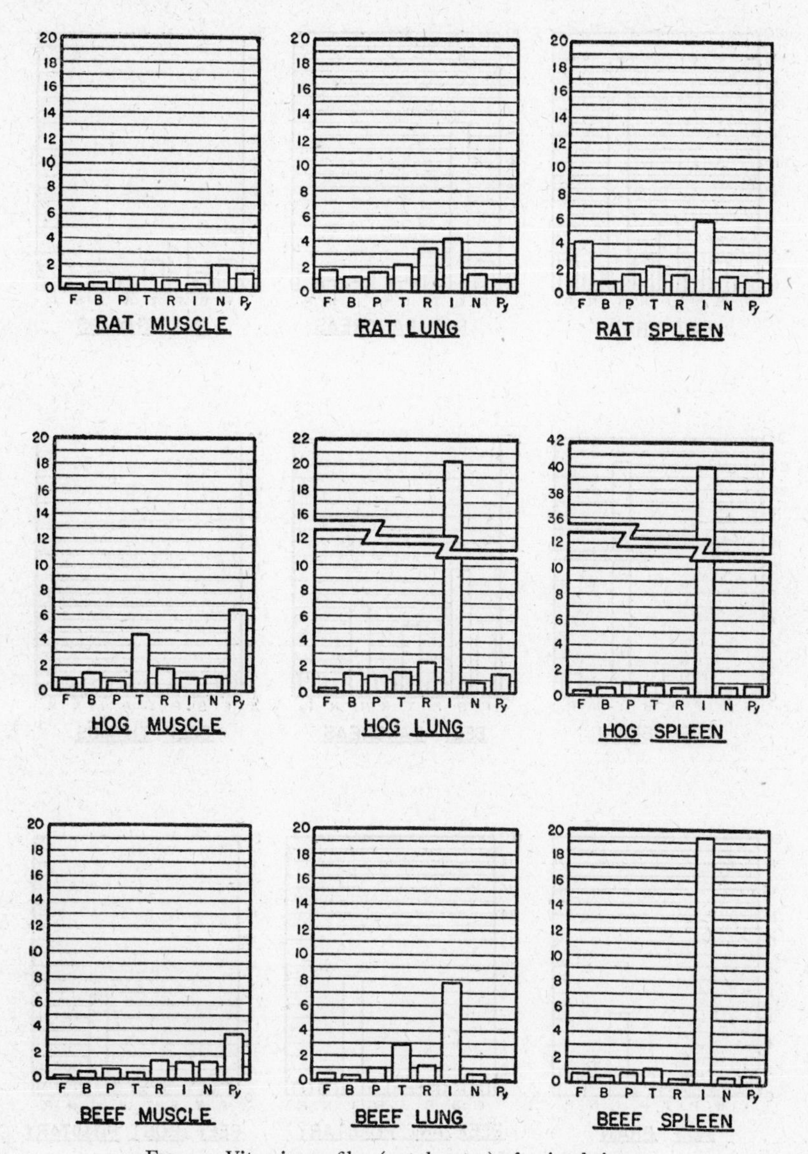

FIG. 7.—Vitamin profiles (autolysates) of animal tissues

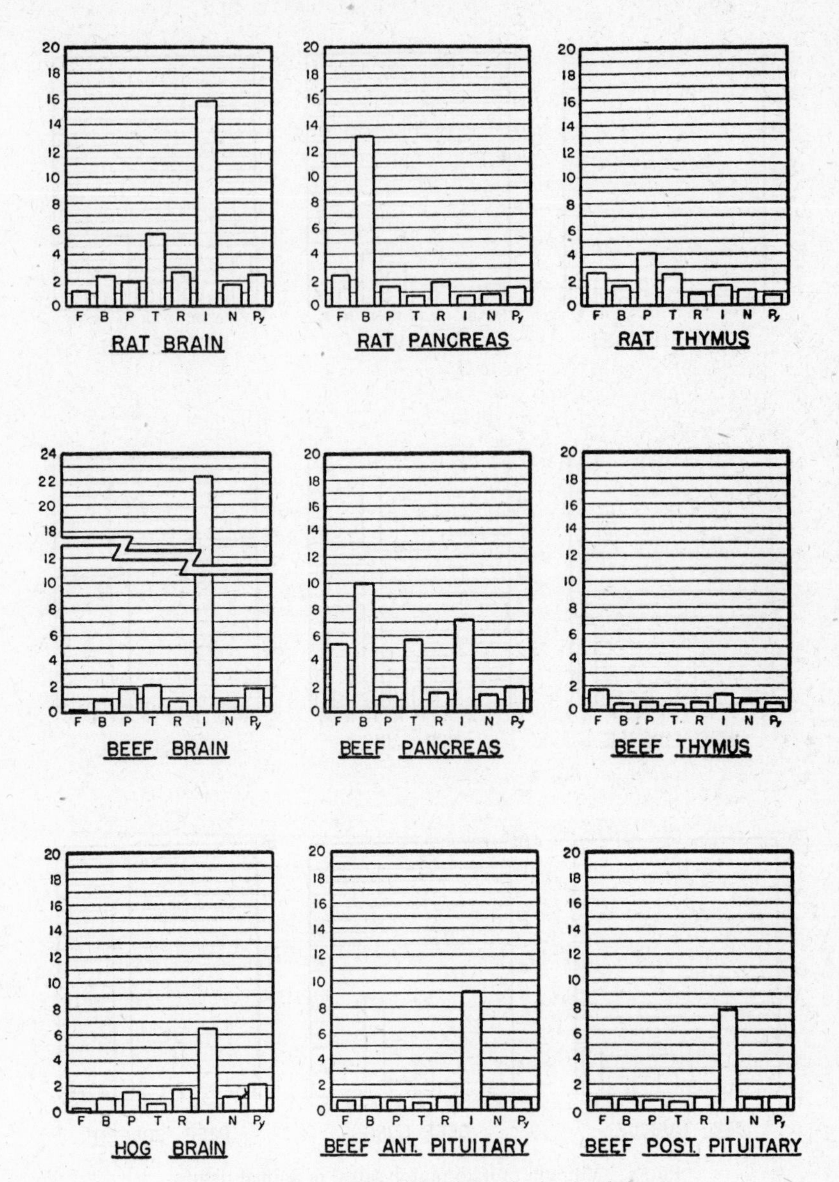

FIG. 8.—Vitamin profiles (autolysates) of animal tissues

Another form of chart is represented in Figures 9 and 10. These represent the distribution of the individual vitamins in different tissues. One of the most interesting observations to be made in connec-

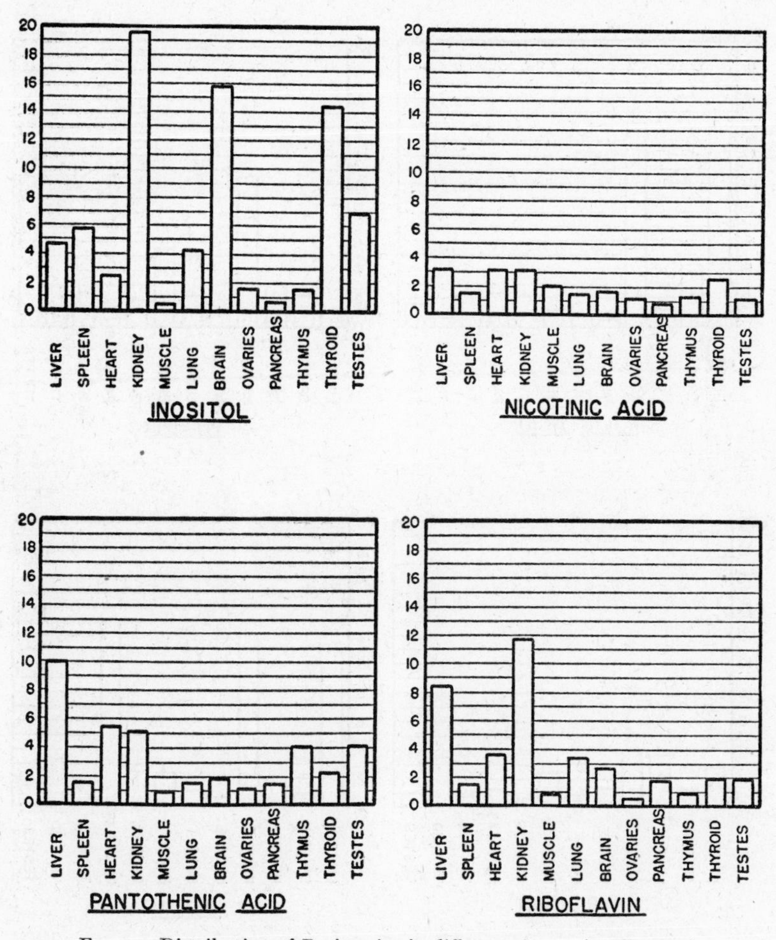

FIG. 9.—Distribution of B vitamins in different tissues (autolysates)

tion with these determinations is the fact that the distributions of the various B vitamins show a positive correlation with each other. Sources which are rich for one B vitamin tend to be rich for the others. Individual tissues offer interesting exceptions. The distribution of inositol is erratic.

In Figures 11 and 12 are shown vitamin profiles of autolysates of embryonic, young, and mature tissues. We do not claim that the methods which we have used or the results obtained from them are

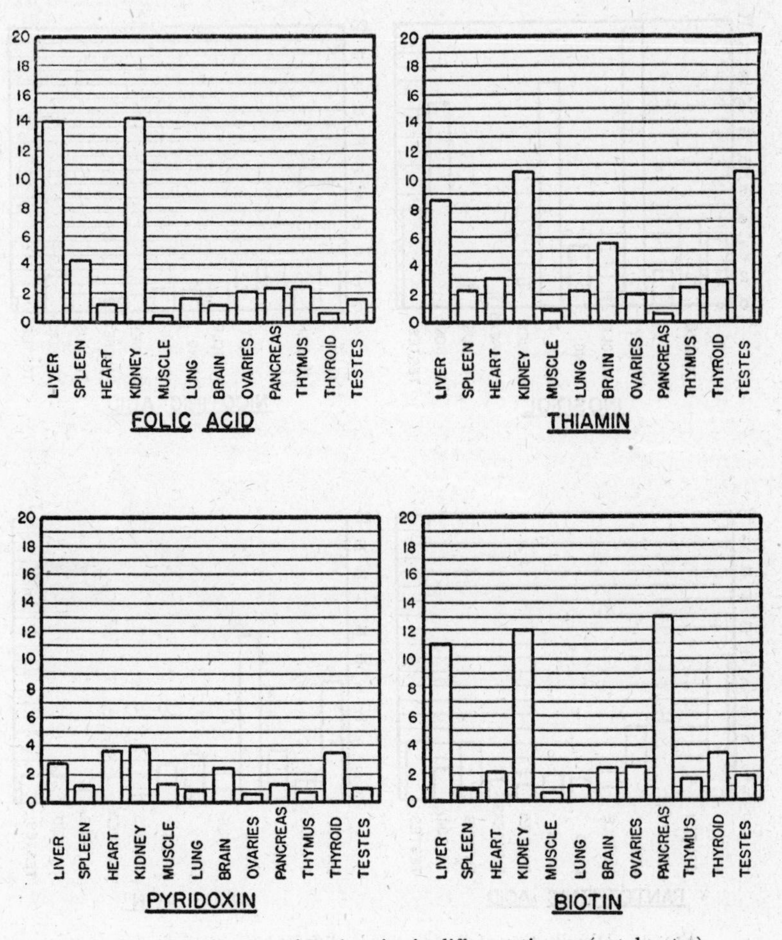

FIG. 10.—Distribution of B vitamins in different tissues (autolysates)

in any sense final. The sample graphs here shown at least suggest what can be done by microbiological methods.

Let us suppose, now, that all the B vitamins have been discovered and that satisfactory methods of one kind or another have been de-

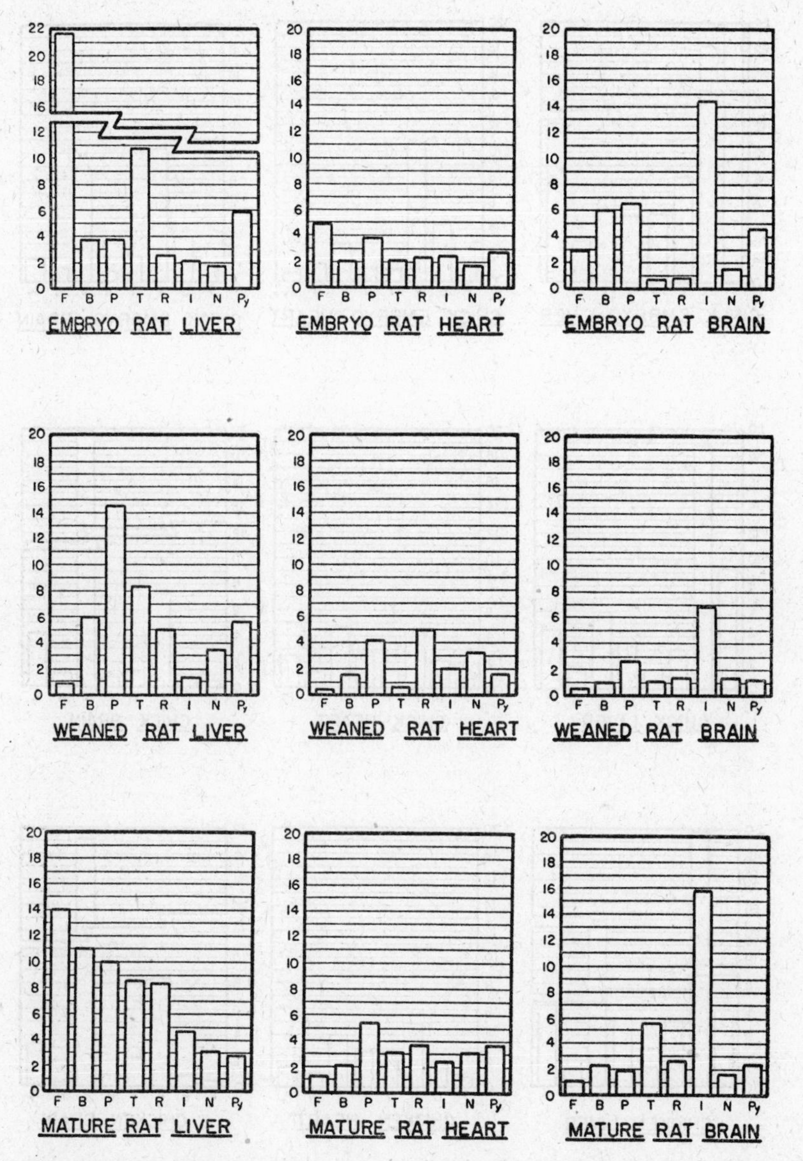

FIG. 11.—Distribution of B vitamins in embryonic, young, and mature rat tissues (autolysates).

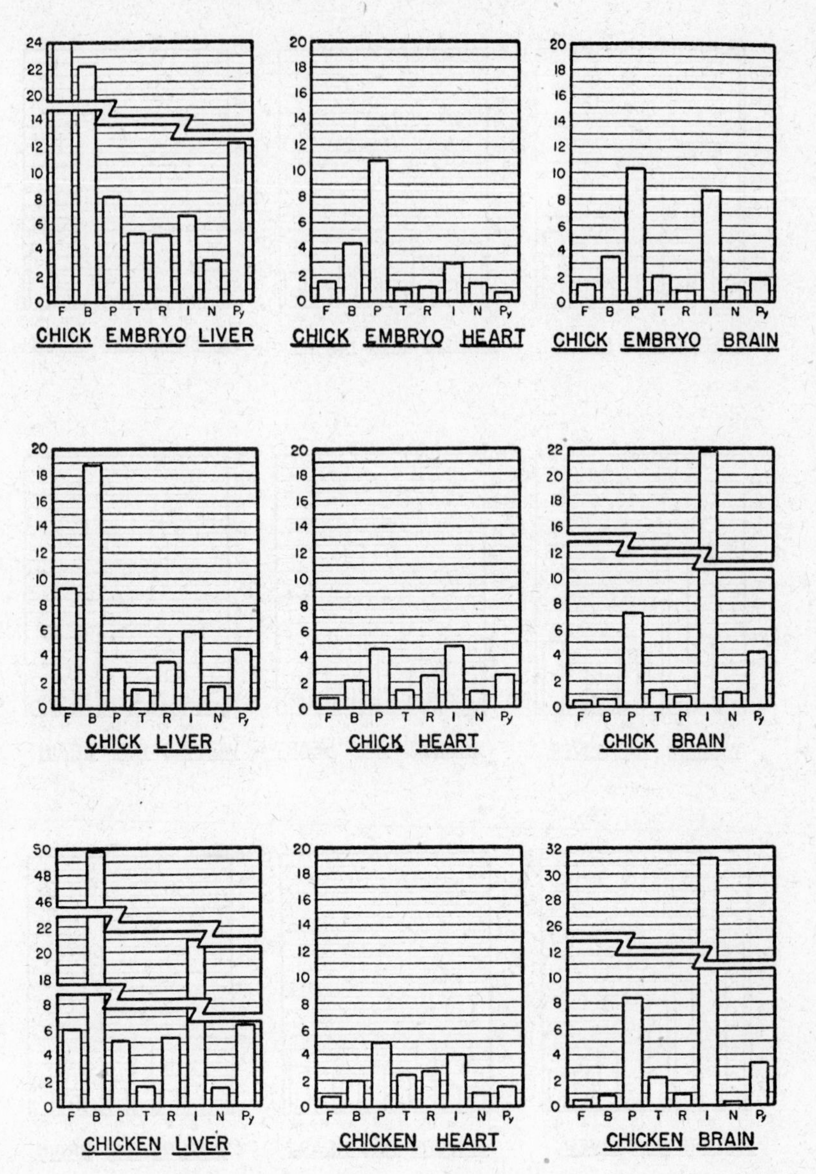

FIG. 12.—Distribution of B vitamins in embryonic, young, and mature chicken tissues (autolysates).

veloped for all of them. Is there still more that microbiological study can do?

There appear to be two more important contributions from this source. First, there is the problem of microbiological production of B vitamins in the intestines of various animals. Recent suggestive work by Elvehjem and co-workers indicate that this phase of investigation may be highly important. Second, there is the question of interrelations, replacements, antagonisms, and synergisms between the various B vitamins. There is almost an indefinite amount of investigation on animals which will have to be done before these problems can be solved. It appears likely that the best place to start is with microörganisms. In connection with yeast-growth studies, a number of interesting and suggestive observations have already been made which may be of a fundamental nature and may carry over into the animal organism. Experiments with microörganisms are relatively so simple, compared with animal experiments, that it is desirable to use them whenever they show promise.

BIBLIOGRAPHY

1. Symposium on Respiratory Enzymes, University of Wisconsin, September, 1941.
2. WILLIAMS, R. J., Biol. Rev., **16**:49, 1941.
3. WILLIAMS, R. J., Enzymologia, **9**:387, 1941
4. MITCHELL, H. K.; SNELL, E. E.; and WILLIAMS, R. J., J. Am. Chem. Soc., **63**:2284, 1941.
5. Univ. Texas Publ. 4137, 1941.

PANTOTHENIC ACID IN HUMAN NUTRITION

EDGAR S. GORDON
Departments of Biochemistry and Medicine, University of Wisconsin

THE importance of pantothenic acid in the nutrition of various species of animals is now well established, but the significance of this factor in the diet of humans is only beginning to be explored. A few brief reports have appeared (1, 2, 3, 4, 5), but in no instance have adequate studies been performed to substantiate the observed clinical effectiveness of this substance. The present report, therefore, is intended to summarize the available knowledge of pantothenic acid in so far as human nutrition is concerned, as well as to present several preliminary observations relative to its therapeutic usefulness.

The first report of a clinical trial of pantothenic acid was that of Spies, Stanberry, Jukes, Williams, and Babcock (4), which indicated a fall up to 50 per cent in the pantothenate level in the blood of patients with pellagra, beriberi, and riboflavin deficiency. Subsequent injection of calcium pantothenate produced a rise in both pantothenate and riboflavin. Likewise, the administration of riboflavin to such patients caused a rise in both factors. From these results the authors concluded that pantothenic acid is necessary to humans and that its function is in some way closely associated with that of riboflavin.

Three months later Musick (5) suggested that deficiency of pantothenic acid and pyridoxine was responsible for the muscular weakness characteristic of B-complex avitaminosis. No assay studies were included.

Quantitative blood and urine studies in dogs have recently been reported by Silber and Klaus (6), who have found that urinary excretion of pantothenate rises within 2 hours following an oral test dose of 4 mg. per kilo body weight. With an oral dose of 1 mg. per kilo the 24-hour excretion amounted to 22–31 per cent of the administered amount. The blood levels rose and fell within 2 hours after oral administration of calcium pantothenate. The effect on riboflavin content of blood and urine reported by Spies *et al.* was not confirmed in this study on dogs.

The assay method used by Silber and Klaus, and by the author in the study of human pantothenate excretion, was that of Strong, Feeney, and Earle (7) and was based upon the growth requirement of *Lactobacillus casei* for pantothenic acid. A culture medium was prepared which contained all of the growth essentials for the organism with the exception of pantothenate. Urine was then added in predetermined dilutions to supply the missing factor. The bacterial growth which ensued during the following 72-hour period was directly proportional to the pantothenate content of the added urine, and the end-point was readily determined by titration of the lactic acid produced by the growing culture with standard alkali, using bromthymol blue as an indicator. Such a procedure has proved to be applicable to a wide variety of assay conditions. By slight modification of the basal medium, riboflavin determinations can be carried out according to the technique of Snell and Strong (8).

In the studies on humans the subjects were chiefly medical students and members of the laboratory staff, all of whom were consuming apparently normal diets, and in none of whom could any manifestations be found suggestive of deficiency disease of any sort. Various hospital patients were also studied because of clinical evidence, more or less clear-cut, of nutritional deficiency disease.

Urine was collected in 24-hour specimens and preserved with a few drops of chloroform and a few drops of toluene to prevent bacterial growth. These small amounts of preservative have been found not to interfere in any way with the subsequent growth of the assay organism.

A series of 58 assays on 40 different subjects revealed an average daily excretion of 3.52 mg., with a range of from 1.14 to 6.36 mg. Individual variations from day to day were found to be quite large and were presumably dependent upon corresponding variations in the pantothenate content of the diet. The distribution of these excretion data are shown in Figure 1. Thus, 19 per cent of this group excrete between 3.0 and 3.5 mg. per 24 hours. None of the normal subjects excreted less than 1.0 mg.

In 12 cases of general nutritional deficiency the range of urinary excretion was from 0.39 to 1.45 mg. per 24 hours, with an average of 0.83 mg. Although 1.0 mg. per 24 hours appears to be a rough divid-

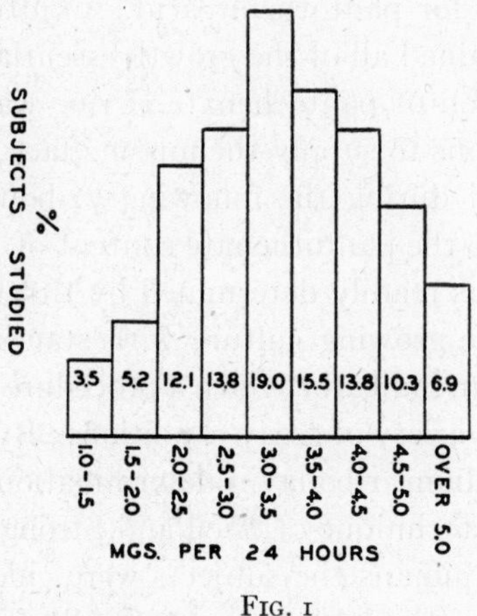

FIG. 1

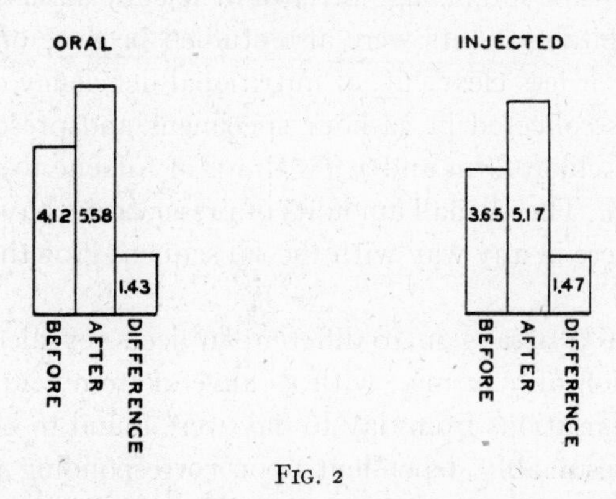

FIG. 2

ing-line between normal and deficient subjects, there is some apparent overlapping of values which makes some further diagnostic procedure highly desirable.

In an effort to find such a test procedure, 10 mg. of crystalline calcium pantothenate were administered either orally or subcutaneously, followed by hourly urine collections. Another series, using 20 mg. of pantothenate both orally and subcutaneously, was also examined. In all cases a pretest 24-hour specimen was collected, and the test dose was given under fasting conditions; diuresis was produced by the administration of 400 cc. of water. The results of the 20-mg. test-dose procedure in normal subjects are shown in Figure 2. Every conceivable analysis of these data has failed to yield a basis for satisfactory separation of normals from deficiency cases. The evidence presented in the chart, however, indicates that calcium pantothenate is quickly and efficiently absorbed from the gastrointestinal tract in normal subjects. The charted results for cases of deficiency disease are almost identical and are therefore not included. Thus it appears that the "test-dose procedure" is not applicable as a diagnostic measure of human pantothenic acid deficiency. Axelrod, Spies, and Elvehjem (9) have shown this to be true also in the case of riboflavin deficiency in humans.

Therapeutic administration of calcium pantothenate to cases of nutritional deficiency, either alone or together with other vitamins, produces a prompt rise in urinary excretion, until the daily output falls well within the established normal range. A similar rise has often been observed to follow the establishment of a good diet without added vitamin supplements.

In attempting to identify a specific biochemical or clinical function of pantothenic acid, it is logical to be guided by the known manifestations of this deficiency in experimental animals. In chicks, this substance is known to be necessary for normal growth and has been shown to prevent typical deficiency lesions of the skin and central nervous system (10). In rats, growth is likewise impaired, and lesions appear in the adrenal cortex, characterized by depletion of lipoid droplets, hemorrhage, and finally necrosis and atrophy, with presumably a concomitant loss of adrenal cortical function (11, 12). Similar adrenal cortical lesions have been produced in dogs, and life has then been maintained with adrenal cortical extract in the continued absence of pantothenic acid from the diet (13). The author has obtained identical results with rats (14).

In the pig, a lack of the filtrate factor causes a retardation of growth and a failure of normal weight gain (15). In addition, as shown in experiments of Wintrobe, Miller, and Lisco (16), changes in the central nervous system brought about by B-complex deficiency, and unaffected by the addition of various pure components to the diet, are partially relieved by the use of liver. In these experiments pure pantothenate was not tried. Subsequent experiments by this same group have corroborated their earlier findings and have indicated, in addition, that pantothenic acid may be at least one of the factors involved in the central nervous system lesions which manifest themselves in the spastic goose-stepping gait (17). Hughes has produced similar evidence (18).

In the silver fox, the lack of filtrate factor leads to the development of an inferior grade of fur with an excessive degree of "silvering" (19). Graying of fur in several other species has been attributed to pantothenic acid deficiency (20, 21, 22), but the evidence is not completely satisfactory at present.

From the available evidence in animals, lesions due to pantothenic acid deficiency in the human may occur in the nervous or endocrine systems or they may involve the skin or hair. Several cases have been of unusual interest in this connection. In two of these showing the classical signs and symptoms of peripheral neuritis associated with a long-standing poor dietary intake and other manifestations of nutritional deficiency, the use of supplements of pure thiamine, riboflavin, nicotinic acid, and pyridoxine failed to produce a therapeutic response. The subsequent addition of 50 mg. daily of pantothenate to the diet resulted in prompt improvement, both subjectively and objectively. In all, 5 cases of peripheral neuritis were treated in this manner, and the response in every instance was excellent. The results, however, are open to the criticism that the improvement noted may have been due to the delayed effect of the other B vitamins administered before the pantothenate. The slow response of this condition to vitamin therapy is well known, and such a possibility cannot be ruled out. Quantitative methods of study were not available at the time of most of these observations. In a few instances such studies confirmed the clinical diagnosis, and the data so obtained are included above.

Another interesting observation occurred in connection with a case of Korsakoff's syndrome in a male alcoholic with severe peripheral neuritis. His mental state was typical of that condition, and the neurological signs of peripheral neuropathy included exquisite tenderness over the nerve trunks and loss of knee and ankle jerks and of vibration and position senses. This entire clinical picture did not respond to the administration of those members of the B complex usually employed, namely, thiamine, riboflavin, and nicotinic acid. There was, however, a marked and rapid response to the addition of pantothenic acid supplements to the diet. This improvement included a rapid clearing of the mental state, but there has thus far been no return of the knee and ankle jerks. It was not possible to perform quantitative urine examinations for pantothenate, but the clinical response strongly suggests a therapeutic effect from that substance.

The possibility of human adrenal insufficiency on a nutritional basis is worthy of passing mention. There have not been any reported cases of this type, although clinicians are becoming increasingly aware of a rising incidence of nontuberculous Addison's disease, the etiology of which is usually described as "idiopathic" or "toxic." It is not unreasonable, therefore, on the basis of animal experiments, to conclude that nutritional deficiency may act either alone or as an important predisposing factor in the production of this condition. Of the nutrients thus far studied, pantothenic acid would appear to be one most worthy of further attention.

The suggestion that pantothenic acid may play a part in maintaining the integrity of nervous tissue, both in experimental animals and in man, comes at a time when many students of nutrition are beginning to question the existing theories as to the specific etiology of nutritional neuropathy. Evidence from several sources has been presented which indicates that thiamine alone neither prevents nor cures the degenerative changes in nervous tissue generally conceded to be due to nutritional deficiency (23, 24, 17). Indeed, the entire basis for thiamine as an antineuritic factor has been questioned. It is abundantly clear, on the one hand, that the error in pyruvate metabolism justifiably attributable to thiamine deficiency is corrected in a matter of hours after restoration of the missing factor and, on the other, that long-continued nutritional deficiency produces permanent irreversible changes in the peripheral nerves. The intermediate stages are not clear, but there is a growing opinion that "nutritional neuropathy" represents a multiple-deficiency disease. Pantothenate may eventually prove to be one of the missing factors.

Because of the wide distribution of pantothenic acid in nature, it is logical to question the incidence of a spontaneous deficiency. Jukes (25) has listed 16 foods as excellent sources, 13 foods as good sources, and a great many foods as moderate-to-poor sources. By studying this list it becomes apparent that pantothenic acid deficiency might easily occur in combination with other B-complex deficiencies. Among experimental animals the ruminants are independent of a dietary supply of this substance because of its synthesis by the bacterial flora of the rumen. This synthesis probably occurs also in most animals, including man; but the site of the bacterial action, in the colon, makes absorption impossible.

Sebrell (26) has designated 2.77 mg. daily as the riboflavin requirement of normal healthy adults. The average daily urinary excretion varies from 700 to 1,200 μg. daily. If the same ratio were tenable for pantothenate, calculated on an average daily excretion of 3.52 mg., the human daily requirement would be from 9 to 11 mg. Such a figure is obviously entirely speculative, since the daily requirement cannot be accurately estimated until experimental pantothenic acid deficiency can be produced in human subjects.

While many of the clinical observations presented above can hardly stand up under close scrutiny, they may, nevertheless, serve as a step toward more carefully controlled studies in the future. They are of sufficient interest to warrant the extension of careful quantitative clinical investigations of nutritional deficiency disease to include pantothenic acid. For the results of animal experimentation have already pointed to a number of leads, the further study of which must be accepted by investigators in the clinical field.

BIBLIOGRAPHY

1. Wilder, R. M.; Browne, H. C.; and Butt, H. R., Arch. Int. Med., **65**: 390, 1940.
2. Spies, T. D.; Hightower, D. P.; and Hubbard, L. H., J.A.M.A., **115**: 292, 1940.

3. Editorial, South. M. J., **33**:906, 1940.
4. SPIES, T. D.; STANBERRY, S. R.; WILLIAMS, R. J.; JUKES, T. H.; and BABCOCK, S. H., J.A.M.A., **115**:523, 1940.
5. MUSICK, V. H., J. Oklahoma M. A., **33**:4, 1940.
6. SILBER, R. H., and KLAUS, U., J. Biol. Chem., **142**:623, 1942.
7. STRONG, F. M.; FEENEY, R. E.; and EARLE, A., Indust. & Engin. Chem. (Anal. ed.), **13**:566, 1941.
8. SNELL, E. E., and STRONG, F. M., Indust. & Engin. Chem. (Anal. ed.), **11**: 346, 1939.
9. AXELROD, A. E.; SPIES, T. D.; and ELVEHJEM, C. A., J. Clin. Investigation, **20**:229, 1940.
10. PHILLIPS, P. H., and ENGEL, R. W., J. Nutrition, **18**:227, 1939.
11. DAFT, F. S.; SEBRELL, W. H.; BABCOCK, S. H.; and JUKES, T. H., Pub. Health Rep., **55**:1333, 1940.
12. MILLS, R. C.; SHAW, J. H.; ELVEHJEM, C. A.; and PHILLIPS, P. H., Proc. Soc. Exper. Biol. & Med., **45**:482, 1940.
13. ELVEHJEM, C. A., to be published.
14. GORDON, E. S., unpublished observations.
15. HUGHES, E. H., Hilgardia, **11**:595, 1938.
16. WINTROBE, M. M.; MILLER, J. L.; and LISCO, H., Bull. Johns Hopkins Hosp., **67**:377, 1940.
17. WINTROBE, M. M.; MUSCHATT, C.; MILLER, J. L.; KOLB, L. C.; STEIN, H. J.; and LISCO, H., J. Clin. Investigation, **21**:71, 1942.
18. HUGHES, E. H., to be published.
19. MORGAN, A. F., and SIMMS, H. D., J. Nutrition, **20**:627, 1940.
20. MORGAN, A. F., and SIMMS, H. D., *ibid.*, **19**:233, 1940.
21. FROST, D. B.; MOORE, R. C.; and DANN, F., Proc. Soc. Exper. Biol. & Med., **46**:507, 1941.
22. EMERSON, G. A., and EVANS, H. M., Proc. Soc. Exper. Biol. & Med., **46**: 655, 1941.
23. BROWN, M. R., J.A.M.A., **116**:1615, 1941.
24. MEIKELJOHN, A. P., New England J. Med., **223**:265, 1940.
25. JUKES, T. H., J. Nutrition, **21**:193, 1941.
26. SEBRELL, W. H., this volume.

BIOTIN

VINCENT DU VIGNEAUD
Department of Biochemistry, Cornell University Medical College

THE story of biotin is a story of the development of three parallel lines of investigation which, evolving independently, gave no indication of their possible connection. Suddenly two of these lines converged. The two remaining lines continued for some time, and then they too merged into one. We now recognize that what were thought to be independent roots of different trees of research were, in reality, roots of the same tree.

In each of these three lines of investigation a search was being made for a biologically active compound responsible for a certain biological effect. In one group of laboratories a search was being made for one of the bios factors, a substance necessary for the growth of yeast. This was finally isolated by Kögl and Tönnis (1) in 1936 and called "biotin." In another group of laboratories a search was being made for a compound which was necessary for the growth of *Rhizobium*, a nitrogen-fixing bacterium. The compound responsible for this was called "coenzyme R" by Allison, Hoover, and Burk (2), its discoverers. In still another group of laboratories attempts were under way to isolate a substance which had the remarkable power of inhibiting in animals the deleterious effects produced by the feeding of raw egg white. This protective factor was called the "protective factor X" by Boas, "the protective factor against egg white injury" by Parsons, and "vitamin H" by György. It was little realized, however, that the groups in these various laboratories were dealing with different manifestations of the same chemical entity.

With the demonstration that biotin, the yeast-growth factor, was the anti–egg-white injury factor, or vitamin H (3), in animals, interest in biotin has vastly increased, since it became clear through this work that biotin played a role in the vital economy of animals and that biotin was an animal vitamin. As a result of this finding, work was stimulated in many laboratories, and utterly new aspects of its activity are coming to light. The chemical work on elucidation of structure is likewise under way. We have, in our own laboratory, gradually been getting a glimpse of its chemical nature and perhaps of its possible structure. The work, of course, is hampered by the small amounts of material available. I need only remind you that Kögl worked up 250 kilos of dried egg yolk to get 1.1 mg. of the crystalline compound. It is true that in our laboratory we have worked out a far superior method of isolation from other raw materials more readily available; yet it is still a precious compound. I hope to tell you in the course of this discussion something as to its chemical nature. As knowledge of the functional groups may be of aid to those working with biotin, I shall discuss the evidence for the functional groups, to give these workers a better understanding of its chemical behavior and even hints perhaps as to why biotin possesses certain peculiar behaviors. I should also like to refer briefly in this presentation to some of the studies we have under way on some of the biological activities of this compound. I should first, however, like to go back to discuss for a moment the development of those independent lines of investigation of which I spoke at the beginning, how they happened to coalesce, and how biotin became recognized as the compound responsible for these apparently different biological activities. Perhaps it might not be uninteresting if I were to digress, in the course of the story, to relate how we happened to be engaged in this particular work and the circumstances that surrounded the realization and demonstration of the identity of vitamin H with biotin and coenzyme R. There are interesting coincidences involved which, although not important scientifically, are nevertheless sometimes of interest in the human side of scientific events.

The first of these biological activities to be run down was the bios, or yeast-growth, factor. The development of the bios field is undoubtedly familiar to all of you, and I shall not attempt to review it here. You are well acquainted with the early recognition by Wildiers (4) in Ide's laboratory in Louvain, Belgium, in 1901, that yeast required the presence of traces of certain factors in the media for its proper growth and that "bios" came to be the name given to this group. As in the case of vitamin B, it was thought at first that bios might be a single compound; but, as further research was done, it was recognized that bios represented a group of compounds. The bios group became separated into subgroups and into individual compounds labeled "Bios I," "Bios II*a*," and "Bios II*b*," etc. It was the Bios II*b* factor, the charcoal adsorbable factor, which particularly occupied the attention of Kögl and Tönnis at Utrecht. From this fraction Kögl and Tönnis isolated in 1936 a crystalline methyl ester of a compound which was extremely potent in influencing the growth of yeast at concentrations as low as one part in 4×10^{11}. Kögl called this compound "biotin." He assigned to the ester the empirical formula of $C_{11}H_{18}O_3N_2S$. Whether there are still other growth substances in the Bios II*b* fraction remains for the future to settle. A thesis has recently been presented at the University of Toronto by Wayman (5), a student of the late Lash Miller, who claims that biotin does not possess the full growth-promoting power of the Bios II*b* fraction.

While this work on the bios factors was under way, Allison, Hoover, and Burk, in 1933, found that several species of the root-nodule bacterium *Rhizobium* required the presence of some substance which could be concentrated from cultures of *Azotobacter*, commercial sucrose, molasses, hydrolyzed yeast, and many other sources. It was heat stable and of low molecular weight. It had a marked effect upon the respiration of *Rhizobia;* and, because of its properties, these investigators called it a coenzyme of respiration—for short, "coenzyme R." Considerable work was done on the properties of this compound, and considerable effort was made over a period of years toward its isolation. In 1939, about four years after the isolation of biotin, West and Wilson (6) suggested that coenzyme R and biotin were identical, on the basis of extensive comparisons of crude preparations. Even somewhat earlier, Nilsson and co-workers (7), in Sweden, began to suspect the identity of this yeast nutrilite with coenzyme R and finally tried some of Kögl's crystalline biotin methyl ester for its effect on the growth of *Rhizobia*. They found that biotin possessed the activities ascribed to coenzyme R, and thus two of these fields of investigation under discussion converged. Coenzyme R became biotin.

It was not realized at this time, however, that biotin and coenzyme R, necessary for the growth of yeast and of *Rhizobia*, were also necessary for animals.

While the work on biotin and coenzyme R was going on, work was also progressing in other laboratories on a very remarkable substance which occurred in yeast, liver, and various other sources and which possessed the power of counteracting the harmful effects of egg white on animals. Boas in 1927 (8) described a definite syndrome which regularly occurred in rats that had been fed a diet containing dried egg white as the source of protein. She found that when young rats were placed on the diet shown in Table 1 characteristic symptoms

TABLE 1

EGG-WHITE DIET USED BY BOAS

Dried egg white	100 gm.	Lemon juice	25 cc.
Wheaten starch	250 gm.	Marmite	25 gm.
Normal salt mixture	25 gm.	Distilled water	300 cc.
Hardened cottonseed oil	75 gm.		

began to appear after 3 weeks. Boas described the syndrome as follows:

> The rats grow well and are usually in good health for from 2 to 3 weeks. Then red scaly patches appear at the corners of the mouth, the coat becomes rough and sticky and the long hairs fall out. The fur on the abdomen shows at first a characteristic ribbed appearance, followed by the development of bald areas. Meanwhile the red patches spread to other parts of the body and the picture is one of an eczematous dermatitis. There are even skin hemorrhages in severe cases. The region round the mouth is always the most severely affected though there is often such marked blepharitis that the eyes are closed. The loss of hair is often extensive. In a few cases oedema of the feet has been seen but this does not usually occur. These rats always have a distinctive, somewhat musty smell, probably due to some constituent of the urine. The body weight remains stationary for a week or two, but falls slowly during the second stage of the disease. This is reached about 2 to 3 weeks after the development of the first signs of deficiency. To the dermatitis, symptoms of nervous upset are now added. There is pronounced spasticity of the limbs, particularly of the hind legs, and the back is arched. The rat assumes in many cases a kangaroo-like posture. . . . . Some of the rats do not show marked spasticity but assume a crouching attitude and display a curious swimming movement with the front paws. Death, which occurs in the final phase, is preceded by a rapid loss of weight, and the animal shows signs of extreme cyanosis. Rigor mortis sets in rapidly. Post mortem there is an almost complete absence of fat and the skin is infiltrated and vascularised.

The absence of fat is particularly worthy of note in passing, in the light of McHenry's recent work (9) on the effect of biotin on fatty infiltration of the liver.

The discovery of a protective factor against this egg-white injury was partly due to coincidence but mainly resulted from the careful work of Margaret Boas. She found that Bond had long used dried egg white in nutrition studies with the rat but had never observed the symptoms which she had found. They compared data and found that their diets were apparently exactly the same. On closer scrutiny, however, they realized that Bond had used potato starch and Boas had used wheat starch. Boas then repeated her work but used potato starch. The animals did not develop the characteristic symptoms, but did when she went back to wheat starch. She therefore postulated that there was some factor in the potato starch which protected against the egg-white injury and which was absent in the wheat starch. She called it the "protective factor X." This was the original discovery of the anti–egg-white injury factor, which we also know as "vitamin H," and now as "biotin." In further work she studied the distribution of the protective factor in a variety of foodstuffs and found it to be present in large amounts in raw potatoes, yeast, milk, and liver.

From her work Boas postulated two alternative hypotheses: (*a*) that when fresh egg white is dried, a heretofore unknown factor is destroyed which can be supplied by fresh eggs, dried yeast, potato starch, etc., or (*b*) that, upon drying egg white, a toxic substance is produced which can be neutralized by a factor X; but she concluded that it would seem to her that the problem was more complicated than either of the two theories.

Boas also granted that it might be a balance between two constituents of the diet. In later work Boas (10) interpreted her evidence as being in favor of the hypothesis that dried egg white contains some toxic substance created in the process of drying. She regarded the data as opposed to the theory that it was a nutritive disorder due to a deficiency. She concluded that the toxic substance was formed from some unknown protein constituent of the egg white. It is interesting to note that she pointed out that the protective factor X had striking similarities in its distribution with the water-soluble B vitamins.

Findlay and Stern in 1929 (11) confirmed the effect of dried egg white. It was in their paper that the first attempt was made to connect this factor with clinical conditions in the human. These workers pointed out what they believed to be a great similarity between the symptoms in the rat and those exhibited by children having Swift's disease, known colloquially as "pink disease." There is also tucked away in this paper an observation which seems to have been overlooked by many subsequent investigators. They found that, if suckling mother rats were placed on the egg-white diet, the characteristic symptoms of egg-white injury were produced in the young. This was done under conditions in which the young did not eat the diet themselves. Although it is true that this could be interpreted on the basis that a highly toxic substance was excreted in the milk, it appeared more likely to Findlay and Stern that a vitamin-like substance was lacking in the milk. They suggested that the egg-white injury symptoms were the result of the absence from the diet of vitamin-like substances different from those hitherto known. Boas and also Findlay and Stern were under the impression that to produce the egg-white injury syndrome it was necessary to dry the egg white. It is perhaps because of this that there was so much discussion of the possible destruction of a vitamin in the egg white or the production of a toxic substance by the drying process. It was not until the work of Parsons and her group at the University of Wisconsin that it became clear that fresh egg white could likewise produce the symptoms. Salmon and Goodman (12), at about the same time, likewise demonstrated that fresh egg white was as effective as dried egg white in producing the harmful effects.

The very thorough and extensive studies of Parsons and her associates (13–24) greatly extended the knowledge of the egg-white injury factor and the distribution of the factor capable of combating it. She made a very extensive study of the occurrence of the protective factor in a variety of foodstuffs. As early as 1934 Parsons demonstrated with Lease that the protective factor was efficacious when given parenterally as well as orally. She concluded that the interrelationship was metabolic in nature between the egg-white toxic effect and the protective factor. In a series of experiments on the cause of the effect of egg-white feeding Parsons found that peptic digestion destroyed the capacity of the egg white to produce the toxic effect. She also found that the toxicity followed the protein fraction when the egg white is completely precipitated with ammonium sulfate, but she found that the toxic substance was absent in purified egg albumin. A very significant finding made by Parsons was that the livers and kidneys of rats which had been kept on a diet high in egg white contained a decreased amount of protective factor. In addition she found that, when animals that had been subjected to the egg-white injury were put on a curative period of 25 days with protective substance in the diet, the amount of protective factor in the liver and kidneys was brought back to normal within error of measurement.

The Wisconsin group also found that the characteristic dermatitis could be produced in the chick, in rabbits, and in monkeys by diets rich in egg white. In addition, Schultz (25) has produced the syndrome in the dog.

From a study of the content and behavior of the protective factor in the feces of rats on raw and cooked egg-white diets Parsons and her associates (24), early in 1940, suggested that raw egg white derives its essential capacity to produce a pathological condition from its ability to combine in the digestive tract with, and hold in an unabsorbable form, the protective factor.

The most extensive studies of the chemical and physical properties of the curative factor of the egg-white injury were carried out by Dr. Paul György (26–34). In his work with the egg-white injury György became very much impressed with the similarity of symptoms in the rat to certain clinical conditions in man. He regarded the lesions as unlike those in pellagra and acrodynia in man that others had likened them to, but as similar to the dermatitis of a seborrheid, desquamative type. Because of this similarity and because he surmised that one was dealing with an induced vitamin deficiency, which has since proved to be correct, György took the step of calling it a vitamin in 1931. He selected the term "vitamin H," the "H" derived from the German *Haut*, or skin, to indicate that it was a vitamin whose lack produced severe skin lesions.

György made the important observation that vitamin H could be extracted from liver only after vigorous hydrolysis and from yeast after autolysis, indicating that vitamin H was present, at least to a considerable extent, in these tissues in a combined form. When the vitamin H was freed, he found that it was easily dialyzable, indicating that it was a relatively small molecule. In electrodialysis experiments he showed that vitamin H was acidic in character, with an isoelectric point between 3 and 3.5.

From 1933 to 1938 György carried on a tremendous number of experiments in attempting to isolate the vitamin and in studying the properties and distribution of the compound throughout nature. It was difficult, however, to obtain accurate data as to its chemical properties. He was able to work out a purification procedure by which he obtained consistently material from liver with a potency of 20–40 units per milligram. In special experiments he obtained a preparation having a further four- or fivefold increased potency. Further attempts to purify these concentrates of vitamin H, however, were to no avail.

It was at this stage that we happened to come into this field. Dr. György felt that he wanted the collaboration of a more strictly chemical group. He visited my laboratory in the spring of 1938, while I was at George Washington University Medical School, and graciously invited me to enter this field of work and attack the problem, and he offered to carry on the difficult task of vitamin-H assay for the joint work. Thus began a very enjoyable collaboration which culminated in the recognition of the vitamin-H activity of biotin on the part of Melville, Burk, and myself at Cornell and of György and Miss Rose at Western Reserve (3, 35, 36).

We accepted György's invitation because we had been much intrigued through the years by the remarkable relationship of this unknown compound in counteracting egg-white injury, and started in with purification and inactivation and reactivation studies to get further information on the properties of the compound.

Some of the data we obtained agreed with data in the literature, but in quite a number of instances it did not. There is no point, though, in going into this work on concentrates, since we now have the pure crystalline material available; and with the latter, one can obtain unequivocal results. I shall, therefore, pass over the work which we did during the following year and a half.

We thought, however, we were doing well when we raised the

potency up to as high as 500 units per milligram through an electrophoretic approach. Our attack, however, changed suddenly, early in 1940, with the realization of the possibility that the vitamin H we were working with was biotin, the yeast nutrilite, which had been isolated in 1936 by Kögl. It is a coincidence that the suspicion that biotin might be vitamin H came at about the same time to both the group at Western Reserve and to the group at Cornell.

At one of our conferences with Dr. György on February 8, 1940, György raised the question as to whether it were possible that vitamin H might be biotin. It so happened that, when the question was asked, I had lying before me on my desk a report by Dr. Melville of the preliminary results carried out by him the day before of actual experiments showing that some of our vitamin-H fractions were highly potent in biotin activity. I had asked Melville to write up the experiments, so that I could show them to György in our conference. It is one of many coincidences that have occurred in the work on biotin and vitamin H and coenzyme R.

Both groups were impressed with the observation of Williams that biotin appeared in a combined form in the liver (37). This fact was strikingly parallel to the fact that vitamin H likewise appeared in combined form. However, György had found that autolysis of liver did not yield vitamin H, whereas Williams had found that autolysis of liver liberated biotin.[1] Only vigorous hydrolysis was found, by György, to liberate vitamin H. Yet the fact that both were apparently found in the combined form in the tissue impressed us more than the conflict as to how they were liberated, and this was sufficient to give the necessary association of ideas, which in turn gave rise to the positive thought of possible identity.

Before going into the proof of identity I cannot refrain from mentioning another coincidence about which Dr. György has told me. In the laboratory of the I. G. Farbenindustrie the very man who pre-

[1] György in a recent personal communication has suggested a possible explanation of this apparent discrepancy. He suggests that, since autolyzed liver is liquefied and is exposed in Williams' growth test to yeast cells, the minute amount of free biotin present in the liver concentrate stimulates initial growth of yeast cells, which, in their turn by virtue of their enzymes, break down the biotin-protein compound remaining in the concentrate and thus liberate all the biotin. He points out that the corresponding enzymes are not present in the intestine of the rat.

pared the vitamin-H concentrates from liver for György, when he was working on the problem abroad some years ago, was the man who made the concentrates of biotin from eggs at the same time for Kögl.

To come now to the question of identity, it became clear, from examining our own data and data in the literature, that there were a great number of parallelisms in the occurrence and distribution of vitamin H and biotin. The similarity in the solubility of the compounds, in the behavior toward various adsorbents, and in their stability toward various reagents was marked. There were, however, some conflicting data—but none too serious or beyond explanation. Experiments have since afforded understanding of what were then apparently discrepancies.

The obvious experiment, of course, was to test the vitamin-H preparations for biotin activity. Dr. Melville made these assays and found that our vitamin-H preparations were extremely potent in biotin activity, and we began to have hopes that finally we had run down vitamin H, on which we had been working for some two years.

It so happened that, while this was going on, Dr. Burk was in my laboratory, working on tumor metabolism, while on leave from the National Cancer Institute. Just as soon as we had obtained these first indications of the possible identity of biotin with vitamin H, I told Dr. Burk of the results; and he immediately pointed out that, if our results indicated the identity of vitamin H with biotin, it also meant that vitamin H must also possess coenzyme-R activity. You will recall that Burk was the codiscoverer, with Allison and Hoover, of coenzyme R. I believe that it is also another rather unusual coincidence to have had in your laboratory the man who discovered coenzyme R at a time when your work indicated that vitamin H might be biotin, which in turn had been shown to be identical with coenzyme R. We therefore invited Burk to join us in our collaboration, and we set about to compare the coenzyme R, as well as the biotin, activities of some of our vitamin-H preparations.

At this time we had just received from Dr. György the vitamin-H assays of the concentration of vitamin H in a number of cells of an electrodialysis experiment which we had done on a liver preparation containing 20 units per milligram (a vitamin-H unit being the daily dose required for complete protection against egg-white injury). The apparatus consisted of 11 cells separated with cellophane membranes. The vitamin-H preparation was placed in cell III, the cathode cell being No. I. Distilled water was placed in the other cells. Electrodialysis was allowed to continue until the voltage (4,500 down to 1,300) remained constant for 24 hours. The vitamin-H assays which we had just received from Dr. György are shown in Table 2.

The solutions from these cells were then assayed for biotin and coenzyme R. The biotin assays we ran were done essentially according to the method of Snell, Eakin, and Williams (37). We also sent samples of these fractions to Allison and Minor of the United States Department of Agriculture at Washington, who kindly ran coenzyme-R assays, using *Rhizobium trifolii*. The results are shown in Table 3. They then sent us cultures of the organism, and we confirmed these results in our own laboratory.

TABLE 2

ELECTRODIALYSIS OF VITAMIN H

	Cell			
	III	IV	V	VI
pH	4.7	3.4	3.1	3.0
Solids mg/cc	4.6	2.7	1.9	1.2
Vitamin H:				
Units/mg	6–8	52	215	160–200
Units/cc	30–40	140	400	200–250

The relative concentrations per milligram were remarkably the same in the different cells. This meant that vitamin-H, biotin, and coenzyme-R activities had all migrated at about the same rate and had stopped at the same cell, thus giving us a very strong indication that the activities resided in a single component. These results were confirmed, and the comparisons extended to other electrodialysis samples. With these results and with other data from our own work and from those in the literature on their similarities in distribution and in physical and chemical properties, we felt confident that vitamin H was truly biotin and felt justified in proposing in the literature the suggestion that they were either identical or closely related compounds (35). We pointed out at that time that, if the suggestion were substantiated that vitamin H was identical with biotin and coenzyme R, it would show that the two latter substances are significant in the vital economy of the mammal. Likewise, in view of the demonstrated role of coenzyme R in the respiration of *Rhizobia*,

TABLE 3

COMPARISON OF CONCENTRATIONS OF VITAMIN-H BIOTIN, AND COENZYME-R ACTIVITY

	CELL			
	III	IV	V	VI
Biotin* per cubic centimeter....	0.00025	0.00005	0.00002	....
Coenzyme R† per cubic centimeter..........	0.001	0.00025	0.0001	0.00014
Relative concentration per milligram:				
Vitamin H..........	1	7.4	31	26
Biotin..........	1	8.5	30	....
Coenzyme R..........	1	6.8	24	26

* Cubic centimeters required to produce half-maximum growth increase (*ca.* 500 per cent increase over inoculum) of bakers' yeast in 16 hours at 30° C. in 12 cc. of yeast-growth medium deficient in biotin.

† Cubic centimeters required to produce half-maximum growth of *Rhizobium trifolii* strain 209 (*ca.* 800 million cells per cubic centimeter) in 4 days at 28° C. in 25 cc. of synthetic sucrose-mineral-nitrate medium (inoculum negligible).

it was likely that vitamin H acts in ways other than simply to protect against egg-white injury, and that it might well function in intermediate carbohydrate metabolism, as do various members of the so-called "vitamin B complex," to which vitamin H, biotin, and coenzyme R might well belong.

Conclusive proof of the identity of these principles had to await, however, the testing of the pure substances for their mutual activities. Through the kindness of Professor F. Kögl a solution of 150 γ of crystalline biotin methyl ester in ethyl alcohol was placed at our disposition for vitamin-H assay. We wish to acknowledge his generosity and co-operation.

In order to obtain some indication of the level at which the biotin methyl ester should be tested for vitamin-H activity by the rat assay method, the yeast-growth activity of this solution was compared with that of a solution of known vitamin-H activity. We found that biotin methyl ester produced a half-maximum growth increase at a concentration of 1 part in 4×10^9. A vitamin-H preparation containing 34 units of vitamin-H activity per milligram produced the same yeast-growth effect at a concentration of 1 part in 1.36×10^7. It could be predicted, therefore, that the biotin methyl ester would show an activity of approximately 10,000 units of vitamin H per milligram by the rat assay method if biotin and vitamin H were identical.

Dr. György and Miss Rose then ran the vitamin-H assays. Rats showing definite vitamin-H deficiency symptoms were used for assay of the solution of the crystalline biotin methyl ester at various levels above and below the amount indicated by the yeast assay. Subcutaneous administration of the biotin ester brought about complete cure of the skin manifestations and resumption of growth in these animals. The minimum effective dose, within the limits of assay error, was found to be 0.1 γ per rat per day for 30 days. In other words, 0.1 γ of biotin could protect against egg-white injury—an amazing potency. This corresponds to an activity of 10,000 units of vitamin H per milligram for the methyl ester of biotin. You may recall that the most potent vitamin-H preparation hitherto reported possessed an activity of 215 units per milligram.

Our vitamin-H solution was derived from liver, whereas Kögl had isolated his material from dried eggs. We felt that, to complete this proof of identity—to place it beyond any question whatsoever—we must isolate the compound from liver and see if it had the chemical properties reported for biotin by Kögl and Tönnis. At this stage of the work Dr. Hofmann joined Dr. Melville and myself in this work, and I should like to pay tribute to the skill and ingenuity of Dr. Hofmann and Dr. Melville which have made possible the advances we have made with the small amount of material available.

The starting material supplied by Dr. György for the isolation was a vitamin-H liver concentrate which had been prepared from the alcohol-insoluble fraction of beef liver which had been subjected to high-pressure hydrolysis. The vitamin-H activity of the solution was 25–35 units per milligram of solids and 1,000 units per cubic centimeter.

One of the final steps in the lengthy fractionation procedure used by Kögl and Tönnis was the conversion of biotin to a biologically active "ester base" by esterification with acidic methanol. We therefore decided to employ esterification of our crude preparation in order to obtain the active material in a form which would be soluble in organic solvents and which might lend itself to purification by chromatographic adsorption procedures.

By adsorption of the crude ester from chloroform solution on aluminum oxide and by elution with acetone, the potency of the material was raised from 25–50 vitamin-H units per milligram to 1,000–2,000 vitamin-H units per milligram, as shown by assay of the fractions by the yeast-growth method. A second adsorption on aluminum oxide and elution yielded material of a potency of 3,000–6,000 vitamin-H units per milligram. From this fraction crystals of the free ester were obtained which melted from 154° to 158° (36, 38). By repeated crystallizations from a mixture of methanol and ether a product of constant melting-point and biological activity was obtained which melted sharply from 166° to 167° (micro-melting-point). Sublimation *in vacuo*, followed by crystallization from a mixture of methanol and ether, did not change the melting-point, crystalline form, or biological activity. The substance crystallized, as shown in Figure 1, in long, thin, platelike needles from the methanol-ether mixture. From a chloroform-petroleum-ether mixture it crystallized in needles, as described by Kögl and Tönnis. The biological activity and melting-point of the pure biotin methyl ester were confirmed by several separate isolations. The compound was optically active.

Expressed in terms of vitamin-H units, the various preparations of purified product that we have prepared have all consistently yielded, by the yeast-growth method, the high value of 27,000 (±10 per cent) vitamin-H units per milligram. Direct vitamin-H assays by Dr. György of the crystals, made on rats by the curative method, were in agreement with this high potency.

The analytical values we obtained for the pure crystalline compound agree most closely with the empirical formula of $C_{11}H_{18}O_3N_2S$. Molecular weight determinations indicated that the empirical formula as derived from the analytical data on the basis of one sulfur atom in the molecule is unquestionably correct. Analyses of several crystalline derivatives and degradation products likewise support this formula. This formula is in agreement with that given by Kögl, although it should be pointed out that Kögl gave no analytical data.

Fig. 1.—Crystalline biotin methyl ester. Magnification 150×

The melting-point for the preparation from which Kögl derived this formula was not given, so one must therefore assume that his previously published melting-point of 148° still applies. It is to be noted that the melting-point of the pure biotin methyl ester obtained by us is higher than the value reported by Kögl and Tönnis, and no explanation for this is as yet apparent. The similarity, however, in solubility, in crystalline form, and in composition leads us to believe that the compound isolated by us from liver is identical with that isolated by Kögl and Tönnis from egg yolk.

As we have stated, the *solution* of crystalline biotin methyl ester supplied us by Kögl showed a potency of 10,000 vitamin-H units per milligram, as compared with the value of 27,000 vitamin-H units per milligram found for our preparations both by comparative assays for yeast growth and for anti–egg-white injury activities. However, we do not know the melting-point or purity of this particular preparation of Kögl's. We therefore do not stress this difference in degree of potency. It is within the range of possibility that the Kögl sample may have suffered loss of potency from the time it was made up until it was assayed here. In fact, Dr. Peterson has compared a solution of Kögl's with one of ours and finds that both had the same potency per milligram. Direct comparison of the crystalline compounds is, of course, the only satisfactory comparison desirable, and we hope that future circumstances will permit such a comparison.[2]

The free crystalline biotin is readily obtained by saponification of the ester with cold alkali (39). Upon acidification of the saponification mixture with HCl, free biotin separates in long thin needles, as shown in Figure 2. The biotin crystallizes out as the free acid even from strongly acid solutions. Biotin melts at from 230° to 232°, with decomposition, and is optically active (+92°). The analytical figures point to a composition $C_{10}H_{16}O_3N_2S$, which is in good agreement with the composition of the monomethyl ester. In the yeast-growth assay the free biotin appears to have the same potency per mole as the ester.

The titration curve run by Dr. Rachele of our laboratory resembles the titration curve of a simple monocarboxylic acid; the neutral equivalent of 244 obtained from the curve agrees with that expected for a monocarboxylic acid of the empirical formula given.

With the crystalline material available it was possible to obtain preliminary information on the stability and behavior of the compound toward various reagents by inactivation and reactivation experiments, using small amounts of material. Dr. Brown collaborated in this phase of the work (40). The results of such inactivation ex-

[2] Kögl and Pons have just reported (48) that they have succeeded in raising the melting-point of their biotin methyl ester from Kögl's previously published value of 148° to 161.5° and that some of the material distributed for biological work was only once-crystallized material, owing to the preciousness of the material. The remaining small difference in the melting-points from the two laboratories may well be due to the methods employed in determining the micro-melting-points.

periments must, of course, be interpreted cautiously. When inactivation has been brought about, it is justifiable to assume that a change in the molecule has occurred; but, when no inactivation has taken place, the possible formation of an active derivative or degradation product cannot be excluded. I shall summarize the data which we have obtained in these inactivation experiments (Table 4).

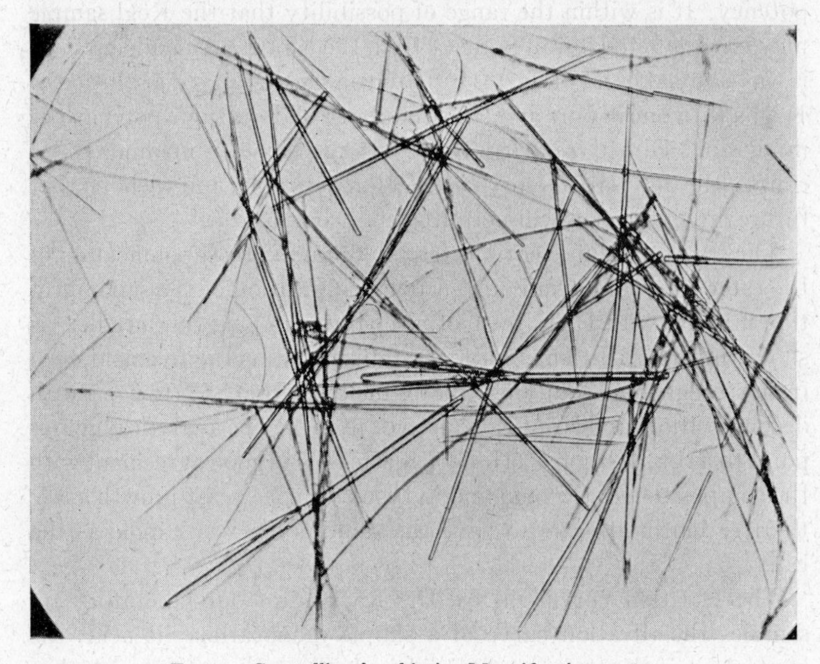

FIG. 2.—Crystalline free biotin. Magnification 150×

The majority of these inactivation experiments done on the crystalline material were carried out on 1- or 2-cc. aliquots of a solution containing 12.5 γ of biotin per cubic centimeter.

In a study of the effect of acid it was found that the use of 20 per cent HCl over fairly long periods of time was required to completely inactivate the samples. The action of alkali resulted in greater inactivation than corresponding strengths of acid. For example, 40–60 per cent inactivation was brought about by the action of 1 N KOH at 120° for 17 hours. Longer periods of treatment or stronger concentrations of alkali led to complete inactivation. Thus, in contrast to other data in the literature, biotin does not appear to be quite as stable to acid and to alkali as had been assumed.

Prolonged aeration of either an acid or an alkaline solution of biotin with air or O_2 had no appreciable effect, but the use of stronger oxidizing agents quickly destroyed the activity. For instance, treatment with 5 per cent H_2O_2 completely destroyed the activity, as did the use of peroxide-containing ether.

TABLE 4

EFFECT OF REAGENTS ON ACTIVITY OF CRYSTALLINE BIOTIN

Reagents Used	Inactivation	Reagents Used	Inactivation
Air or O_2	−	$(CH_3CO)_2O$–CH_3COOH with Zn	−
5 per cent H_2O_2	+	$CH_2=C=O$	−
Ether peroxides	+	C_6H_5COCl—NaOH	−
H_2—Pd	−	C_6H_5COCl—C_5H_5N	−
H_2—PtO_2	−	C_6H_5NCO	−
Na in liquid NH_3	−	NaOH	+
Chloramine T	+	KOH	+
Aqueous Br_2	+	$KOCH_3$	+
SO_2	+	Methylation	−
HCl in CH_3OH	−	Benzylation	−
CH_2N_2	−	CH_2O	+
HCl	+	HONO	+
HCl—HCOOH	+	Ninhydrin	−
H_2SO_4, concentrated	−	NH_2OH	−
CH_3COOH—H_2SO_4	−	*p*-$NO_2C_6H_4NHNH_2$	−
CH_3COCl—NaOH	−	*u. v. l.*, irradiated	−
$(CH_3CO)_2O$—NaOH	−		

The fact that biotin has been found by others to be inactivated by nitrous acid has led to the assumption on the part of some that biotin was very likely an α-amino acid. We confirmed the inactivation with nitrous acid; and, in addition, we observed that biotin is rapidly and completely inactivated by chloramine T. We found, however, that ninhydrin has no effect whatsoever on the activity of the compound at various hydrogen-ion concentrations, and the absence of any reaction with this reagent strongly indicated to us that biotin was not an α-amino acid.

The action of *p*-nitrophenylhydrazine in acidified alcohol and of hydroxyl amine in alkaline solution also failed to bring about inactivation, thus indicating the absence of an aldehyde or ketone.

In actually tackling the characterization of the functional groups by direct chemical means, we first directed our attention toward the nitrogen and oxygen. Two of the three oxygens, of course, had been accounted for by the carboxyl group, leaving one oxygen to be accounted for. Possibility after possibility of what the nitrogen might be was eliminated, such as various ring forms, etc. There is no point, however, to going into the many negative experiments in this direction. It became very puzzling as to what the nature of the nitrogen might be. However, the break came when a cleavage product was obtained after treatment of the biotin with strong barium hydroxide for 20 hours at 140°. This treatment brought about the formation of a new compound which could be isolated in excellent yield. The analyses of the free compound led to the empirical formula $C_9H_{18}O_2N_2S$. It was clear that the split product had lost only one carbon and one oxygen and had acquired two hydrogens. Micro–Van Slyke analyses indicated the presence of two primary amino groups in the molecule, whereas none was indicated in the biotin by nitrous acid treatment. On benzoylation by the Schotten-Baumann method, an alkali-soluble dibenzoyl derivative (melting-point, 182°–183°) was formed. The new compound contained, therefore, two primary amino groups and a carboxyl group. I will refer to it as the "diaminocarboxylic acid."

The most logical interpretation we can place on the formation of a diaminocarboxylic acid with the loss of one carbon atom and one oxygen atom from biotin is the cleavage of a cyclic urea derivative. The conversion of the biotin to the basic diaminocarboxylic acid fits in with the interpretation offered. The inactivation of biotin by nitrous acid, in spite of no liberation of nitrogen gas, may possibly be due to the formation of a nitroso derivative, a property of urea derivatives. The hydrolytic cleavage of biotin may be written as follows (41):

DEGRADATION OF BIOTIN TO DIAMINOCARBOXYLIC ACID

$$C_8H_{13}S\left\{\begin{array}{l}-COOH\\ -NH\\ \quad\rangle CO\\ -NH\end{array}\right. \longrightarrow \left[C_8H_{13}S\left\{\begin{array}{l}-COOH\\ -NH_2\\ -NH-COOH\end{array}\right.\right] \longrightarrow C_8H_{13}S\left\{\begin{array}{l}-COOH\\ -NH_2\\ -NH_2\end{array}\right. + CO_2$$

It will be noted that the urea structure and the carboxyl group account for all of the oxygen and the nitrogen, leaving the sulfur to be accounted for. Again many possibilities were eliminated, and we suspected that the sulfur was present as a thio ether. Positive evidence was afforded by the effect of H_2O_2 on the compound.

It had been observed by us that biotin is extremely sensitive to peroxides. Accordingly, pure biotin was treated with excess hydrogen peroxide. From the reaction mixture it was possible to isolate a crystalline oxidation product in 90 per cent yield. The analyses of the pure compound point to the composition $C_{10}H_{16}O_5N_2S$, in which two atoms of oxygen have been added to the biotin molecule without loss of carbon or hydrogen. The presence of a carboxyl group in the compound was shown by the formation of a methyl ester on treatment with diazomethane.

The addition of two oxygen atoms to the molecule without loss of carbon or hydrogen, along with evidence eliminating various other possibilities, pointed to an oxidation by the peroxide treatment of a thio ether to the corresponding sulfone.

It is obvious that, if biotin is a urea derivative and if the barium hydroxide treatment yields a diaminocarboxylic acid, then we should be able to resynthesize biotin from the diaminocarboxylic acid by closing the ring again through urea formation. This we have been able to accomplish by treatment of the diaminocarboxylic acid with phosgene, as shown by the following equation.

RESYNTHESIS OF BIOTIN FROM A DEGRADATION PRODUCT

$$C_8H_{13}S\left\{\begin{array}{l}COOH\\ NH_2\\ NH_2\end{array}\right. + \begin{array}{c}Cl\\ \diagup\\ C{=}O\\ \diagdown\\ Cl\end{array} \longrightarrow C_8H_{13}S\left\{\begin{array}{l}COOH\\ N\diagup H\\ \quad\diagdown C{=}O\\ N\diagup\\ \quad\diagdown H\end{array}\right.$$

Diaminocarboxylic Acid *Phosgene* *Biotin*

By this reaction biotin of the same melting-point and crystalline form was obtained (42). A mixed melting-point of the synthetically prepared biotin with the isolated natural biotin showed no depression of the melting-point. Conversion to the ester and the comparison of its properties with biotin methyl ester confirmed the identity. The synthetic compound showed the same specific rotation as natural biotin. Furthermore, assay of the synthetic compound showed it to have the same yeast-growth activity as the naturally occurring biotin. I believe this evidence proves, beyond a shadow of doubt, the urea structure for biotin. Furthermore, it demonstrates that no racemization occurred during the $Ba(OH)_2$ treatment.

Through this work we therefore arrived at what we feel convinced are the functional groups of biotin.[3] That biotin should be a urea derivative particularly intrigued us. It has no doubt occurred to many as you have listened to this discussion that when I mentioned that biotin is a urea derivative you immediately thought of the possible connection of this fact with the combination of biotin with avidin, thinking of the effect of urea on proteins. I have already given you the history of the development of the egg-white injury factor and the protective factor. When the latter was shown by our work with György to be biotin, Williams, who had been interested in biotin, immediately saw that, if vitamin H and biotin were one and the same compound, as we claimed, then, just as the egg-white injury factor would produce a vitamin-H deficiency, the addition of egg white to the media used for the growth of yeast should produce a deficiency of biotin, with the resultant lack of growth on the part of the yeast. Such proved to be the case. In fact, Williams produced evidence that the egg-white injury factor united with biotin in a fairly stable combination—broken, however, by hydrolysis.

It was therefore reasonable to assume that this was the explanation of the syndrome produced in animals by feeding egg white, that the egg-white injury factor united with the vitamin H in the intestinal tract and the combined vitamin H was carried out of the body by way of the feces, thereby producing a vitamin-H or biotin deficiency. Williams and co-workers (43) assayed the feces and tissues for biotin and vitamin H after the feeding of egg white and found that the combined biotin was increased in the feces while the biotin content of the tissues was decreased. In a collaborative study with György this hypothesis was tested by vitamin-H studies on the

[3] In two papers just come to hand, Kögl and co-workers arrive at the same conclusions with regard to the nature of the functional groups (48, 49).

rat (44). The results of the study appear to have substantiated it. Williams named the egg-white injury factor "avidin," to indicate its avidity for vitamin H or biotin, and set about to purify it. He has obtained the avidin in crystalline form, as he has announced at this symposium. It appears to be a protein.

It is, of course, an intriguing question as to why biotin is capable of forming such a union with avidin, the egg-white injury factor. The finding that biotin is a cyclic urea derivative tempts one to think that this might be the grouping that confers on biotin this peculiar behavior. It is at least an intriguing hypothesis which we have been putting to the experimental test.

Dr. György has just informed me of a very interesting experiment he has recently performed, and that is, that avidin is not effective when given parenterally. In fact, from his data one would conclude that the administration of the avidin-biotin combination is broken up when the combined material is administered to the body by injection and that biotin that was utilized with the avidin is free, so that one can actually cure the syndrome in the rat by biotin combined with the avidin. It would appear, therefore, that the syndrome in the rat produced by egg white is an induced biotin deficiency. So far the syndrome in rats is not produced by a diet deficient in biotin, that is, by a natural or synthetic diet in which avidin has not been given. We have fed diets very low in biotin and, in fact, carried them into the third generation on a diet lower in biotin than any hitherto fed. We are going ahead with this, attempting to get a diet absolutely free of biotin. However, it may be difficult to produce a biotin deficiency in the rat because of the synthesis of biotin by the intestinal flora. A true biotin deficiency, however, has been produced in the chick without the aid of avidin. This has been accomplished by Ansbacher and Landy (45) with the heat-treated diet and by Elvehjem (46) with a nontreated diet. It would seem that the chick requires much larger amounts of biotin than the rat, and one is able therefore to produce a biotin deficiency by a biotin-low diet. That the symptoms produced on the diet were truly a result of a biotin deficiency was demonstrated by the administration of crystalline biotin, which we were happy to be able to furnish these workers.

I mentioned earlier in the presentation the work of McHenry on fatty infiltration in the rat. McHenry has recently reported that he had reason to believe that, when biotin was fed in fairly large amounts to rats on a low fat diet, the fatty infiltration of the liver occurred. This was done with concentrates of biotin. In recent work McHenry has confirmed this[4] with crystalline biotin, which we were glad to place at his disposal for the work. He has found that the administration of 5 γ of biotin per day for 1 week increased the fat content of the liver over the controls. This discovery of McHenry's may lead to some elucidation of the role of biotin in the body.

We have followed up with Dr. Burk and Dr. Winzler the earlier work of Allison, Hoover, and Burk in 1933, in which it was shown that coenzyme R markedly increases the rate of oxygen consumption by the legume-nodule organism *Rhizobium*. Working with yeast, we find, as reported at the meetings of the Federation of American Societies for Experimental Biology earlier this year (47), that biotin increases the fermentation of yeast even more markedly than its respiration, and respiration even more immediately than yeast growth. The profound role of biotin as a catalyst in intermediary metabolism is definitely established. Yeast grown at low biotin levels possesses respiration and fermentation rates some twentieth of the normal rate. Addition of biotin to this yeast increases both anaerobic and aerobic fermentation rates perceptibly after but a few minutes, and manifold over a period of hours. Corresponding respiration rate increases commence after about one hour, and growth or turbidity increases after some two hours. For these metabolic increases to occur, readily available nitrogen is necessary. For this purpose ammonia is best, and it is absorbed by the yeast only when biotin is present. We have also been studying for the past year and a half, in collaboration with Dr. Burk in our laboratory and Dr. C. P. Rhoads and Charles Kensler at Memorial Hospital, the influence of biotin and of avidin-containing diets on butter-yellow tumor formation.[5]

There are still other biological aspects that I should like to consider in this discussion; yet the field of biotin research is so new in its application to animal metabolism that we might more profitably

[4] Personal communication.

[5] The discussion which was given of this phase of the work has appeared elsewhere (50).

await more concrete data. I am also sorry to have to forego any attempt at reviewing the considerable work that has been done on bacterial metabolism and biotin.

BIBLIOGRAPHY

1. Kögl, F., and Tönnis, B., Ztschr. f. physiol. Chem., **242**:43, 1936.
2. Allison, F. E.; Hoover, S. R.; and Burk, D., Science, **78**:217, 1933.
3. du Vigneaud, V.; Melville, D. B.; György, P.; and Rose, C. S., Science, **92**:62, 1940.
4. Wildiers, E., Cellule, **18**:313, 1901.
5. Wayman, M., The purification of Bios II*b*. Thesis, University of Toronto, 1941.
6. West, P. M., and Wilson, P. W., Science, **89**:607, 1939.
7. Nilsson, R.; Bjälfve, G.; and Burström, D., Naturwissenschaften, **27**: 389, 1939.
8. Boas, M. A., Biochem. J., **21**:712, 1927.
9. McHenry, E. W., and Gavin, G., J. Biol. Chem., **140**:lxxxvii, 1941.
10. Fixsen, M. A. B., Biochem. J., **25**:596, 1931.
11. Findlay, G. M., and Stern, R. O., Arch. Dis. Childhood, **4**:1, 1929.
12. Salmon, W. D., and Goodman, J. G., J. Nutrition, **8**:1, 1934.
13. Parsons, H. T., J. Biol. Chem., **90**:351, 1931.
14. Parsons, H. T., and Kelly, E., Am. J. Physiol., **104**:150, 1933.
15. Parsons, H. T., and Kelly, E., J. Biol. Chem., **100**:645, 1933.
16. Parsons, H. T.; Lease, J. G.; and Kelly, E., J. Biol. Chem., **100**:lxxvii, 1933.
17. Lease, J. G., and Parsons, H. T., J. Biol. Chem., **105**:l, 1934.
18. Parsons, H. T., and Lease, J. G., J. Nutrition, **8**:57, 1934.
19. Lease, J. G., and Parsons, H. T., Biochem. J., **28**:2109, 1934.
20. Parsons, H. T., J. Biol. Chem., **116**:685, 1936.
21. Parsons, H. T.; Lease, J. G.; and Kelly, E., Biochem. J., **31**:424, 1937.
22. Lease, J. G.; Parsons, H. T.; and Kelly, E., Biochem. J., **31**:433, 1937.
23. Parsons, H. T., and Johnson, D., J. Biol. Chem., **123**:xci, 1938.
24. Parsons, H. T.; Gardner, J.; and Walliker, C. T., J. Nutrition, **19**: Suppl. 19, 1940.
25. Schultz, F., personal communication to Dr. György.
26. György, P., Ztschr. f. ärtzl. Fortbild., **28**:377, 417, 1931.
27. György, P., in Lehrbuch der Kinderheilkunde, p. 562. Berlin, 1933.
28. György, P., in Pfaundler, M. von, and Schlossmann, A., Handbuch der Kinderheilkunde (4th ed.), **10**:45, 1935. Berlin.
29. György, P.; Sullivan, M.; and Karsner, H. T., Proc. Soc. Exper. Biol. & Med., **37**:313, 1937.
30. György, P., J. Biol. Chem., **119**:xliii, 1937.
31. György, P., *ibid.*, **131**:733, 1939.

32. György, P.; Kuhn, R.; and Lederer, E., J. Biol. Chem., **131**:745, 1939.
33. Birch, T. W., and György, P., J. Biol. Chem., **131**:761, 1939.
34. György, P., and Rose, C. S., Proc. Soc. Exper. Biol. & Med., **43**:73, 1940.
35. György, P.; Melville, D. B.; Burk, D.; and du Vigneaud, V., Science, **91**:243, 1940.
36. György, P.; Rose, C. S.; Hofmann, K.; Melville, D. B.; and du Vigneaud, V., Science, **92**:609, 1940.
37. Snell, E. E.; Eakin, R. E.; and Williams, R. J., J. Am. Chem. Soc., **62**:175, 1940.
38. du Vigneaud, V.; Hofmann, K.; and Melville, D. B., J. Biol. Chem., **140**:643, 1941.
39. du Vigneaud, V.; Hofmann, K.; Melville, D. B.; and Rachele, J. R., J. Biol. Chem., **140**:763, 1941.
40. Brown, G. B., and du Vigneaud, V., J. Biol. Chem., **141**:85, 1941.
41. Hofmann, K.; Melville, D. B.; and du Vigneaud, V., J. Biol. Chem., **141**:207, 1941.
42. Melville, D. B.; Hofmann, K.; and du Vigneaud, V., Science, **94**:308, 1941.
43. Eakin, R. E.; McKinley, W. A.; and Williams, R. J., Science, **92**:224, 1940.
44. György, P.; Rose, C. S.; Eakin, R. E.; Snell, E. E.; and Williams, R. J., Science, **93**:477, 1941.
45. Ansbacher, S., and Landy, M., Proc. Soc. Exper. Biol. & Med., **48**:3, 1941.
46. Hegsted, D. M.; Oleson, J. J.; Mills, R. C.; Elvehjem, C. A.; and Hart, E. B., J. Nutrition, **20**:599, 1940.
47. Burk, D.; Winzler, R. J.; and du Vigneaud, V., J. Biol. Chem., **140**:xxi, 1941.
48. Kögl, F., and Pons, L., Ztschr. f. physiol. Chem., **269**:61, 1941.
49. Kögl, F., and Man, T. J. de, Ztschr. f. physiol. Chem., **269**:81, 1941.
50. du Vigneaud, V.; Spangler, J. M.; Burk, D.; Kensler, C. J.; Sugiura, K.; and Rhoads, C. P., Science, **95**:174, 1942.

CHOLINE

WENDELL H. GRIFFITH
Department of Biochemistry, St. Louis University School of Medicine

CHOLINE was recognized as a component of the sinapin of mustard seed by von Babo and Hirschbrunn in 1852 and as a component of the lecithin of ox bile by Strecker in 1862. The constant occurrence of this base in two phospholipids has been adequately confirmed since the demonstration of the structure of lecithin by Diacanow in 1867 and by Strecker in 1868 and since the original observations on sphingomyelin by Thudichum in 1884. Although the wide distribution of lecithins and sphingomyelins in animal cells early indicated the biochemical importance of choline, its nutritional significance was not disclosed until after the discovery of insulin by Banting and Best in 1922. Subsequent investigations by Allan, Bowie, Macleod, and Robinson (1), by Hershey (2), and by Best and Hershey (3) of the metabolism of depancreatized dogs supplied with insulin paved the way for the demonstration that the lipotropic activity of dietary lecithin depended upon the choline moiety. In 1932 Best and Huntsman (4) reported the occurrence of fatty livers in rats fed a high-fat, low-choline ration and the prevention of the deposition of this excess liver lipid by dietary supplements of choline. These experiments initiated a detailed study of the relation of this substance to the metabolism and distribution of lipids in the animal body, a study which has continued to engage the attention of Best and his associates.

Investigations at Toronto and in many other laboratories during the last nine years have brought to light a surprising number of relationships of choline to metabolism in general and to certain metabolites in particular and have emphasized the dietary indispensability of this substance or of its precursors not only for the maintenance of the integrity of tissues but even for survival. Although the present discussion must be limited to a small portion of the very interesting and significant data recorded in the following researches, their enumeration will serve to indicate the varied nature of the manifestations of choline deficiency and the importance of this substance in the animal organism.

Following the original studies on depancreatized dogs, Chaikoff (5) showed that choline prevents fatty livers in animals in which the pancreatic duct had been ligated, as well as in depancreatized dogs. Schaefer, McKibben, and Elvehjem (6) reported severe anorexia and growth failure in puppies on a low-choline diet. Davis (7) noted that choline depresses the polycythemia induced by cobalt. Abbott and De Masters (8) found that choline is essential for normal nutrition and for egg production in chickens. Jukes (9, 10) observed that choline is necessary for the growth of chicks and young turkeys and that, with manganese, it prevents perosis, or "slipped tendon disease," in these birds. Best (4) showed, as noted previously, that marked deposition of liver fat occurs on low-choline diets. Griffith (11) found that, if young rats are used, a severe pathological state results which is characterized by renal hemorrhagic degeneration, as well as by the deposition of liver fat. Sure (12) reported that choline is required for normal lactation and for the normal nutrition of newborn rats. Sharpless (13) noted that choline prevents papillomatous lesions in the forestomach of rats on a diet containing 89 per cent white flour. Chaikoff (14), utilizing the administration of radioactive phosphorus (P^{32}), observed that choline accelerates the formation and removal of phospholipids in rat livers. Blumberg and McCollum (15) observed that cirrhosis of the liver results from the prolonged feeding of a low-choline diet. György, Poling, and Goldblatt (16) noted that supplements of choline and cystine afford definite but not regular protection against liver necrosis, cirrhosis, and cancer resulting from the addition of dimethylaminoazobenzene (butter yellow) to the diet. Du Vigneaud (17) found that choline supplies a methyl group which permits the *in vivo* formation of methionine from homocysteine. As a result of this and subsequent observations, Du Vigneaud has emphasized the importance of transmethylation and of dietary sources of utilizable methyl groups.

Choline is characterized by the presence of a trimethyl quaternary nitrogen. It is, therefore, strongly basic and decomposes in alkaline solution with the liberation of trimethylamine. It is freely soluble in water and alcohol and insoluble in ether and chloroform. It forms relatively stable salts with acids and is available in the form of the synthetic choline chloride. Derivatives useful in its isolation and determination include, among many others, the chloroplatinate, the chloroaurate, the enneaiodide, and the reineckate. The latter two have been particularly useful in quantitative procedures. Hunt (18) in 1915 showed that choline could be determined biologically by conversion to acetylcholine and measurement of its depressor action.

Choline occurs in nature largely as a constituent of phospholipids. Many estimations of free choline in plant and animal tissues are recorded in the literature, but it is questionable whether the reported values actually represent free choline, in view of the wide distribution of the choline phospholipids and in view of the possibility of the autolytic liberation of free choline. The latter process is well illustrated in the experiments of Johnston, Irvin, and Walton (19), who found that the free choline of bile increased rapidly on standing, even though the bile was preserved in an icebox with toluene and chloroform. According to the analyses of Jacobi, Baumann, and Meek (20), the total choline in rat tissues amounts to about 1 mg. per gram of body weight.

Procedures have been developed in several laboratories (21, 22, 23) for the determination of the phospholipid partition in blood and in other tissues, and doubtless more exact information regarding the distribution of the choline phospholipids, especially sphingomyelin, will be forthcoming. A water-soluble compound which appears to be the choline ester of sphingosine phosphoric acid has been isolated from tissues by Booth (24) and by King and Small (25), and phosphocholine was detected in liver by Inukai and Nakahara (26). The only choline derivative which has been isolated from animal tissues and which is not known to occur as a part of a choline phospholipid is acetylcholine, a most interesting compound which may be extremely important in myoneural physiology (27, 28). Woolley and Peterson (29) have isolated the anhydride of the sulfuric acid ester of choline from mold tissue.

Little is known of the metabolic function of sphingomyelins and of the base sphingosine. The investigations by Thannhauser and Reichel (30) of the structure of this choline phospholipid and of the possible occurrence of "sphingosine fats" are therefore of unusual interest. In this connection the isolation of the choline ester of sphingosine phosphoric acid may be extremely significant. It is not possible to state whether this compound exists as such in tissues or whether it is formed from sphingomyelin as an autolytic product. If the latter is the case, then the occurrence of a readily hydrolyzable sphingomyelin in tissues and its presence in significant amounts in plasma suggest that this choline phospholipid may participate actively in metabolism. No information is available regarding the precursors or dietary importance of sphingosine. The choline ester of sphingosine phosphoric acid resembles, in some respects, a mononucleotide; and it would indeed be interesting if this molecule were found to serve as a coenzyme in some enzymatic system.

The results of a dietary deficiency of choline in young rats will be discussed in detail because these experimental animals show, for the most part, the same effects as those previously noted in adult rats, and show, in addition, marked degenerative changes which have not been observed in the older animals. Young male rats, 21–26 days of age and 38–42 gm. in weight, develop moderately severe hemorrhagic degeneration on the following low-choline food mixture: casein 18 per cent, lard 19 per cent, sucrose 49 per cent, salt mixture 4 per cent (31), calcium carbonate 1 per cent, agar 2 per cent, dried brewers' yeast 6 per cent, and fortified fish-liver oil 1 per cent. As will be discussed later, this ration is a suboptimal source of cystine, and optimum supplements of cystine aggravate the effects of the deficiency of choline. The cystine-supplemented diet plus choline is an adequate food mixture for short experimental periods, permitting an average gain in weight of 3–4 gm. daily for at least a 30-day period. The level of dietary fat is relatively unimportant (32), and the carbohydrate may be sucrose or glucose or certain preparations of starch. Some brands of starch, however, are highly protective (33). The severity of the deficiency is markedly increased by decreasing the methionine content of the diet through use of other proteins than casein, which is high in methionine. In young rats on the above food mixture the deposition of liver fat and the severity of renal lesions are unaffected by dietary supplements of manganese, thiamine, riboflavin, pyridoxine, pantothenic acid, ascorbic acid, vitamin K, so-called "vitamin P" or citrin, biotin, inositol, or an aqueous extract of beef liver (33, 34).

The feeding of the cystine-supplemented diet results in a spectacular series of events which reach a crisis within 6–8 days (35, 36). This critical period may terminate with the death of the rat, or it may be followed by a rapid, partial recovery which permits survival. Recovery and survival on the same diet that produces severe degeneration of tissues are highly interesting and, as yet, unexplained phenomena. A marked increase in liver fat occurs within 48 hours, and it is thus evident that young rats have no available reserve of choline for use in lipid metabolism. The accumulation of liver lipids is maximal after 4–6 days, and during this interval there is no interference with appetite or with growth. The largest concentration of liver fat, 25–30 per cent of the liver weight, is uniformly found in the most rapidly growing animals; i.e., in those fed otherwise adequate diets and containing just enough choline to prevent tissue degeneration.

Renal degeneration occurs between the sixth and eighth days; the animal becomes noticeably sick, and there is a marked elevation of the nonprotein nitrogen of the blood. The renal lesion develops over a 24–48-hour period and is characterized by an increase in size and weight and by hemorrhagic discoloration of the kidneys. Severely affected rats show an extensive regression of the thymus, and ocular hemorrhage is frequently observed. Neither thymectomy nor adrenalectomy influences the result of the choline deficiency (33). Proteinuria, but not hematuria, occurs. A temporary failure of renal function is indicated by a diminished rate of excretion of phenol red and of inulin during this acute stage (33). Recovery is noteworthy because of the rapidity with which renal function improves. This repair process is also evident in the gross appearance of the kidneys, which at the end of a 10-day period (4 days after the onset of the hemorrhagic degeneration) show little or no sign of hemorrhage. These "recovery" kidneys are enlarged and pale brown in color and are frequently rough and scarred with a white incrustation, the so-called "frosted" kidney. The subsequent history of surviving animals is variable, although evidence is at hand that the renal damage may persist for months and involve the glomeruli as well as the tubules. Whatever the explanation of the recovery process may be, it certainly does not represent the sudden beginning of an unlimited synthesis of choline, because the liver remains fatty throughout the recovery period.

The acute lesion has been studied by Christensen (37) and by György and Goldblatt (38) and may be described as follows: The principal changes in the kidney are vascular congestion and tubular degeneration. The enlarged and deep-red appearance is caused primarily by the congestion of the peripheral cortical capillaries and the capsular blood vessels. Evidence of hemorrhage, if present, is found only in the capsule and at the edge of the cortex. Blood in the outermost part of the cortex may come from ruptured blood vessels of the capsule. Glomerular and other renal blood vessels usually appear normal, but in severely affected animals glomeruli in the peripheral cortex are also congested. Tubules in the deep part of the cortex and in the outer part of the medulla are always filled with casts and are markedly necrotic.

The effects of choline deficiency are exaggerated by the feeding of a diet low in methionine as well as in choline. As a result of the use of the low-methionine protein, arachin, Engel and Salmon (39) were able to demonstrate hemorrhage in the adrenals, lungs, and myocardium, as well as in the eyes and kidneys. The severity of the degenerative state in these young rats is indicated by the fact that no animals at all survived. It may be of significance in this connection that Weichselbaum (40) has noted a rapidly occurring and fatal hepatic hemorrhage in rats on a diet devoid of both cystine and methionine.

The prevention of all of the effects of choline deficiency listed above is accomplished by dietary supplements of choline chloride, the fatty liver being abolished by 4–6 mg. and the renal lesions by 1–2 mg. daily. The weight of the kidneys during the acute degenerative phase is an accurate measure of the extent of the renal damage and of the absence of choline and of its precursors. The weight of the liver, and especially the weight of liver fat, is a reliable index of the extent of the choline deficiency only if sufficient choline is present to prevent severe renal lesions. The severely affected rats consume little or no food during the period of hemorrhagic degeneration, so that the weights of the liver and of liver fat are extremely variable in these poorly nourished animals (41, 42).

The problem of the occurrence of a fatty liver in rats on a low-choline diet has been complicated, first, by the observation of Beeston and Channon (43) that a supplement of cystine in a low-protein–low-choline diet increases the deposition of liver fat and the need of choline; and, second, by the observation of Tucker and Eckstein (44) that a supplement of methionine decreases the deposition of liver fat and the need of choline. Thus, the two sulfur amino acids appear to act in direct opposition to each other.

An explanation of the lipotropic action of methionine and of betaine is provided by the investigations of Du Vigneaud and his associates (17, 45, 46, 47). These workers have concluded that trans-

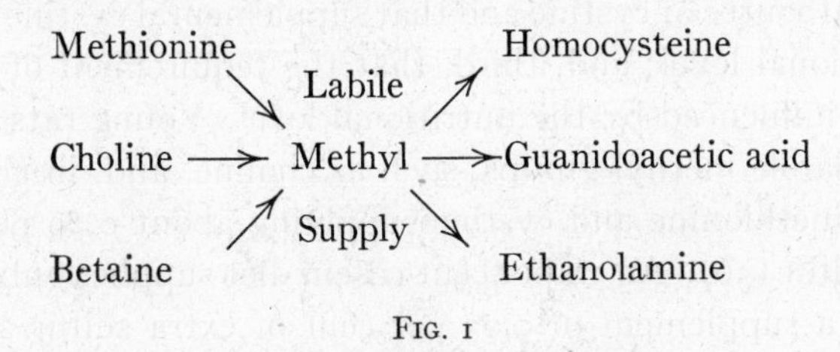

FIG. 1

methylation is an important metabolic function which is concerned with the shifting of certain specific methyl groups, *as such*, from one metabolite to another and that normal transmethylation is dependent upon a dietary supply of compounds containing these utilizable or labile methyls. These workers have been able to demonstrate, first, that supplements of choline or betaine in a diet which contains homocystine but which is devoid of methionine and cystine stimulates the growth of young rats, owing to the formation of needed methionine from homocysteine and a methyl group supplied by the choline or betaine; second, that isotopic hydrogen administered to rats in the methyl group of methionine could be isolated later in tissue choline and creatine; and, third, that the methyl groups of creatine and of sarcosine are not labile, since neither compound permits growth if added to the methyl-deficient diet containing homocystine. The labile methyl group supply which occurs in foods and in tissues includes at least the three substances: choline, methionine, and betaine (Fig. 1). The possible methylation of ethanolamine, indicated in Figure 1, will be discussed later.

The opposite effect of the second sulfur-containing amino acid, cystine, has been interpreted by others as demonstration of a direct and antagonistic relationship between cystine and choline, with possibly the formation of a cystine-choline complex. However, Griffith (48) has proposed that the cystine effect is not directly related to the metabolism of choline but is due to a stimulation of metabolism which is the result of a supplement of cystine in a cystine-deficient diet. The basis for this conclusion is, first, that the effect of cystine on the requirement for choline is not proportional to the cystine added to the diet, a result also reported by Channon (49); second, that the 18 per cent casein diet which was employed is actually a suboptimal source of cystine and that supplemental cystine improves the nutritional level; and, third, that the requirement of choline is markedly influenced by the nutritional level. Young rats require a source of labile methyl groups, such as choline, and, in addition, a source of methionine and cystine supplying about 0.19 per cent of dietary sulfur (36). An 18 per cent casein diet supplies only 0.14 per cent, and a supplement of 0.05 per cent of extra sulfur as cystine results in longer and heavier animals, and *the gains in weight and length are possible with little or no increase in the food consumption.* This difference in efficiency of utilization of food is most pronounced during a 20-day period; i.e., in rats 25–45 days of age—indicating a greater need of cystine during this part of the growth period. The extra supplement of sulfur is apparently used as cystine, but it may be supplied as methionine. It is pertinent that 24–26 per cent of casein, rather than 18 per cent, is required to supply an adequate level of sulfur amino acids in an unsupplemented diet. The cystine supplement in an 18 per cent casein diet, which produces the maximum stimulation of growth and increase in efficiency of utilization of food, is approximately the same as the supplement which results in the greatest deposition of excess liver fat. For instance, in a basal diet containing a partly protective level of choline (0.5 mg. of choline chloride per gram of food), supplements of 0.05 and 0.1 per cent of cystine increase the liver fat, but the effect of 1 or 2 per cent of cystine is no greater than that of 0.1 per cent. These observations, together with the demonstration that increases in the caloric intake also increase the need of choline, point to the conclusion that the apparent direct antagonism of cystine and choline is really the manifestation of a greater need of choline at the higher nutritional level resulting from an adequate supply of cystine. It would be of interest to know the number of other dietary essentials, the requirement of which is modified, as is that of choline, by the use of a diet adequate in the very important sulfur amino acids. It is suggested that due consideration be given the character of a food mixture before it is concluded that an effect of a cystine supplement is directly related to the cystine rather than to a stimulation of metabolism, which in turn brings to light previously unrecognized deficiencies.

The feeding of high-casein diets for the purpose of determining the level of casein and of methionine which would obviate the necessity of a choline supplement demonstrated that 30 per cent of casein was required (36). These experiments also led to the conclusion that methionine, which is used as a source of labile methyl groups and of the by-product homocysteine, is not also available as a source of cystine sulfur. This result supports the suggestion by Toennies (50) that homocysteine may not be used as a precursor of cysteine unless sufficient labile methyl groups are supplied to permit the conversion of homocysteine into methionine. The observation by Singal and Eckstein (51) and by Griffith and Mulford (42) that supplemental homocystine in low-choline diets increases the requirement of choline, as does cystine, does not mean necessarily that homocysteine is converted directly into cystine but may only signify that homocysteine is using part of the already inadequate labile methyl group supply in the formation of methionine.

The lipotropic action of methionine has been demonstrated by Eckstein (44) and confirmed by Channon (52) and by Best (53). Methionine also protects young rats against hemorrhagic degeneration (41), and its methyl group appears to be completely available for the function of transmethylation if the utilization of choline is taken as the standard (42). Betaine was shown in the original experiments by Best and Huntsman (4) to possess choline-like activity. This has been confirmed by Welch (54), by Platt (55), and by Du Vigneaud (56). Where comparisons were possible, there has been agreement on the point that betaine is less active than choline; Platt reported its activity to be 30 per cent of that of choline. Griffith and Mulford (33, 42) obtained a similar result and suggested that only one of the three methyl groups of betaine is labile. The basis for this conclusion is the fact that 3.56 mg. of betaine hydrochloride are required to equal the effect of 1 mg. of choline chloride. The molecular weight ratio of these two compounds is 1.1:1.0, so that 1.1 mg. of betaine hydrochloride should have the same lipotropic action as 1 mg. of choline chloride if the three betaine methyl groups are used as efficiently as the three methyl groups of choline. The results of the comparison of the betaine activity with that of choline as a standard correspond to the 96 per cent utilization of one methyl group or to the 32 per cent utilization of three methyl groups. The latter view is not acceptable because, in such a case, greater variations than those observed would have resulted from changes in the level of the betaine supplement.

Additional support for this difference between the betaine methyl groups is supplied by the results of using sarcosine as a possible source of labile methyl groups. Sarcosine, which may be considered a product obtained by the removal of two of the three betaine methyl groups, is demethylated in the animal organism and is believed to be rapidly changed to glycine. Gordon and Jackson (57) reported that sarcosine increased the rate of detoxication of benzoate to hippurate in rats, and Abbott and Lewis (58) made similar observations in the rabbit. Bloch and Schoenheimer (59) administered betaine containing isotopic nitrogen to rats and concluded that a direct and rapid conversion to glycine had occurred. Handler, Bernheim, and Klein (60) noted that betaine was broken down by liver tissue to glycine and formaldehyde. However, the demethylation of sarcosine does not give rise to a labile methyl because Du Vigneaud found that sarcosine does not permit the *in vivo* formation of methionine from homocysteine (46), and Griffith and Mulford were unable to demonstrate that this *N*-methyl derivative possesses protective action against the labile methyl groups deficiency which characterizes hemorrhagic degeneration in young rats (33). It seems definite that the word "demethylation" must be used with due regard for the mechanism involved. Betaine is demethylated, the methyl group serving as a labile methyl group. Sarcosine is also demethylated, but the mechanism is such that the methyl group loses its identity—probably because of oxidation.

The question then arises: "Which methyl groups are potentially labile?" From the results with glycine betaine it might be supposed that any other betaine should also yield at least one methyl group to the labile methyl group supply. This is not the case. Best (61) and Du Vigneaud (17) reported that ergothioneine is not lipotropic in older rats; and Carter (62) found similar negative results with the betaines of serine, threonine, and allothreonine. We have tested the betaines of serine and allothreonine and also the *N*-methyl derivatives of *dl*-valine and *dl*-leucine (all four generously given to us by Dr. Carter) and find that none of these protects against hemorrhagic degeneration in young rats. However, a number of compounds, other than methionine and betaine, have been reported to have lipotropic activity. Channon has shown that homocholine is even more active than choline (63) and that the ethyl derivative, triethyl-β-hydroxyethylammonium hydroxide, is about two-thirds as lipotropic as choline (64). Singal and Eckstein (51) have added the sulfoxide of methionine to this list, but Channon (65) has reported that *S*-methyl cysteine is without lipotropic effect. Alanine betaine was found active by Welch and Welch (54); and cystine betaine, *S*-ethylcysteine, and dithiodiglycollic acid by Singal and Eckstein (51). It is difficult, at present, to explain the presence of some of these compounds in the list of lipotropic substances. Possibly their effects depend upon physiological properties only indirectly related to choline metabolism. Possibly, also, the explanation lies in the fact that the formation of choline from any part of a precursor involves not only the labile methyl but also the unknown molecule to which the methyl is transferred. Little information is available as yet regarding the identity and dietary indispensability of this methyl acceptor. If a diet contains suboptimal levels of both labile methyl and the compound which is to be methylated, then provision of these precursors should result in lipotropic benefit. It is to be hoped that the availability of these lipotropic compounds as sources of labile methyl may also be determined in the young rat. This animal is so sensitive to a lack of labile methyl that its deficiency may be demonstrated on diets which are more nearly adequate in other respects, particularly with regard to the dietary protein, than those commonly used in fatty liver experiments.

The substance to which methyl is transferred in the synthesis of choline was referred to above as an "unknown substance." In this connection one thinks immediately of ethanolamine, the base of cephalin. Neither Best (4) nor Platt (55) nor Griffith (33) has found ethanolamine to be lipotropic. This is not unexpected, because the compound could not be methylated if the diet is low in labile methyl. We have fed moderately protective levels of betaine with ethanolamine and have found no more protection than that afforded by the betaine alone, so that it is evident that the 18 per cent casein diet supplies adequate amounts of ethanolamine *if* it actually is the precursor of choline. As a result of the feeding of ethanolamine, choline,

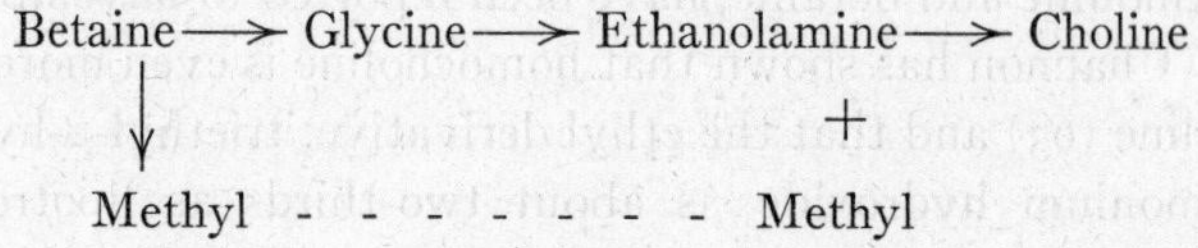

Betaine ⟶ Glycine ⟶ Ethanolamine ⟶ Choline

↓ +

Methyl - - - - - - - Methyl

Fig. 2

glycine, betaine, and ammonia, each containing isotopic nitrogen (N^{15}), Stetten (66) has concluded that ethanolamine serves as a precursor of choline and has suggested the reactions illustrated in Figure 2. In this scheme glycine occupies an important position as one of the principal sources of ethanolamine. In our laboratory we have attempted to produce both ethanolamine and methyl deficiency by feeding low-choline diets containing added benzoate. However, the results are inconclusive, as yet, owing in part to the fact that ethanolamine serves as a precursor of glycine in such experiments. Chargaff (67) has studied the formation of the choline phospholipid, lecithin, and of the ethanolamine phospholipid, cephalin, and has interpreted his experiments as suggesting the demethylation of lecithin to cephalin rather than the methylation of cephalin to lecithin. It remains to be determined whether the serine phospholipid reported by Folch and Schneider is involved in the ethanolamine-choline relationship (68).

If one accepts the deposition of liver fat and the renal hemorrhagic degeneration as typical indexes of labile methyl deficiency, then the pertinent question arises: "How does choline prevent these abnormalities?" The relation of choline to the fatty liver appears direct in view of the recognized role of the choline phospholipids, especially of lecithin, in the transport of fatty acids. However, the exact mechanism of fatty acid transport and utilization are still unknown, so that a conservative view of the role of choline in lipid metabolism would be that of Best (61), that "dietary choline increases slightly the phospholipid content of the liver and this promotes the transport of fatty acids, as phospholipids, from the liver to other tissues or promotes the utilization of fatty acids in the liver itself."

A satisfactory explanation of renal hemorrhagic degeneration must include both the cause of the onset of the degeneration and the reason for partial recovery without change in the food mixture. No such explanation has an acceptable experimental basis yet, but it seems probable that the two choline phospholipids are involved, since both may be important in cellular organization as well as in lipid metabolism. It may be that the whole picture is complicated by variations in the dietary or metabolic supply of labile methyl, of certain fatty acids, of phosphoric acid, of ethanolamine, or of sphingosine. It is also possible that manifestations of choline deficiency may be due to the failure of formation of other essential methyl-containing compounds, including constituents of tissues, products of detoxication, and various other metabolites. Indeed, choline may not be directly involved except as it supplies labile methyl for other methylations. Although this might conceivably be the case as far as the renal lesions are concerned, it does not seem probable as an explanation of the prevention of fatty livers. Choline, after all, does occur in lecithin and in sphingomyelin, and Welch (69) has shown that the feeding of arsenocholine results in a lipotropic effect with the arsenic derivative actually used and incorporated into the phospholipid fraction.

The literature contains numerous references to the occurrence of renal pathology in rats on experimental diets high in protein or in individual amino acids, cystine particularly. It appears significant that excess cystine in a diet adequate in choline fails to damage the kidneys during the period in which renal pathology is so easily produced in the absence of choline. In this connection it is of interest that rats fed the normal stock ration for over a year after recovery from an original 10-day period on the low-choline diet showed definitely pathological kidneys even though repair and restoration of marked degree had occurred (33). It is possible, therefore, that renal damage reported in some of the earlier investigations may have been due to an unrecognized choline deficiency at the beginning of the experimental period.

In conclusion, we would emphasize the peculiar importance of choline as a dietary essential without which young animals develop deficiencies which are spectacular in their onset and severity. Because of the unexplained partial recovery of less severely affected animals, pathological changes may be observed only as these animals happen to come to autopsy later, at which time the pathology may be wholly unrelated to the dietary regime. It is entirely possible that subsequent research may show that the animal organism is able to synthesize choline in unlimited quantities from precursors. However, until such precursors are identified and shown to be available in commonly used foodstuffs, choline should be regarded as indispensable in diets, as first suggested by Best (70). The new questions and new problems which have resulted from the characterization of choline as a lipotropic and antihemorrhagic molecule, which with methionine probably constitutes the bulk of the body's supply of labile methyl, present a fascinating challenge to workers in this field.

BIBLIOGRAPHY

1. Allan, F. N.; Bowie, D. J.; Macleod, J. J. R.; and Robinson, W. L., Brit. J. Exper. Path., **5**:75, 1924.
2. Hershey, J. M., Am. J. Physiol., **93**:657, 1930.
3. Best, C. H., and Hershey, J. M., J. Physiol., **75**:49, 1932.
4. Best, C. H., and Huntsman, M. E., J. Physiol., **75**:405, 1932.
5. Entenman, C.; Montgomery, M. L.; and Chaikoff, I. L., J. Biol. Chem., **135**:329, 1940.
6. Schaefer, A. E.; McKibben, J. M.; and Elvehjem, C. A., Proc. Soc. Exper. Biol. & Med., **47**:365, 1941.
7. Davis, J. E., Am. J. Physiol., **127**:322, 1939.
8. Abbott, O. D., and De Masters, C. U., J. Nutrition, **19**:47, 1940.
9. Jukes, T. H., J. Biol. Chem., **134**:789, 1940.
10. Jukes, T. H., J. Nutrition, **20**:445, 1940.

11. Griffith, W. H., and Wade, N. J., J. Biol. Chem., **131**:567, 1939.
12. Sure, B., J. Nutrition, **19**:71, 1940.
13. Sharpless, G. R., Proc. Soc. Exper. Biol. & Med., **45**:487, 1940.
14. Perlman, I., and Chaikoff, I. L., J. Biol. Chem., **127**:211, 1939.
15. Blumberg, H., and McCollum, E. V., Science, **93**:598, 1941.
16. György, P.; Poling, E. C.; and Goldblatt, H., Proc. Soc. Exper. Biol. & Med., **47**:41, 1941.
17. Du Vigneaud, V.; Chandler, J. P.; Moyer, A. W.; and Keppel, D. M., J. Biol. Chem., **131**:57, 1939.
18. Hunt, R., J. Pharmacol. & Exper. Therap., **7**:301, 1915.
19. Johnston, C. G.; Irvin, J. L.; and Walton, C., J. Biol. Chem., **131**:425, 1939.
20. Jacobi, H. P.; Baumann, C. A.; and Meek, W. J., J. Biol. Chem., **138**:571, 1941.
21. Kirk, E., J. Biol. Chem., **123**:623, 637, 1938.
22. Thannhauser, S. J.; Benotti, J.; and Rheinstein, H., J. Biol. Chem., **129**:709, 1939.
23. Erickson, B. N.; Arvin, I.; Teague, D. M.; and Williams, H. H., J. Biol. Chem., **135**:671, 1940.
24. Booth, F. J., Biochem. J., **29**:2071, 1935.
25. King, E. J., and Small, C. W., Biochem. J., **33**:1135, 1939.
26. Inukai, F., and Nakahara, W., Proc. Imp. Acad. (Tokyo), **11**:260, 1935.
27. Dale, H. H., and Dudley, H. W., J. Physiol., **68**:97, 1929.
28. Alles, G. A., Physiol. Rev., **14**:276, 1934.
29. Woolley, D. W., and Peterson, W. H., J. Biol. Chem., **122**:213, 1937.
30. Thannhauser, S. J., and Reichel, M., J. Biol. Chem., **135**:1, 15, 1940.
31. Hawk, P. B., and Oser, B. L., Science, **74**:369, 1931.
32. Griffith, W. H., J. Biol. Chem., **132**:639, 1940.
33. Griffith, W. H., and Mulford, D. J., unpublished experiments.
34. Griffith, W. H., and Mulford, D. J., J. Nutrition, **21**:633, 1941.
35. Griffith, W. H., J. Nutrition, **19**:437, 1940.
36. Mulford, D. J., and Griffith, W. H., J. Nutrition, **23**:91, 1942.
37. Christensen, K., J. Biol. Chem., **133**:xx, 1940.
38. György, P., and Goldblatt, H., J Exper. Med., **72**:1, 1940.
39. Engel, R. W., and Salmon, W. D., J. Nutrition, **22**:109, 1941.
40. Weichselbaum, T. E., Quart. J. Exper. Physiol., **25**:363, 1935.
41. Griffith, W. H., and Wade, N. J., J. Biol. Chem., **132**:627, 1940.
42. Griffith, W. H., and Mulford, D. J., J. Am. Chem. Soc., **63**:929, 1941.
43. Beeston, A. W., and Channon, H. J., Biochem. J., **30**:280, 1936.
44. Tucker, H. F., and Eckstein, H. C., J. Biol. Chem., **121**:479, 1937.
45. Du Vigneaud, V.; Chandler, J. P.; Cohn, M., and Brown, G. B., J. Biol. Chem., **134**:787, 1940.
46. Du Vigneaud, V.; Chandler, J. P.; and Moyer, A. W., J. Biol. Chem., **139**:917, 1941.

47. Du Vigneaud, V.; Cohn, M.; Chandler, J. P.; Schenck, J. R.; and Simmonds, S., J. Biol. Chem., **140**:625, 1941.
48. Griffith, W. H., J. Nutrition, **21**:291, 1941.
49. Channon, H. J.; Manifold, M. C.; and Platt, A. P., Biochem. J., **34**:866, 1940.
50. Toennies, G., J. Biol. Chem., **132**:455, 1940.
51. Singal, S. A., and Eckstein, H. C., J. Biol. Chem., **140**:27, 1941.
52. Channon, H. J.; Manifold, M. C.; and Platt, A. P., Biochem. J., **32**: 969, 1938.
53. Best, C. H., and Ridout, J. H., J. Physiol., **97**:489, 1940.
54. Welch, A. D., and Welch, M. S., Proc. Soc. Exper. Biol. & Med., **39**:7, 1938.
55. Platt, A. P., Biochem. J., **33**:505, 1939.
56. Chandler, J. P., and Du Vigneaud, V., J. Biol. Chem., **135**:223, 1940.
57. Gordon, W. G., and Jackson, R. W., J. Biol. Chem., **110**:151, 1935.
58. Abbott, L. D., Jr., and Lewis, H. B., J. Biol. Chem., **131**:479, 1939.
59. Bloch, K., and Schoenheimer, R., J. Biol. Chem., **135**:99, 1940.
60. Handler, P.; Bernheim, M. L. C.; and Klein, J. R., J. Biol. Chem., **138**: 211, 1941.
61. Best, C. H., and Ridout, J. H., Ann. Rev. Biochem., **8**:349, 1939.
62. Carter, H. E., and Melville, D. B., J. Biol. Chem., **133**:109, 1940.
63. Channon, H. J.; Platt, A. P.; and Smith, J. A. B., Biochem. J., **31**:1736, 1937.
64. Channon, H. J., and Smith, J. A. B., Biochem. J., **30**:115, 1936.
65. Channon, H. J.; Manifold, M. C.; and Platt, A. P., Biochem. J., **34**:866, 1940.
66. Stetten, D., Jr., J. Biol. Chem., **140**:143, 1941.
67. Chargaff, E.; Olson, K. B.; and Partington, P. F., J. Biol. Chem., **134**: 505, 1940.
68. Folch, J., and Schneider, H. A., J. Biol. Chem., **137**:51, 1941.
69. Welch, A. D., Proc. Soc. Exper. Biol. & Med., **35**:107, 1936.
70. Best, C. H., and Huntsman, M. E., J. Physiol., **83**:255, 1935.

THE ECONOMY OF PHOSPHORUS IN THE ANIMAL ORGANISM

FRANKLIN C. McLEAN
Department of Physiology, University of Chicago

APPRECIATION of the part played by phosphorus in carbohydrate metabolism, and thereby in the transfer and storage of energy in the organism, has been mainly a development of the past decade. It seems desirable, at this time, to attempt to see the relations of phosphorus to the animal organism as a whole, so that these newly discovered functions of this element may be examined in perspective. With so much emphasis upon the recently discovered reactions in which phosphorus is concerned, there is the possibility that other equally important functions may be temporarily lost sight of. Moreover, and in view of the multiple role of phosphorus in the organism, it is of some interest to see how the organism regulates the assimilation of this substance, and its flow through the blood and tissues, in such a way as to distribute it among the many demands which compete for it. In following these complicated regulatory processes we shall find, as might be anticipated, that enzymes, hormones, and vitamins are all involved.

FORMS OF PHOSPHORUS

Before entering upon these tasks it may be well to recapitulate the types of phosphorus compounds found in the animal organism and to give some idea of the correlation of the functions of these compounds with the chemical characteristics of this element.

First, all or almost all of the compounds of phosphorus—inorganic and organic—found in the organism are derivatives of orthophosphoric acid, H_3PO_4.

Second, of approximately 700 gm. of phosphorus in the adult human organism, about 600 gm. are in the skeleton, and the presence of this large amount of phosphorus in the bones depends upon the ability of orthophosphoric acid to form difficultly soluble compounds with calcium. Upon this same characteristic depends another very interesting phenomenon—the formation, under appropriate conditions, of a colloidal complex of calcium and phosphate in the plasma.

Third, orthophosphoric acid is a weak tribasic acid. Its dissociation constants are such that at pH 7.4 approximately 85 per cent of the total inorganic phosphate of the plasma is in the form of the divalent ion $HPO_4^{=}$, while 15 per cent is monovalent $H_2PO_4^{-}$ and only about 3.5 parts per 100,000 is trivalent $PO_4^{\equiv}$. The theory of the buffer action of the plasma was largely developed in terms of these ions, although, as is now known, the buffer value of the plasma phosphate is negligible in comparison with that of the other buffer systems. The buffer action of the phosphates is important, however, in accomplishing the excretion of excess acids in the urine, and a deficiency in phosphorus may lead to acidosis by a diminution in this function.

Fourth, phosphates enter into combination with lipids and with certain proteins, such as casein. The role of the phosphate in these combinations is not yet clear, but with reference to the phosphoproteins it is worth mentioning that the phosphate linkage with the protein portion of some of the complex respiratory enzymes appears to be of importance in the activation of these substances.

Fifth, phosphate enters into a considerable number and variety of chemical combinations, which have in common their solubility in acid, their extreme lability, and their association with the utilization of carbohydrate. In the latter connection two groups of compounds may be distinguished: (1) combinations of the phosphate with the substrate, i.e., the carbohydrate or one of the intermediary products of its metabolism; and (2) combinations of phosphate with more or less complex substances serving as catalysts to various reactions in the metabolic cycle of the carbohydrates. An additional substance of the acid-soluble group, phosphocreatine, seems to be unique in that it serves as a reservoir of energy immediately available for the contraction of muscle. As this energy is expended, the phosphate radical is lost from the compound, but it is promptly restored with the aid of energy derived from the metabolic processes just mentioned. A further source of stored energy in muscle, with a secondary reservoir in the liver, is glycogen. Glycogen itself is not in combination with phosphate, but phosphate compounds are essential to its synthesis and to its breakdown into immediately available forms of carbohydrate.

The organism appears to be able to synthesize all of the complex organic compounds of phosphorus from inorganic phosphate. This is not to say that it can synthesize all of the organic substances with which phosphate is united. The human organism, for example, cannot synthesize thiamine. But, given thiamine, the organism can transform it into the active form—diphosphothiamine. Moreover, it would appear that this ability to form organic combinations with phosphate is very widespread within the human organism, as it is among various other organisms, since only a negligible concentration of phosphate in organic form is carried in the plasma. Phosphorus taken into the gastrointestinal tract in organic combination is, as a rule, split off and absorbed in the same manner as if ingested as inorganic phosphate. This ability of the organism to meet its manifold needs for phosphorus from simple inorganic phosphate is probably a necessity from the standpoint of survival.

SOURCE, REQUIREMENTS, AND ABSORPTION

As phosphorus is present nearly everywhere in the animal organism, so is it present nearly everywhere in nature. Ultimately, of course, the source of the phosphorus which flows through the animal organism in a never ending stream is the soil. For man the flow is first to the plant foods, then either direct to the human organism or indirectly by way of the animal tissues which man consumes. Fertilization of the soil consists in supplying it with phosphorus, as well as with nitrogen—two elements without which most plants cannot grow. In the sea, where phosphorus may not be abundant, a deficiency of this element may limit plant life and thereby animal life. A deficiency of phosphorus in the soil may similarly limit plant and animal life.

The daily requirement for phosphorus in the adult human organism is in the neighborhood of 1 gm. and is even higher in the growing child, in whom the needs of the skeleton must be met. But a deficiency in intake of phosphorus, taken by itself, scarcely constitutes a problem in nutrition. The typical southern dietary is deficient in phosphorus, but the importance of this is overshadowed by the other concomitant deficiencies. Moreover, the phosphorus content of human milk is much lower than that of cow's milk, and may, in breast-fed infants, be the limiting factor in the rapidity of mineralization of the skeleton, but this cannot be regarded as a true deficiency. On the other hand, a deficient absorption of phosphate, in the presence of an adequate intake, is not uncommon, creating for the organism the same physiological problems that would be created by a true deficiency in intake of this element.

On an ordinary intake of phosphorus a considerable proportion of that ingested appears in the stools. But it is not correct to subtract the amount in the stools from that taken in and to assume that the difference represents that actually absorbed. A large amount of phosphorus, perhaps equivalent to the daily intake, is poured into the gastrointestinal tract in the various secretions, most of which are reabsorbed. It is thus conceivable that the same phosphate ion might be released into the gastrointestinal tract and reabsorbed a dozen times before being finally ejected with the excreta.

VITAMIN D

These difficulties are largely avoided by the concept of *net absorption*, which is defined by the difference between the intake and that lost in the stools. And the net absorption of phosphate, as well as that of calcium, is influenced by vitamin D, the details of the mode of action being wholly obscure. Vitamin D thus plays an important, and, in the infant in particular, a decisive part in regulating the supply of phosphorus to the organism. We shall see that the first effect of a deficient assimilation of phosphorus is a failure of calcification of the bones, and that this, by removing the largest demand for the element, generally leaves an amount adequate for all other purposes, except under the most rigorous experimental conditions.

In spite of constantly recurring suggestions that vitamin D has other points of action in the organism, and particularly that it is concerned locally with the deposition of the minerals of bone, there is no satisfactory evidence for any such actions, except in large and toxic doses, with which we are not here concerned. On the other hand, and while we may feel that we have ruled out the possibility that the deposition of bone mineral is influenced directly and locally by vitamin D, we cannot feel so sure about the absence of systemic effects. But we do feel that the burden of proof is still upon those who would maintain that there are such effects.

TRANSPORT

Transport of phosphorus within the animal organism is, of course, mainly a function of the circulating blood. Even here, there are unsolved problems. In the fluid portion of the blood, the plasma, as well as in the tissue fluids, phosphate is present almost entirely in the inorganic form, there being a total of only about 0.5 millimoles per liter of organic phosphate in these fluids. But the red blood cells are rich in organic acid-soluble compounds of phosphorus, and there is abundant evidence that these compounds are not simply fixed substances, in transit from one part of the organism to another; they are labile and are engaged in the transformations typical of similar compounds elsewhere, and specifically in the reactions of the glycolytic cycle.

Just what functions are served by the phosphoric esters in the red blood cells or by the glycolysis with which they are concerned is not clear. The need for transfers of energy within the red cells is not immediately apparent. Physiologists have become accustomed to think of the nonnucleated red blood cells of mammals as playing a purely passive role in the transport of oxygen and of carbon dioxide and in the regulation of the acid-base balance; and this idea has been strengthened by the fact that these cells, in the presence of an abundant supply of oxygen, consume negligible amounts of it. Now we must accustom ourselves to the facts that anaerobic glycolysis, with its transfer of energy, is actively carried on within these cells and that the amounts of energy concerned are not insignificant. For the moment one can only speculate as to the use to which this energy is put, and there is a temptation to relate it to some other perplexing problems concerning the red blood cells as well as tissue cells. For example, we are still very much in the dark as to why sodium and potassium behave so differently in the animal organism. In most tissues sodium is almost entirely extracellular, while potassium is predominantly intracellular; and in most species, but to a somewhat lesser degree, this difference is reflected in the red blood cells. The failure of the sodium and potassium in the plasma to come to equilibrium with that in the cells has generally been attributed to impermeability of the cells, including the red blood cells, to these ions; but recent work with radioactive isotopes has confused, rather than clarified, this concept. It has been suggested from several sources that the differences between the concentrations of sodium and potassium inside the red cell and those in the plasma and the apparent impermeability of the red cell to these substances are actually maintained by a process which requires the expenditure of energy, and Danowski (1) has brought forward experimental evidence supporting this point of view.

Such a view, if found to be valid, would materially modify our outlook upon the Donnan equilibrium, although there is no indication that it would invalidate this formulation as a description of the distribution of water and electrolytes between the plasma and the red cells. In fact, recent work by Guest and Rapoport (2) on the anion equivalencies of the organic phosphates of the red blood cells and upon the influence of diphosphoglycerate on the distribution of diffusible ions between the plasma and red cells has cleared up some of the obscure points in the earlier results.

RICKETS

One of the most constant and most characteristic sequelae of what may be called a "functional deficiency" in phosphate—generally as the result of a deficiency in intake of vitamin D—is the lowering of the concentration of inorganic phosphate in the blood plasma. The simplest conception of rickets is that which attributes all of the symptoms and findings in this disease to the lowered plasma phosphate. It will be noted that I adhere rather closely to this concept of rickets, putting the burden of proof upon those who would maintain that there are findings not to be interpreted in this light. In this connection I may call attention to the fact that Freudenberg (3) has recently attributed the rather mild acidosis of rickets, frequently cited as evidence for the view that rickets is actually a systemic disease, to the fact that the phosphate available for excretion in the urine is not sufficient to carry out adequately the elimination of acid from the organism.

In addition to the lowered inorganic phosphate of the plasma in clinical and experimental rickets, there are numerous reports of a diminished content of acid-soluble organic phosphorus in the red cells during this disorder and of increases in the concentrations of these substances under conditions which lead to the healing of rickets. Moreover, similar findings have been reported for the soft tissues, offering an example of the usefulness of the blood picture as reflecting the state of the labile phosphorus reserves of the whole body.

Guest and Rapoport (2) have reported that the development of rickets induced in rats by a high-calcium, low-phosphorus diet is associated with decreases first of inorganic phosphorus and of an-denosinetriphosphate and then of diphosphoglycerate in the blood cells. During the development of rickets the concentration of diphosphoglycerate decreases progressively. A rapid increase in concentration of diphosphoglycerate following any of the procedures which induce healing appears to be a sign of rapid mobilization of phosphorus in the body and of the availability of such phosphorus for transport to the calcifying bones.

Such findings have frequently been cited as evidence that vitamin D has some specific effect upon the organic phosphorus compounds of the blood and tissues. The findings may be as readily explained, however, by assuming that the organic compounds of the red blood cells, and presumably of other cells as well, are in equilibrium with the inorganic phosphate of the plasma and that a lowering in concentration of the one leads automatically to a lowering of the other. A disturbing note is that Freeman and McLean (4) have reported that puppies fed a diet extremely low in phosphorus, over a period of 100 days, failed to show a significant decrease in the acid-soluble phosphorus of the red blood cells, regardless of whether or not vitamin D was administered in antirachitic doses. I do not attempt to explain this discrepancy.

The problem of calcification, with which I can deal only in its broadest outlines, may be stated in the form of a question: How, and under what conditions, does calcium, in combination with phosphate, leave the circulating fluids of the body and become deposited in solid form in the tissues?

We can describe one mechanism by which a compound of calcium and phosphate may leave the blood, although this mechanism is of doubtful applicability to calcification.

If calcium or phosphate is added to serum, nothing seems to happen, unless these substances are added in very large amounts. In other words, it is not practicable, within ordinary limits, to precipitate calcium in combination with phosphate from serum.

COLLOIDAL CALCIUM PHOSPHATE

It is now well established that in the presence of a protective colloid, such as serum protein, increase in calcium and phosphate concentrations beyond a critical level gives rise to formation of a colloidal complex of these two substances. The chemical composition of this complex and the mechanism of its formation are not clearly defined; but, since the conditions for its appearance in the plasma approximate very closely the conditions for calcification *in vitro*, it is not unreasonable to suppose that the conditions for formation of a colloidal complex, in a protein-containing solution, depend upon solubility relationships.

Something is now known concerning the behavior of this colloidal complex in the animal organism. When the level of phosphate or of calcium in the plasma is increased, the colloidal complex is formed. There is a definite time factor in the process, as shown in collaboration with Hinrichs (5), the formation of the colloidal complex proceeding more rapidly as the concentrations of the ions are increased, and very slowly nearer the critical levels. As the substance is formed, it is very quickly removed from the circulating plasma; and Gersh (6) has shown that it is taken up by the histiocytes, or the so-called "reticulo-endothelial system," of the liver and spleen. Here it is redissolved and put back into solution in the circulating fluids. The formation of this substance acts as a limiting factor upon the possible simultaneous increase in phosphate and in calcium concentrations in plasma. It accounts for the low plasma calcium, with concurrent tetany, frequently observed, together with phosphate retention, in Bright's disease. Whether the colloidal complex has any direct relationship to calcification is not known, but it represents at least one form in which calcium and phosphate may be removed from the blood. It is of interest that the formation of this colloidal complex, with the consequent removal of calcium ions from the blood, occurs much more readily in serum than in solutions of casein. This suggests the possibility of some mechanism for catalyzing the reaction in serum, but this possibility has not been adequately explored.

CALCIFICATION

It has been apparent for some time that calcification, being essentially the deposition of a difficultly soluble salt in solid form, must be concerned with the solubility of that salt, and that consequently it should be possible to define the conditions for calcification in relation to a solubility product constant. But the difficulties in realization of this definition have been many. Howland and his associates (7), some years ago, in the absence of any method for determining either calcium or phosphate-ion concentrations in the serum, introduced a simple empirical product—Total calcium *times* Total phosphate—and found that the presence or absence of rickets in infants could be correlated with this product. In spite of various attempts to refine this formulation, the problem of an adequate definition of the humoral conditions for calcification has only recently been resolved. This is not the place for a detailed account of this work, which has been done in collaboration with Lipton, Bloom, and Barron (8), but it may be said that for calcification of rachitic cartilage to occur *in vitro* the solubility product constants of both secondary and tertiary calcium phosphates must be exceeded and that this has been found to be true over a range of pH 5.7–8.7.

Since the conditions are such that saturation with $CaHPO_4$ at pH 7.4 can only be attained in solutions already saturated with the tertiary compound, the solubility of this salt is critical for calcification in the living animal, as was postulated some years ago by Shear and his associates. Thus we have the seeming paradox that the solubility of this salt, which is not present in bone, nevertheless determines the deposition of the bone mineral.

As already mentioned, this finding is a refinement of the empirical product of Howland; and, taken together with the local factor to be discussed, it is adequate to account for the calcification of the bones in growing animals and for the failure of this calcification, which is known as "rickets." What it fails to account for is the fact that adults, with concentrations of calcium and phosphate in the plasma identical with those of the rachitic child, can still carry on the physiological turnover of bone mineral and can calcify the callus of a healing fracture.

COMPOSITION OF BONE SALT

The finding that the solubility of $CaHPO_4$ is critical for calcification is easily reconciled with current conceptions, both as to the chemical composition of the bone salt and as to the mode of its formation. The chemical composition has been studied by x-ray diffraction methods and, lately, with the aid of radioactive elements. For some years this work had the goal of identifying the bone salt with a pure crystalline substance of constant composition and a high degree of stability. More recently it has appeared better to abandon this attempt in favor of one compatible with the view that the bone salt is not a pure substance, is not of constant composition, and is not stable. That it belongs in the apatite group of minerals, all of which have the same basic crystalline structure, is now firmly established; but it does not correspond exactly to any of the pure substances in this group or to any mixture of them. Instead, on what may be regarded as a base of hydroxy-apatite, the bone salt is an isomorphous mixture, with substitutions of carbon for both phosphorus and calcium in the crystal structure (9). Other substitutions occur, notably magnesium, sodium, and potassium for calcium; and these substitutions continue to take place long after the mineral is laid down.

FORMATION OF BONE SALT

Corresponding changes in the ideas concerning the mode of formation of the bone salt have taken place. The problem is complicated by the facts that even the sequence of events when a solution of phosphoric acid is titrated with lime water is not yet entirely clear and that the deposition of bone salt is a much more complicated process. But to replace the classical idea of precipitation, in which all the constituent ions collide, combine, and are deposited in a solid phase, we have now the concept of the bone salt being formed as the result of a series of reactions and transformations. While it is by no means certain that the following description correctly records the events as they occur, it does illustrate the current conception of the mode of formation of the bone salt:

1. $CaHPO_4$ is aggregated, presumably in submicroscopic particles.
2. Three molecules of $CaHPO_4$ condense to form one molecule of $Ca_3(PO_4)_2$, leaving one molecule of H_3PO_4. By reaching this stage in two steps the necessity of a fifth order reaction is avoided.
3. $Ca_3(PO_4)_2$ is unstable, but there are quickly added $(OH)_2^=$, $CO_3^=$, and perhaps other ions, to complete the crystal structure characteristic of the apatite minerals.
4. Further additions to, and substitutions in, the molecule continue over a long period of time, the mineral increasing in stability and decreasing in solubility.

From this point of view, then, and from the correlations of calcification with ion products, it seems reasonable to suppose that the solubility products of both secondary and tertiary calcium phosphates must be exceeded in order for the corresponding stages in the formation of the bone salt to take place. From the same point of view it is also possible to see why the bone salt, once formed, is less soluble than the salts formed in the process of its deposition, and that consequently the solution of bone salt from bone is negligible, even in the presence of low ion products in the plasma. The correlation of calcification with critical ion products in the plasma also reveals the mechanism for protection of the organism's other needs for calcium and phosphate. During the period of growth, by far the greater part of the phosphate ingested goes to the skeleton. But if the supply of phosphorus or of calcium fails, the ion product falls, and calcification ceases. Consequently, the intake of phosphorus may be markedly reduced, without seriously affecting the supply available for other than skeletal purposes.

All of the above discussion concerning the humoral factor in calcification presupposes a calcifiable tissue, for, even when saturation of the fluids of the body with calcium and phosphate is attained, calcification occurs only in certain predetermined places. For this reason it is necessary to recognize a *local factor* which determines the occurrence and localization of calcification when favorable humoral conditions are present.

PHOSPHATASE

It would be peculiarly appropriate, in this symposium, to be able to clarify the role of phosphatase in calcification and to identify it with the mechanism of the local factor. But it is hardly possible to go further, either with affirming or with denying a relationship of this enzyme to the deposition of the bone salt, than Robison (10) was able to go when he left the problem in 1934.

Phosphatase is present in especially high concentrations in three tissues—bone, kidneys, and intestines. In only one of these tissues can the enzyme be primarily concerned with calcification. Robison's original hypothesis was that bone phosphatase, by catalyzing the breakdown of phosphoric esters, raises the local concentration of inorganic phosphate high enough to exceed the solubility product of the bone salt and that deposition of the salt occurs. This hypothesis was supported by experiments in which calcification of rachitic cartilage occurred *in vitro* in media in which all of the available phosphorus was in the form of phosphoric esters. The hypothesis, however, immediately encountered two objections: (1) the fact that the plasma and diffusible fluid of the body, from which the phosphate would presumably be derived, contain so little organic phosphate that, if it were all transformed into the inorganic form, the concentration of the latter would not be significantly altered; and (2) the fact that calcification occurs only in predetermined places made it necessary to postulate a *second* mechanism, corresponding to what we have called the "local mechanism." Robison attempted to meet the first objection by assuming that the inorganic phosphate came from the phospheric esters either of the red blood cells or of the hypertrophic cartilage cells, and he also attempted to identify the second mechanism with phosphatase activity, but the verdict still stands as not proved. The presence of phosphatase in the bones in high concentration, particularly during the period of rapid growth and of deposition of the bone salt, suggests some relationship to this deposition. With Freeman, we have recently found (4) that phosphatase is associated with the layer of osteoblasts applied to the surface of growing bone and also with the hypertrophic cartilage cells of the zone of provisional calcification. On the other hand, the enzyme is not found in the matrix of osteoid tissue awaiting calcification. The significance of these findings is not clear.

It has been suggested that the absorption of both carbohydrates and fatty acids depends upon a transient phosphorylation and that the reabsorption of glucose through the renal tubules depends upon the same process. Such mechanisms, as yet not proved, would account for the high concentrations of phosphatase in the kidneys and in the intestines.

THE LOCAL FACTOR

During the past year, in collaboration with Lipton, Barron, and Bloom (11), I have been engaged in a frontal attack upon the problem of the nature of the local factor. After reviewing the various possibilities which had been suggested, and the available facts, the latter chiefly from the work of Robison, it appeared to us that the process, whether concerned with phosphatase or not, is probably enzymatic in nature. This was supported by the observations that heating to 60° C. causes a complete but irreversible inhibition of calcification of rachitic cartilage *in vitro*. Other influences, including iodoacetate, fluoride, alcohol, acetone, chloroform, drying over phosphorus pentoxide, and leaching in phosphorus-free saline solutions, caused a partial inhibition, usually easily overcome by adding an excess of phosphate to the solutions used. Our search for a method for producing a satisfactory reversible inhibition of the local factor, with which the nature of the process could be further investigated, has so far failed.

We attempted also to find some correlation of calcification in the matrix of hypertrophic rachitic cartilage with the anaerobic glycolysis of the tissue, this work being stimulated by an apparent correlation between the appearance of glycogen in the cartilage cells and the calcifiability of the matrix and by the reports in the literature that calcification *in vitro* is inhibited by iodoacetate and by fluoride. On account of the low oxygen consumption of cartilage, aerobic studies were not possible. Here, again, we failed to find any demonstrable interrelationship. While it is true that a 70–90 per cent inhibition of glycolysis by iodoacetate or by fluoride is accompanied by a slight reduction in calcification, this is easily overcome by adding slightly more phosphate. The addition of glucose to the incubating medium, while increasing anaerobic glycolysis about eightfold, had no appreciable effect upon calcification. Moreover, glycolysis proceeded at the same rate, whether or not the incubating medium contained enough phosphate to induce calcification in the cartilage matrix.

The addition of adenosine triphosphate and of creatine to the incubating medium had no effect upon calcification. Addition of glutathione and thioglycolic acid, both of which are reported to inhibit phosphatase activity, still gives excellent calcification in the presence of a phosphate ester and in the absence of inorganic phosphate. The work has had to be interrupted, but we hope to return to it at the earliest opportunity.

RESORPTION OF BONE

The function of the skeleton in the storage of calcium is well known. Obviously, phosphorus is also accumulated in the bones, but apparently no great physiological need is served thereby.

The simplest conception of the release of calcium and phosphorus from the bones into the blood stream would be the converse of calcification, or decalcification. But simple decalcification, or solution of the bone minerals in the fluids of the body, does not appear to occur to any appreciable extent. Instead, for the body to obtain access to the minerals stored in bone, some of the bone itself, including its organic matrix, must be destroyed.

The whole process of formation and destruction of bone, serving the need for storage and delivery of bone mineral as needed, is beautifully illustrated in female birds during the egg-laying cycle, as recently studied in detail in the laboratory of Dr. William Bloom (12). In the pigeon, in which maturation of the ovarian follicle is initiated by copulation, there begins at the same time a remarkable process in the marrow cavities of the long bones. Here an entire secondary system of bone, concerned only with the storage of the calcium needed for the eggshell, is built up within a few days, extending as a network throughout the marrow cavities. This is true bone, although not needed for ordinary skeletal support; and calcium is deposited in it, as it is formed, in the usual combination with phosphorus, as bone salt.

When the eggshell is about to be formed, there is a sudden reversal from bone formation to bone destruction, and calcium and phosphate are liberated. The calcium goes into the eggshell, in the form of almost pure calcium carbonate, while some of the phosphate is excreted and some is used again in the next cycle. It is of interest, also, that during this same period there appears in the blood a phosphoprotein, called "serum vitellin," having approximately the composition of ovovitellin and apparently concerned with the deposition of the latter in the egg. The formation of medullary bone can be brought about by the administration of sex hormones. In the pigeon, but apparently not in some other birds, both female and male hormones must be administered to produce the reaction (13). The reversal of the process from bone formation to bone destruction, which occurs spontaneously and with great rapidity in the laying bird, has not been duplicated experimentally, and its mechanism remains unexplained.

Under usual physiological conditions this destruction or resorption of bone is regulated by the parathyroid hormone, which thus regulates the concentration of calcium ions in the blood plasma. Efforts have been made to establish the phosphate level in the blood, rather than the calcium level, as the effective stimulus to functional activity of the parathyroid glands, but the arguments are not convincing. The function of the parathyroid glands seems not to be primarily related to the phosphorus needs of the organism, for the phosphorus released from the bones under their influence is not utilized elsewhere but runs to waste in the urine and is lost to the body. This is accomplished by an effect of the parathyroid hormone upon excretion of phosphate through the kidneys. When bone salt is liberated from bone under the influence of parathyroid extract, both calcium and phosphate, in definite proportions, are poured into the blood. But the calcium concentration in the plasma rises, while the phosphate concentration usually falls or remains unchanged. This differential effect, resulting from the increased excretion of phosphate in the urine, permits the parathyroid hormone to regulate the concentration of calcium in the plasma, without the interference of a rise in phosphate concentration which would make a concurrent rise in calcium concentration impossible.

SUMMARY

1. Phosphorus flows through the organism in the blood stream, chiefly in the form of the ions of orthophosphoric acid. This flow usually forms an adequate supply of this element for metabolic needs of the organism, these needs being protected by the fact that all withdrawal of the mineral for calcification stops long before the supply for other needs is threatened.

2. In addition to compounds of phosphorus with proteins and lipids, phosphate enters into a considerable number and variety of chemical combinations which have in common their solubility in acid, their extreme lability, and their association with the utilization of carbohydrate, their chief function being in the transfer, rather than in the storage, of energy. Only in the case of creatine phosphate does there appear to be any appreciable storage of energy in the form of energy-rich phosphate bonds, this stored energy being held ready to meet the demands of muscular contraction.

3. The organism appears to be able to synthesize all of the complex organic compounds of phosphorus from inorganic phosphate.

4. The problem of calcification, including the humoral conditions necessary for the deposition of bone salt, and the nature of the local factor have been considered, together with the processes involved in the resorption of bone.

BIBLIOGRAPHY

1. Danowski, Thaddeus S., J. Biol. Chem., 139:693, 1941.
2. Guest, G. M., and Rapoport, S., Physiol. Rev., 21:410, 1941.
3. Freudenberg, E., Schweiz. med. Wchnschr., 20(69):285, 1939.
4. Freeman, Smith, and McLean, F. C., Arch. Path., 32:387, 1941.

5. McLean, F. C., and Hinrichs, M. A., Am. J. Physiol., 121:580, 1938.
6. Gersh, I., Am. J. Physiol., 121:589, 1938; Anat. Rec., 70:331, 1938.
7. Howland, J., Harvey Lect., 18:189, 1922–23.
8. McLean, F. C.; Lipton, M. A.; Bloom, W.; and Barron, E. S. G., to be published.
9. Gruner, J. W.; McConnell, D.; and Armstrong, W. D., J. Biol. Chem., 121:771, 1937.
10. Robison, R., and Rosenheim, A. H., Biochem. J., 28:684, 1934.
11. McLean, F. C.; Lipton, M. A.; Barron, E. S. G.; and Bloom, W., unpublished work.
12. Bloom, W.; Bloom, M. A.; and McLean, F. C., Anat. Rec., 81:443, 1941.
13. Bloom, M. A.; Bloom, W.; and McLean, F. C., Am. J. Physiol., 133:216, 1941.

VITAMIN K

D. W. MacCORQUODALE
Abbott Laboratories, North Chicago, Illinois

IN CONNECTION with his studies on sterol metabolism Dr. Henrik Dam, of the University of Copenhagen, described in 1929 a hemorrhagic disease in the chick which was characterized by a greatly prolonged blood-clotting time (1). Newly hatched chicks were placed on a special fat-free diet. After two or three weeks there developed extensive subcutaneous intramuscular and abdominal hemorrhages. Anemia was usually severe, and the ability of the blood to coagulate was lost almost entirely. This scurvy-like syndrome was also observed by other investigators, but in 1935 Dam showed that a cure could not be effected by means of any of the known vitamins and correctly concluded that the disease was caused by deficiency of a hitherto unknown dietary factor, for which he suggested the name "Koagulationsvitamin," or vitamin K (2). The newly discovered factor was found to be present generally in green leafy vegetables and in hog-liver fat. Cereals and fruits were found to contain little of it, the tomato being a notable exception.

Early experiments directed toward the isolation of the vitamin utilized hog-liver fat as the source material, but Dam and Almquist and Stokstad (3) found alfalfa to be a particularly rich source of the substance; and it was from this material that the pure vitamin was first isolated in 1939 by McKee, Binkley, MacCorquodale, Thayer, and Doisy (4) at St. Louis University and by Dam and Karrer and their collaborators (5) in the European laboratories.

The formation of vitamin K by bacteria was demonstrated by Almquist and Stokstad (3) at the University of California. They found that vitamin-K-free protein material which was moistened and allowed to stand exposed at room temperature for several days rapidly developed strong antihemorrhagic potency. They also found (6) that an ether extract of the droppings from deficient chicks would afford protection when incorporated in a diet which would otherwise cause development of the disease. These findings were correctly ascribed to bacterial synthesis—in the one case *in vitro*, and in the other in the intestinal tract of the chick. Almquist *et al.* (7) subsequently showed that substances with antihemorrhagic activity were formed as a result of the metabolic processes of a considerable number of bacteria. McKee, Binkley, Thayer, MacCorquodale, and Doisy (8) found vitamin-K activity in the feces of the horse, cow, sheep, hog, and man; and in 1939 (4) they isolated the vitamin formed by the bacterial putrefaction of fish meal. It proved to be a different compound from that obtained from alfalfa. The vitamin

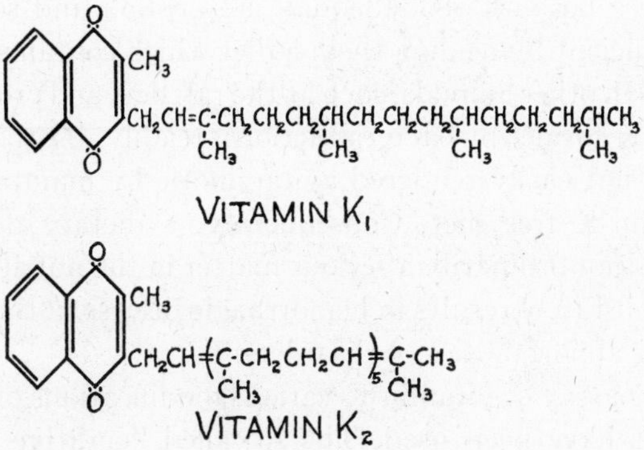

O
CH$_3$
CH$_2$CH=C-CH$_2$CH$_2$CH$_2$CHCH$_2$CH$_2$CH$_2$CHCH$_2$CH$_2$CH$_2$CHCH$_3$
CH$_3$ CH$_3$ CH$_3$ CH$_3$
O

VITAMIN K$_1$

O
CH$_3$
CH$_2$CH$\{$C-CH$_2$CH$_2$CH$\}_5$C-CH$_3$
CH$_3$ CH$_3$
O

VITAMIN K$_2$

Fig. 1

from alfalfa was a light-yellow oil at ordinary temperatures. It crystallized at low temperatures and had a melting-point of approximately -20° C. The vitamin from putrefied fish meal was obtained as a light-yellow crystalline solid melting at 53°5–54°5 C. The vitamin from alfalfa was designated "K$_1$," and that from putrefied fish meal "K$_2$." The empirical formulas were found to be $C_{31}H_{46}O_2$ and $C_{41}H_{56}O_2$, respectively. The St. Louis group have shown vitamin K$_1$ to have the structural formula of 2-methyl–3-phytyl–1, 4-naphthoquinone, and vitamin K$_2$ the probable structural formula 2-methyl–3-difarnesyl–1, 4-naphthoquinone (Fig. 1). Vitamin K$_1$ has been synthesized in numerous laboratories, but the synthesis of K$_2$ has not yet been accomplished, although this will undoubtedly be achieved in due time.

Animals suffering from vitamin-K deficiency exhibit a remarkable tendency to bleed profusely as a result of minor injuries. Trivial bruises usually result in extensive subcutaneous hemorrhages. Wounds which in the case of a normal animal would be considered insignificant lead to extensive and frequently fatal hemorrhage in the deficient animal. Blood drawn from such an animal shows very little tendency to coagulate and may remain fluid for many hours.

Two sources of vitamin K are ordinarily available to the animal. These are the preformed vitamin K_1 in the diet and the vitamin K_2 which is formed by bacterial action in the intestinal tract. Some animals, notably fowls, are not able to utilize the vitamin from the second source because of inadequate absorption and so are easily rendered deficient by feeding them a diet which contains little or no vitamin K. In other animals, such as the rat, dog, and probably man, the vitamin K_2 formed by bacterial action is readily absorbed; and such animals are not easily rendered avitaminotic by maintaining them on a vitamin-K–free diet. Consequently, a dietary deficiency of vitamin K is not ordinarily a serious matter in the nutrition of these animals, for it rarely results in hemorrhagic disease in the absence of contributing abnormalities or disorders.

For the bioassay of vitamin K various modifications of two different methods have been used. The so-called "curative procedure" was first used by Dam and his collaborators. It consists of keeping newly hatched chicks upon a diet containing little or no vitamin K until a definite degree of deficiency has developed. Graded doses of the vitamin-containing material are then administered, and the effect determined by measuring the clotting power of the blood. The preventive method was developed by Almquist and in principle consists of determining the amount of active material which it is necessary to add to the diet in order to prevent the development of the syndrome, as determined by measuring the clotting time of the blood.

There appears to be some relationship between chlorophyll and vitamin K in plants. Dam, Glavind, and Nielsen (9) have shown that the vitamin is formed in the chloroplasts of the plant cell, which also contain the chlorophyll. Leaves which are grown in the dark, and so contain no chlorophyll, are found to contain little or no vitamin K. Plants, such as the spruce and pine, which can form chlorophyll in the dark can also form vitamin K in the dark. Lower plants, such as the mushroom, which contain no chlorophyll, also contain no vitamin K.

Concerning the action of vitamin K in the animal organism much remains to be disclosed. The discovery of this vitamin and the demonstration of its relation to the blood-clotting mechanism have stimulated wide interest in this important problem. According to the most generally accepted theory, the rupturing of tissue cells or the disintegration of blood platelets liberates a kinase known as "thrombokinase" or "thromboplastin." In the presence of calcium ions this acts upon a proenzyme prothrombin present in the blood to form an enzyme known as "thrombin." Thrombin then acts upon the soluble blood-protein fibrinogen to form "fibrin," which is insoluble and separates in a weblike form, enmeshing the formed elements of the blood to form a clot. It was shown by Dam, Schønheyder, and Tage-Hansen (10) that the failure of the clotting mechanism in avitaminosis K is due to a deficiency of prothrombin. Newly hatched chicks placed on a vitamin-K–free diet show a steady decline in the prothrombin level of the blood. At the end of three or four weeks the prothrombin level has dropped to a few per cent of the normal value, and the blood shows only a feeble tendency to coagulate. Administration of vitamin K results in a rapid rise in prothrombin, and in the course of a few hours the clotting time of the blood is found to be within normal limits. If, on the other hand, blood is drawn from a deficient chick and the vitamin is added directly to it, no effect upon the clotting time is observed. This shows that the role of vitamin K in blood clotting is not a direct one but that the vitamin is essential for the formation of prothrombin.

Vitamin K does not form part of the prothrombin molecule. If this were the case, it would be expected that orally administered prothrombin would show vitamin-K activity due to liberation of the vitamin resulting from digestion of the protein complex. Dam, Glavind, Lewis, and Tage-Hansen (11) prepared a prothrombin concentrate from the blood of normal hens. Large doses of this were fed to chicks suffering from vitamin-K deficiency, but no vitamin-K activity was observed.

The site of formation of prothrombin is undoubtedly the liver. Animals from which most of the liver has been removed show a rapid decline in the blood prothrombin level. Moreover, the administration of large doses of vitamin K to such animals is ineffective in increasing the prothrombin. The same is true of animals whose livers have been damaged by chloroform or by other means. The prothrombin level in the blood is definitely related to liver function.

Although vitamin K is necessary for the organism in order that prothrombin may be formed, the availability of the vitamin does not insure that the animal will not suffer from hypoprothrombinemia. Any condition that interferes with the proper utilization of the vitamin will have the same result. A badly damaged liver is not able to form adequate amounts of prothrombin even when large amounts of vitamin K are brought to it by the blood stream. There must be enough normal intestinal mucosa to allow the absorption of sufficient vitamin K to meet the requirements of the body. If the intestinal mucosa is damaged to such an extent that absorption is greatly reduced, a deficiency of prothrombin may result. The well-known role of the bile in promoting absorption of lipoids is highly important with regard to vitamin K. The vitamin is highly insoluble in water, and in the absence of bile its absorption in the intestinal tract is negligible. Ligation of the bile duct or formation of a biliary fistula results in a rapid fall in the blood prothrombin level in animals kept on a diet which is adequate for unoperated animals. Administration of a vitamin-K supplement is ineffective in such animals unless accompanied by bile or bile salts. Elliott, Isaacs, and Ivy (12) have shown that administration of large amounts of mineral oil to rats can interfere with the absorption of vitamin K to such an extent as to bring about a condition of hypoprothrombinemia.

The manner in which vitamin K participates in the formation of prothrombin in the liver is not known. The action is not specific but is shared by a large number of derivatives of 1, 4-naphthoquinone and by compounds which are converted into such quinones in the body. McCawley and Gurchot (13) have put forward an interesting speculation in this connection. They draw attention to the fact that under certain conditions the redox potential of vitamin K_1 is not far from that of *p*-benzoquinone. The latter has been shown to exert an inhibiting effect on protein hydrolysis by papain and by cathepsin of the liver. The action of cathepsin has been shown to be a reversible one, so that, if vitamin K_1 acts similarly to benzoquinone and inhibits the lytic action of cathepsin on prothrombin, the net result would be a stimulation in the synthesis of prothrombin.

The ability of vitamin K to promote the formation of thrombin is shared by a large number of synthetic compounds. Except for a few compounds of low activity, the active compounds are all derivatives of 1, 4-naphthoquinone or compounds readily converted into this type of structure by metabolic processes. The most potent known substance is 2-methyl–1, 4-naphthoquinone, and it appears

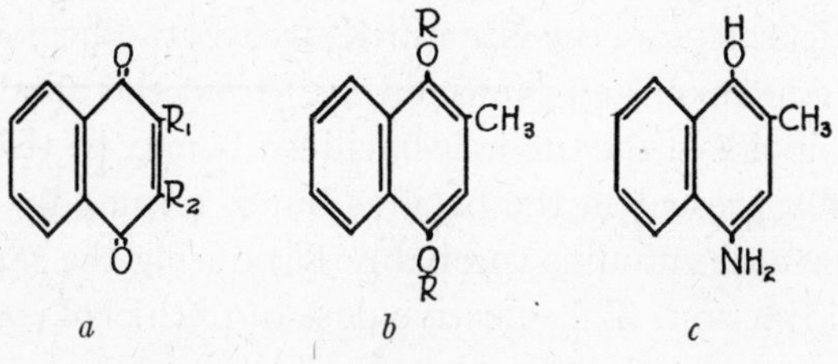

FIG. 2

that the methyl group in the 2-position is necessary for any high degree of activity.

Fieser, Tishler, and Sampson (14) have compared the activities of a large number of compounds and have made a number of generalizations. Naphthoquinone itself has only feeble activity, but with the introduction of a methyl group in the 2-position an extremely potent substance is obtained (Fig. 2*a*, $R_1 = CH_3$, $R_2 = H$). Any change in this structure brings about a diminution of activity. Introduction of a second methyl group in the 3-position causes a large decrease in potency ($R_1 = CH_3$, $R_2 = CH_3$). If one side chain remains a methyl group and the other is progressively increased in length, we find first a diminution in potency followed by an increase, the maximum activity among the compounds tested being found with the phytyl group (vitamin K_1). Except for the removal of the phytyl group, any change in the substituents of the vitamin-K molecule results in diminution of activity. The substitution of an ethyl group for the methyl group results in a compound with only one-thousandth the activity of the vitamin. The presence of the double bond in the $\beta\gamma$ position in the side chain is important for the activity of the vitamin. Saturation of this linkage brings about a considerable drop in potency (values vary from 1/8 to 1/24). A double bond in any other position of a side chain appears to have little influence on activity. Any substitution in the aromatic ring of the naphthoquinone nucleus results in practically complete loss of activity.

The first report of a synthetic compound having antihemorrhagic activity was made by Almquist and Klose (15), who found that phthiocol (2-methyl-3-hydroxy-1, 4-naphthoquinone [Fig. 2*a*, R_1= CH_3, R_2=OH]) was effective in preventing the hemorrhagic diathesis in chicks kept on the vitamin-K–free diet. Phthiocol was first isolated by Anderson and Newman (16) from the alkaline hydrolysate of the lipoids of the tubercle bacillus. It may be that phthiocol is not actually present in the bacillus but is formed by cleavage of one of the natural vitamins (probably K_2) during the saponification of the lipoid fraction. The effective dose of phthiocol is at least five hundred times as great as the dosage of vitamin K_1.

It has already been mentioned that certain types of compounds which are easily oxidized to quinones may possess antihemorrhagic activity, presumably because of oxidation in the body. The diacetates of the vitamin K_1 and K_2 hydroquinones are about half as active as the vitamins, and they possess the advantage of much greater stability. Water-soluble antihemorrhagic compounds are formed by combining the hydroquinones with dibasic or tribasic acids. The resulting derivatives are utilized in the form of the sodium salts. The disulfate, the diphosphate, and the disuccinate esters have been investigated. Apparently these derivatives of the simpler quinones are more efficiently utilized than the corresponding derivatives of the natural vitamins. The diphosphate of 2-methyl-1, 4-naphthohydroquinone (Fig. 2*b*, $R=PO_3H_2$) is reported to be as active as the quinone on a molecular basis, and the same is true for the 3-sodium sulfonate.

The aminonaphthols constitute another class of active compounds. The 2-methyl-4-amino-1-naphthol (Fig. 2*c*) is as active as the corresponding 2-methyl–1, 4-naphthoquinone to which it is oxidized. The isomeric 3-methyl–4-amino–1-naphthol is slightly less active. The aminonaphthols are utilized in the form of the water-soluble hydrochloride salts. Other easily oxidizable compounds found to be active are the 5, 8-dihydro derivatives of the 1, 4-naphthoquinones and naphthohydroquinones, the 2-methyl-naphthylamines and the 2-methylnaphthols. The latter have a remarkably high degree of potency, indicating very efficient utilization.

Molitor and Robinson (17) have investigated the acute and chronic toxicity in mice of a few of the naphthoquinones. For vitamin K_1 no toxic effects were observed even when very large doses were administered. For phthiocol the lethal dose was found to be about 0.2 gm. per kilogram of body weight and for 2-methyl–1, 4-naphthoquinone about 0.5 gm. per kilogram of body weight. Daily feeding for 30 consecutive days of 0.1 gm. of phthiocol and of 0.35 gm. of 2-methyl–1, 4-naphthoquinone per kilogram of body weight was found to cause a marked diminution in the number of erythrocytes and in the percentage of hemoglobin in the blood.

Rapid progress has been made in clarifying the biochemical aspects of the vitamin-K problem and in developing valuable clinical applications, but the fundamental question of the exact relation of vitamin K to prothrombin formation still stands as a challenge to physiologists and biochemists.

BIBLIOGRAPHY

1. Dam, H., Biochem. Ztschr., **220**:158, 1930.
2. Dam, H., Nature, **135**:652, 1935.
3. Almquist, H. J., and Stokstad, E. L. R., J. Biol. Chem., **111**:105, 1935.
4. McKee, R. W.; Binkley, S. B.; MacCorquodale, D. W.; Thayer, S. A.; and Doisy, E. A., J. Am. Chem. Soc., **61**:1295, 1939.
5. Dam, H.; Geiger, A.; Glavind, J.; Karrer, P.; Karrer, W.; Rothschild, E.; and Salomon, H., Helvet. chim. acta, **22**:310, 1939.
6. Almquist, H. J., and Stokstad, E. L. R., J. Nutrition, **12**:329, 1936.
7. Almquist, H. J.; Pentler, C. F.; and Mecchi, E., Proc. Soc. Exper. Biol. & Med., **38**:336, 1938.
8. McKee, R. W.; Binkley, S. B.; Thayer, S. A.; MacCorquodale, D. W.; and Doisy, E. A., J. Biol. Chem., **131**:327, 1939.
9. Dam, H.; Glavind, J.; and Nielsen, N., Ztschr. f. physiol. Chem., **265**:80, 1940.

10. DAM, H.; SCHØNHEYDER, F.; and TAGE-HANSEN, E., Biochem. J., **30**:1075, 1936.
11. DAM, H.; GLAVIND, J.; LEWIS, L.; and TAGE-HANSEN, E., Skandinav. Arch. f. Physiol., **79**:121, 1938.
12. ELLIOTT, M. C.; ISAACS, B.; and IVY, A. C., Proc. Soc. Exper. Biol. & Med., **43**:240, 1940.
13. McCAWLEY, E. L., and GURCHOT, C., Univ. California Publ. Pharmacol, **1**:325, 1940.
14. FIESER, L. F.; TISHLER, M.; and SAMPSON, W. L., J. Biol. Chem., **137**:659, 1941.
15. ALMQUIST, H. J., and KLOSE, A. A., J. Am. Chem. Soc., **61**:1611, 1939.
16. ANDERSON, R. J., and NEWMAN, M. S., J. Biol. Chem., **101**:773, 1933.
17. MOLITOR, H., and ROBINSON, H. J., Proc. Soc. Exper. Biol. & Med., **43**:125, 1940.

VITAMIN K: CLINICAL ASPECTS[1]

H. P. SMITH AND E. D. WARNER
Department of Pathology, State University of Iowa

IT IS the purpose of the present paper to discuss certain of the principles involved in the clinical use of vitamin K. The use of this vitamin in adults will be discussed quite briefly. For more extended discussion of adult therapy the reader is referred elsewhere (1–4). In the present paper we shall give somewhat more extended treatment to therapy during infancy.

Before undertaking to discuss either the infant or the adult, it will be well to outline briefly the question of prothrombin determination, for it is mainly through prothrombin determinations that the results of therapy are judged. Admittedly, there are still uncertainties regarding all of the prothrombin methods now in use, and in the field of fundamental biology these differences are important. In the field of clinical medicine these technical problems are not quite so important, for the clinician is primarily interested in the fluctuations which occur in a given patient, and all of the current methods fulfil this limited purpose reasonably well. The prothrombin methods of Schønheyder, Dam, and Plum (5–7) were used for much of the work which has been done abroad. The method of Quick (8–10) and the methods developed in our laboratory (11–16) have been used more extensively in this country. For clinical work it is desirable that the method used be one which is simple, easily learned, and readily performed. We have worked out the details of one such method (15, 16) which can be done with whole blood. We refer to this as the "bedside test" for prothrombin activity. The test merely involves the addition of thromboplastin to the blood the moment it is drawn. Normal blood clots in about 25 seconds. With a deficiency of prothrombin, clotting may not occur for several minutes. The Abbott Company has recently placed a suitable type of dried thromboplastin on the mar-

[1] The work which has been done in our own laboratory was supported in part by the Graduate College and in part by the John and Mary R. Markle Foundation.

ket,[2] and has also devised a small kit containing the necessary tubes and pipettes for the test.

The "bedside test" requires 1 cc. of blood, which is drawn with a syringe. Recently several groups of workers (17–24) have found that the test can be performed equally well with a single drop of blood obtained by a stab wound. Kato (26), Bray and Kelley (27), Řerábek (25), and the Copenhagen workers (7) have also devised micromethods. These methods are especially useful in work on infants, in which it is often difficult to obtain large amounts of blood.

THE USE OF VITAMIN K IN ADULTS

The vitamin-K compounds which occur in nature appear to be fat-soluble, almost without exception. This is also true of some of the synthetic vitamin-K analogues, but not of all. It is now a matter of common knowledge that the fat-soluble compounds are not readily absorbed from the intestine unless bile or bile salt is present to aid in the absorption. With obstruction of the biliary tract or with biliary fistulas bile does not reach the intestine, and vitamin K is not absorbed in adequate amounts. Likewise, there is difficulty in the absorption of vitamin K in the group of disorders variously classified as sprue, nontropical sprue, and celiac disease (28–34). It has also been shown that absorption is difficult in certain cases of intestinal fistulas (31) and in chronic ulcerative colitis (31, 34, 35). It thus appears that defective absorption may occur independently of bile deprivation. Furthermore, Elliott, Isaacs, and Ivy (36) have shown that excessive use of mineral oil may interfere with absorption of the fat-soluble forms of vitamin K, apparently by holding them in solution and thus preventing their absorption by the mucosa. In summary, then, faulty absorption may be due to lack of bile, to faulty function of intestinal mucosa, or, third, to mechanical factors, such as mineral oil.

In cases of bile deprivation the oral administration of the fat-soluble forms of vitamin K must be accompanied by oral administration of bile or bile salt to aid in the absorption. Bile and bile salt is

[2] Dried thromboplastin, prepared from brain, has also been placed on the market by E. R. Squibb and Sons and by the Difco Laboratories. With these products we have obtained results almost identical to those obtained with the lung extract; however, the end points of the clotting reaction are not quite so sharp.

irritating, however; and it often produces vomiting, especially in patients with biliary-tract disease. Following operation for relief of biliary obstruction, the patients are often nauseated even without this treatment. In such cases it is almost impossible to administer the bile salt successfully.

In order to avoid having to give bile salts, attempts have been made to administer oily solutions of vitamin K subcutaneously, intramuscularly, or intravenously. Very few have advocated the intravenous technic because of the danger of oil embolism. The intramuscular and subcutaneous methods have been given a trial. Dam and Glavind (37, 38) have reported some success along these lines. Our own experience included one case in which the bleeding tendency was quite marked. Unfortunately, this patient bled extensively into the tissue at the site of injection. We therefore gave up this type of therapy.

Most of these difficulties can be prevented by using the water-soluble analogues of vitamin K. It has been shown (39, 40) in our laboratory, both in animals and in man, that the water-soluble forms are readily absorbed from the intestine without the aid of bile salt. They can be given intravenously or intramuscularly in cases where vomiting precludes oral administration. It now seems to be the opinion of most workers that water-soluble forms are preferable to the fat-soluble forms of vitamin K in clinical medicine.

One of the most serious problems encountered in the treatment of the jaundiced bleeder is the marked tendency of the prothrombin level to fall abruptly after any operation which may be performed (34, 41–43, 94, 95). Even when the prothrombin level is normal or nearly so prior to operation, one often observes that it falls to 50 per cent or less within a day or two after operation. This, of course, is a matter of great concern, for postoperative bleeding of this type is far more common and serious than bleeding prior to operation. An additional complication lies in the fact that these patients often vomit persistently for several days after operation, and it is very difficult to give vitamin K by the oral route. One can easily see the merit of being able to give vitamin K intramuscularly or intravenously in such a case. One can thereby avoid a dangerous delay in giving effective treatment.

The question as to why the prothrombin level often falls so markedly after operation has aroused considerable debate. It is known that chloroform anesthesia causes injury to the liver, and liver injury of various types causes a fall in the plasma prothrombin level (12, 13, 44–47). It has been suggested that other anesthetics may likewise produce enough injury to the liver to interfere with the normal production of prothrombin. However, observation shows that the prothrombin rarely falls more than a few per cent after operation, except in cases of operation on the biliary tract (48, 96). It has therefore been suggested (49) that manipulation of the liver during operations on the biliary tract may cause functional impairment of the liver. However, vitamin K does not correct the prothrombin deficiency caused by experimental liver injury (47, 50, 51), whereas the vitamin does relieve the postoperative fall seen in biliary-tract disease. It would thus appear that these patients are suffering from a genuine lack of vitamin K. It now seems almost certain that the tissues of the body normally contain important reserve stores of vitamin K or of prothrombin or of both. In the patient with obstruction of the biliary tract these reserves are eventually depleted. At operation, considerable quantities of prothrombin are consumed in forming fibrin clots in the margins of the wound; and when the reserves of vitamin K are depleted, the prothrombin level falls. It is quite clear that such patients should be treated prophylactically with vitamin K before operation and should be given energetic treatment during the first few days after operation. In this way the fall can be minimized or prevented altogether.

In evaluating the prothrombin response of patients to vitamin-K therapy it is important to recognize that other factors, in addition to the vitamin, influence the prothrombin level. The importance of liver function, mentioned above, is generally recognized. In fact, hypoprothrombinemia which does not respond to the administration of vitamin K is accepted by most workers as evidence of hepatic disease.

A mild degree of hypoprothrombinemia is known to be very common in chronically debilitated patients. This was found to be true of patients at the University Hospital at Iowa City. Similar prothrombin values were found among cases of nutritional deficiency studied at Birmingham, Alabama, in collaboration with Dr. Tom D. Spies (52). In neither group was vitamin-K therapy effective. This mild hypoprothrombinemia evidently is the result of the general debility rather than the lack of any specific factor.

In a recent study (53) the prothrombin level, as determined by the two-stage method (11–14), was found to be less than two-thirds normal in most cases of pernicious anemia in relapse. Vitamin-K therapy was without effect, but the administration of liver extract resulted in a prompt rise in the prothrombin level. The degree of hypoprothrombinemia, while in general more severe in the cases with very severe anemia, does not correlate well with the degree of anemia. Other types of anemia, even though of long standing, have not shown this rather marked lowering of prothrombin. It may well be that the lowered prothrombin level in pernicious anemia reflects some degree of hepatic insufficiency which is corrected by specific liver therapy. It is equally possible, of course, that the marked response to liver therapy signifies that some factor, other than vitamin K, is needed for prothrombin production. This factor might be the substance concerned in the manufacture of red blood cells, or it might be some other substance present in the liver extract.

HEMORRHAGIC DISEASE OF THE NEWBORN

It is now known that hemorrhagic disease of the newborn is caused by a deficiency in the prothrombin content of the blood (19–24, 27, 54–93, 97). This, in turn, is due to a deficiency in vitamin K. It will be well to review a number of the more pertinent facts before discussing the reasons for the lack of this vitamin.

Most workers report that even in "normal" infants the prothrombin falls to dangerously low levels on the second, third, or fourth day of life. Bleeding occurs at this time if the prothrombin level is extremely low, especially if trauma is present to provide a precipitating factor. Such trauma may be of recent origin, but in some cases the blood apparently begins to ooze again from lesions sustained during delivery. Such "delayed bleeding" may occur in any portion of the body but is probably most common within the cranial cavity or from tears in the liver or other abdominal viscera.

Far more common than "delayed bleeding" is the "early type"

suffered by the infant at birth or immediately thereafter. In this type of bleeding, birth trauma is obviously a factor of great importance, but it has been suggested that the infant may already suffer from serious prothrombin deficiency at this time. Prothrombin assays made at birth support this contention. However, a survey of the literature reveals marked disagreement regarding the prothrombin level at the time of birth. It is commonly held that the discrepancies in the literature are due mainly to differences in methods used for the assay of prothrombin. While these differences are undoubtedly important, we believe, nevertheless, that genuine differences do exist in the clinical material studied and that prothrombin deficiency is common in some series but not in others. In support of this contention we wish to present a partial analysis of several reports, chosen more or less at random from the literature. It will then be possible to discuss the way in which a deficiency develops and the various methods of combating the disorder.

The prothrombin levels (untreated) during the first 9 days of life.—In Figure 1 are plotted the prothrombin values obtained in several laboratories. These results are given as percentage of normal adult levels, thus showing quite clearly some rather marked discrepancies.

Curves *1* and *2* were obtained (56) in Iowa City by our "bedside" method and by the method of Quick, respectively. The extremely high initial values with the bedside test are probably due to faulty control of temperature in our earlier studies; recent determinations give values almost identical to our results with Quick's method, shown in the second curve.

In distinct contrast to the Iowa City results are the data obtained in Milwaukee (66) by Quick and Grossman (curve *3*). In the latter series the initial values are 25 per cent lower, the fall occurs earlier, and recovery is more prompt. Careful study of the technic (Quick's method) seemed to eliminate the possibility that there were significant differences in analytical procedure. It seems necessary to conclude that the prothrombin levels in the two series were actually different.

A far more striking discrepancy is supplied by the Chicago series (70) of Kato and Poncher (curve *6*). In this series the level was lowest at birth and, on the average, was only 15 per cent of normal.

These results were obtained by use of a microadaptation of the method of Quick. Kato (26) has reported that this method gives results almost identical to those obtained with the original method

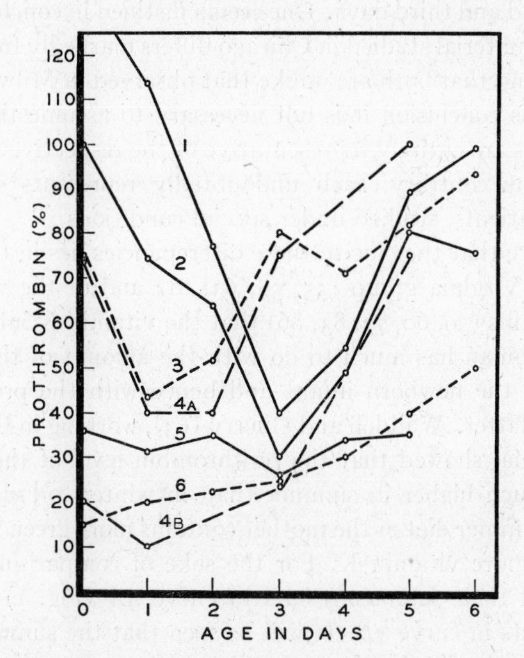

FIG. 1.—Prothrombin levels (untreated) during the first 6 days of life.

Curves *1* and *2*, by Owen, Hoffman, Ziffren, and Smith (56) in Iowa City. Curve *1* by the "bedside test"; curve *2* by the method of Quick.

Curve *3*, by Quick and Grossman (66), in Milwaukee, using the method of Quick.

Curves *4A* and *4B*, by Waddell and Guerry (63) in Charlottesville, Virginia, using a microadaptation of Quick's method devised by Kelly and Bray (68). Curve *4A* was obtained during winter and early spring; curve *4B*, during late spring and early summer. Waddell and Guerry expressed their results in the form of prothrombin time (in seconds). In order to facilitate comparison, we have converted these values into "percentage of normal adult values" with the aid of the conversion curve of Quick.

Curve *5*, by Owen, Hoffman, Ziffren, and Smith (56), in Iowa City, using the two-stage prothrombin method of Warner, Brinkhous, and Smith (11–14).

Curve *6*, by Kato and Poncher (70) in Chicago, using a micromethod devised by Kato (26).

of Quick. Dr. C. A. Owen, of our laboratory, has recently confirmed this. On applying Kato's method to newly born infants in Iowa City he found levels similar to those obtained by Quick's method and far higher than those reported by Poncher and Kato. Furthermore, Astrowe, Palmerton, and Lea (97), using the method of Kato, found moderate prothrombin reduction at birth, followed by a marked fall on the second and third days. One seems justified in concluding that the clinical material studied in Chicago differs markedly from that in Iowa City and that both are unlike that observed in Milwaukee. In reaching this conclusion it is not necessary to assume that any of these reports are entirely representative of the respective communities. On the contrary, each undoubtedly represents specialized classes of patients, studied under special conditions.

We believe that the clue to these discrepancies lies in the conclusion of the Virginia group (55, 58, 63, 81) and of the workers at Johns Hopkins (59, 60, 73, 83, 86) that the vitamin-K intake of the pregnant woman has much to do with the amount of the vitamin received by the newborn infant and hence with the prothrombin level of the latter. Waddell and Guerry (63), working in Charlottesville, Virginia, showed that the prothrombin level of the newborn infant is much higher in summer than in winter, presumably because the summer diet of the mother contains more green vegetables and hence more vitamin K. For the sake of comparison we have summarized their summer results in curve *4A* (Fig. 1) and their winter results in curve *4B*. It will be seen that the summer results are quite similar to the data of Quick and Grossman; the winter levels are almost as low as the values reported by Kato and Poncher. Neither Quick and Grossman nor Kato and Poncher were explicit regarding the season in which their studies were made or regarding the nature of the diet. It seems probable that certain classes of the population, especially the very low-income class, may be more or less deficient in vitamin K at all seasons of the year, and this is particularly likely to occur in large cities, such as Chicago and Milwaukee. It is worthy of note that, in the metropolitan district of New York, Beck, Taylor, and Colburn (20) found low prothrombin values and an unusually high incidence of hemorrhage. On the other hand, the birth level in Iowa City, shown in Figure 1, is uniformly high. The reason, it would appear, is that most of the pregnant women in this series come from rural areas where the diet is of good quality. Furthermore, most of them arrive at the University Hospital several days in advance of delivery. While there, they are placed on an abundant well-balanced diet which is probably in marked contrast to the prenatal treatment received by indigent patients in the large cities.

All of the prothrombin methods thus far mentioned are one-stage methods. Curve 5, on the other hand, shows results obtained with the two-stage technic of Warner, Brinkhous, and Smith. According to this method, the prothrombin level at birth is low, and during the next few days there tends to be a small decrease, which is temporary. Normal levels are not reached for several months. Owen, Hoffman, Ziffren, and Smith (56), from whose paper these results were taken, suggested that the difference in results between the one-stage and the two-stage method is due to an alteration in the conversion rate of the prothrombin. They believe that altered rate of conversion may compensate for a relative lack of prothrombin.

In addition to the data given in Figure 1, there are additional reports which are of considerable interest. Dam, Tage-Hansen, and Plum (62) in Copenhagen at first reported that the birth level is almost normal but that on the second or third day it falls to less than 5 per cent of normal. Later, Plum (84) likewise noted a fall but found that the level was quite low even at birth. One may surmise that seasonal variations would explain this downward revision of the birth level in this clinic.

One additional point of interest is evident from the data given in Figure 1. The postnatal fall in prothrombin occurs most commonly on the second day. In the Iowa City series, however, the minimal levels are reached at the end of the third day. The slow fall in this series is associated with high initial levels, but there is obviously a delay in recovery. We believe that this is associated with the fact that in this hospital the newborn infants are rather carefully segregated from the mothers and nursing is not effectively begun as early as in certain other hospitals.

The amount of vitamin K needed by the infant, and the source of the supply.—As mentioned above, the great importance of vitamin K in maintaining normal prothrombin levels in young infants is now thoroughly established. Waddell and Guerry (55) showed that hemorrhagic disease of the newborn can be cured by the administration of vitamin K to the infant. Later, they showed that the fall of prothrombin can be prevented by prophylactic administration of the vitamin to the infant (58). Hellman (59, 60, 73) and his associates reported similar results and found that the infant could also be given protection if the vitamin were administered to the mother during the last few days of pregnancy. This is in accord with the concept of seasonal fluctuations already mentioned. From the work which they

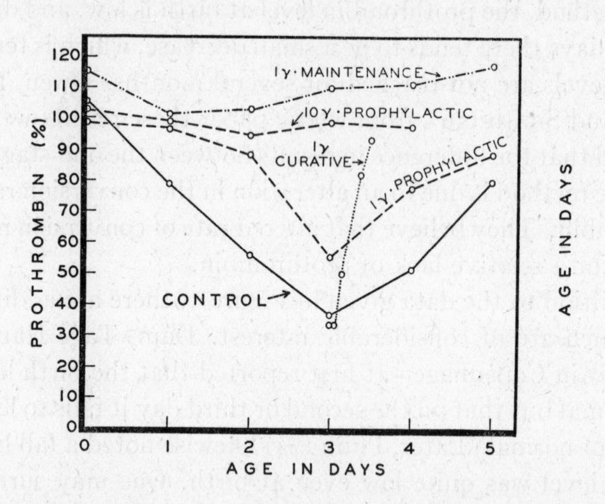

FIG. 2.—Response of infants to variable dosage of vitamin K. The compound used as a source of vitamin-K activity was the water-soluble 4-amino-2-methyl-1-naphthol (Synkamin) kindly supplied by Parke Davis and Company. Administration was by intramuscular injection. These data are adapted with slight amplification, from the data of Sells, Walker, and Owen (24).

have done it is evident not only that the low levels sometimes seen at birth are due to vitamin-K deficiency in the mother but also that the postnatal fall results from the fact that nursing is not effective until the flow of mother's milk becomes abundant, i.e., on about the fourth day postpartum.

Before discussing the merits of treating either the mother or the infant we wish to discuss briefly the problem of normal vitamin-K requirements of the infant. This problem has recently been studied by Sells, Walker, and Owen (24) of our laboratory. Their results, slightly amplified by new data, are given in Figure 2. In securing data for this chart the vitamin was given (*a*) prophylactically, in one dose on the first day of life; (*b*) as a single curative dose on the second, third, or fourth day of life; or (*c*) in the form of daily maintenance doses. The uppermost curve shows that 1 μg., given daily, is adequate to maintain the prothrombin at the normal level. It had not been anticipated that such an exceedingly small amount of the vitamin would be effective, for the customary therapeutic dose, 1 mg., is one thousand times as large as this. Data, not given in the chart, showed that the same response could often be obtained with ½ μg., but at this level the prothrombin fell somewhat in some cases.

On giving the vitamin prophylactically on the first day of life it was found that 10 μg. would usually suffice to prevent the fall shown in the untreated controls (Fig. 2). A single dose of 1 μg. had some effect but did not afford complete protection. An intermediate dose of 5 μg. was also tried and was found to give complete protection to some infants but not to others. It is evident from these studies that the prophylactic method involves definite "wastage" of the vitamin, for, when given in this way, 5–10 μg. are required to give the same protection obtained with 3–4 μg. in divided doses over a period of 4 or 5 days.

In Figure 2 is also shown one experiment involving a single curative dose of 1 μg., given on the third day of life. The prothrombin level, 30 per cent of normal before the vitamin was given, rose to the 95 per cent level in 10 hours. Additional studies made with smaller doses show that complete recovery is sometimes effected with a dose one-half as large as this, but as a rule the recovery is slow and is often incomplete.

These studies, showing that the minimal vitamin-K requirement of the infant is extremely low, raise important questions as to how the needs of the infant are met. Practically all workers have commented on the fact that the prothrombin level rises out of the danger zone as soon as the infant receives adequate amounts of milk. Salomonsen (64, 65, 75, 80) showed that 30–60 cc. of milk daily suffices to keep the prothrombin at safe levels, but it is evident that the colostrum, being scanty in amount, is not adequate. It is known that milk is not a particularly rich source of vitamin K, and for this reason some workers have concluded that the milk served merely to introduce a bacterial flora into the intestinal tract and that vitamin

K was produced in adequate amounts by these bacteria. It is, indeed, well established that many types of bacteria do produce vitamin K, but there are no data whatever regarding how much of the vitamin is formed in the intestine during the first few days of life or how much is absorbed. The assumption that the bacteria are important is purely hypothetical and is designed to fill what appeared to be a gap in the chain of scientific reasoning. From the data we have quoted it is evident that 1 μg. daily is adequate. The work of Sells, Walker, and Owen has shown quite clearly that a reasonable intake of milk does contain adequate amounts of preformed vitamin K to meet these mimimal requirements. The vitamin K contained in milk could be extracted with either and shown to be effective. The extracted residue, containing the proteins and most of the carbohydrates, would presumably support bacterial activity in the intestine, and yet it was found to be relatively ineffective in preventing the fall in prothrombin. It seems necessary to conclude that the effectiveness of milk is due mainly to its content of vitamin K rather than to the role of inciting bacterial synthesis of the vitamin in the intestine.

In summary, it is evident that vitamin K is transmitted through the placenta; and, when large amounts are given to the pregnant woman, a certain amount of the vitamin is stored in the fetus. However, under ordinary circumstances very little is stored; and, owing to lack of food intake, the young infant quickly develops a deficiency unless the vitamin is artificially supplied. If the diet of the mother has been reasonably adequate, as in the Iowa City series, the prothrombin of the infant is at a safe level at birth. A single prophylactic dose of 10 μg. is enough to maintain this level during the critical four days which follow. This same protection can be obtained by giving 1,000 μg. to the mother. It would appear that the vitamin may be distributed between mother and fetus almost in proportion to body weight. At any rate, the fetus obtains at least the necessary 10 μg., and perhaps more. There is, thus, no good reason for believing, as some do, that vitamin K does not pass readily through the placenta. Nor is there any reason for doubting that the tissues of the infant are competent to manufacture adequate amounts of prothrombin, provided vitamin K is present in proper amounts. In support of this view, attention is called to the prompt and complete response observed on administering minimal quantities of vitamin K to K-deficient infants (Fig. 2).

In the practical matter of prophylactic therapy the question arises as to whether one should treat the mother or the infant or both. In treating the mother, most workers advocate giving 1–5 mg. daily during the last few days of pregnancy. With one exception (88) all workers agree that prolonged treatment is not necessary. Even a single dose, given less than 2 hours before delivery, appears to be effective in preventing the postnatal fall (91). There are some who doubt that prothrombin deficiency is an important factor in causing "early" hemorrhage, i.e., the type which affects the infant at birth or immediately thereafter. These workers prefer to give vitamin-K treatment to the newborn infant, not to the mother. No doubt this is a safe procedure in certain communities and with certain classes of patients. However, the data which we have already discussed show that in certain classes and at certain seasons the prothrombin level of the infant may be dangerously low at the time of delivery.

It will no doubt be impossible to impress upon all concerned the desirability of giving synthetic vitamin K prophylactically to pregnant women. In many cases it should be possible to meet essential needs of these women by placing proper stress on dietary factors. It is suggested that, in planning the diet of the pregnant woman, due consideration be given to the inclusion of items rich in vitamin K. These might include green vegetables and tomatoes, and perhaps even canned spinach in the winter months when fresh vegetables are scarce. The use of synthetic vitamin K can well be employed under the more ideal conditions of medical practice.

In case the mother has received large supplements of vitamin K during the last few days of pregnancy, it is probably not necessary in most cases to give additional treatment to the newborn infant. If, however, the mother has had merely a "normal" diet, it is evident that the infant will require special attention. The flow of mother's milk is extremely scanty for the first few days. In order to face this critical period the infant should be given 5 or 6 ounces of milk formula daily or should be given vitamin K in the form of special medication. With most classes of patients it is possible to secure co-operation on one or another of these programs, depending upon financial, social, or educational status of the family.

BIBLIOGRAPHY

1. Warner, E. D., New International Clinics, 3d ser., 2:92, 1940.
2. Brinkhous, K. M., Medicine, 19:329, 1940.
3. Butt, H. R., and Snell, A. M., Vitamin K. Philadelphia: W. B. Saunders Co., 1941. Pp. 172.
4. Koller, F., Das Vitamin K. Leipzig: George Thieme, 1941. Pp. 151.
5. Schønheyder, F., Biochem. J., 30:890, 1936.
6. Dam, H., and Glavind, J., Biochem. J., 32:1018, 1938.
7. Plum, P., and Dam, H., Klin. Wchnschr., 19:815, 1940.
8. Quick, A. J., J. Biol. Chem., 109:lxxiii, 1935.
9. Quick, A. J.; Stanley-Brown, M.; and Bancroft, F. W., Am. J. M. Sc., 190:501, 1935.
10. Quick, A. J., Am. J. Physiol., 114:282, 1936.
11. Warner, E. D.; Brinkhous, K. M.; and Smith, H. P., Arch. Path., 18: 587, 1934.
12. Warner, E. D.; Brinkhous, K. M.; and Smith, H. P., Am. J. Physiol., 114:667, 1936.
13. Smith, H. P.; Warner, E. D.; and Brinkhous, K. M., J. Exper. Med., 66: 801, 1937.
14. Warner, E. D.; Brinkhous, K. M.; and Smith, H. P., Am. J. Physiol., 125:296, 1939.
15. Ziffren, S. E.; Owen, C. A.; Hoffman, G. R.; and Smith, H. P., Proc. Soc. Exper. Biol. & Med., 40:595, 1939.
16. Ziffren, S. E.; Owen, C. A.; Hoffman, G. R.; and Smith, H. P., Am. J. Clin. Path., 4:Tech. Suppl., 13, 1940.
17. Karabin, J. E., and Anderson, E. R., J. Lab. & Clin. Med., 26:723, 1941.
18. White, C. S.; Abramson, D. J.; Weinstein, J. J.; and Sproul, M. T., Virginia M. Monthly, 68:27, 1941.
19. Bruchsaler, F. S., J. Pediat., 18:317, 1941.
20. Beck, A. C.; Taylor, E. S.; and Colburn, R. F., Am. J. Obst. & Gynec., 41:765, 1941.
21. Willumsen, H. C.; Stadler, H. E.; and Owen, C. A., Proc. Soc. Exper. Biol. & Med., 47:116, 1941.
22. Lawson, R. B.; Wynell, D. B.; and Branning, W. S., North Carolina M. J., 2:234, 1941.
23. Huber, C. P., and Shrader, J. C., J. Lab. & Clin. Med., 26:1379, 1941.
24. Sells, R. L.; Walker, S. A.; and Owen, C. A., Proc. Soc. Exper. Biol. & Med., 47:441, 1941.

25. Řeřábek, J., Klin. Wchnschr., **20**:368, 1941.
26. Kato, K., Am. J. Clin. Path., **10**:147, 1940.
27. Bray, W. E., and Kelley, O. R., Am. J. Clin. Path., **10**:154, 1940.
28. Fanconi, G., Deutsche med. Wchnschr., **64**:1565, 1938.
29. Butt, H. R.; Snell, A. M.; and Osterberg, A. E., Proc. Staff Meet., Mayo Clin., **13**:753, 1938.
30. Engel, R., Med. Welt., **13**:120, 1939.
31. Clark, R. L., Jr.; Dixon, C. F.; Butt, H. R.; and Snell, A. M., Proc. Staff Meet., Mayo Clin., **14**:407, 1939.
32. Hult, H., Nord. med., **3**:2428, 1939.
33. Koller, F., and Wuhrmann, F., Klin. Wchnschr., **18**:1058, 1939.
34. Butt, H. R.; Snell, A. M.; and Osterberg, A. E., J.A.M.A., **113**:383, 1939.
35. Stewart, J. D., and Rourke, G. M., New England J. Med., **221**:403, 1939.
36. Elliott, M. C.; Isaacs, B.; and Ivy, A. C., Proc. Soc. Exper. Biol. & Med., **43**:240, 1940.
37. Dam, H., and Glavind, J., Lancet, 720, 1938.
38. Dam, H., and Glavind, J., Acta med. Scandinav., **96**:108, 1938.
39. Warner, E. D., and Flynn, J. E., Proc. Soc. Exper. Biol. & Med., **44**:607, 1940.
40. Smith, H. P., and Owen, C. A., Rev. Gastroenterol., **7**:520, 1940.
41. Snell, A. M.; Butt, H. R.; and Osterberg, A. E., Am. J. Digest. Dis. & Nutrition, **5**:590, 1938.
42. Scanlon, G. H.; Brinkhous, K. M.; Warner, E. D.; Smith, H. P.; and Flynn, J. E., J.A.M.A., **112**:1898, 1939.
43. Stewart, J. D.; Rourke, G. M.; and Allen, A. W., Ann. Surg., **110**:693, 1939; Stewart, J. D., Ann. Surg., **109**:588, 1939; Stewart, J. D., and Rourke, G. M., J.A.M.A., **113**:2223, 1939.
44. Warner, E. D., J. Exper. Med., **68**:831, 1938.
45. Quick, A. J., J.A.M.A., **110**:1658, 1938.
46. Warren, R., and Rhoads, J. E., Am. J. M. Sc., **198**:193, 1939.
47. Andrus, W. DeW.; Lord, J. W., Jr.; and Moore, R. A., Surgery, **6**:899, 1939.
48. Cullen, S. C.; Ziffren, S. E.; Gibson, R. B.; and Smith, H. P., J.A.M.A., **115**:991, 1940.
49. Lord, J. W., Jr., Surgery, **6**:896, 1939.
50. Brinkhous, K. M., and Warner, E. D., Proc. Soc. Exper. Biol. & Med., **44**:609, 1940.
51. Bollman, J. L.; Butt, H. R.; and Snell, A. M., J.A.M.A., **115**:1087, 1940.
52. Warner, E. D.; Spies, T. D.; and Owen, C. A., South. M. J., **34**:161, 1941.
53. Warner, E. D., and Owen, C. A., Am. J. M. Sc., **203**:187, 1942.
54. Brinkhous, K. M.; Smith, H. P.; and Warner, E. D., Am. J. M. Sc., **193**:475, 1937.

55. WADDELL, W. W., JR.; GUERRY, DU P., III; BRAY, W. E.; and KELLEY, O. R., Proc. Soc. Exper. Biol. & Med., **40**:432, 1939.
56. OWEN, C. A.; HOFFMAN, G. R.; ZIFFREN, S. E.; and SMITH, H. P., Proc. Soc. Exper. Biol. & Med., **41**:181, 1939.
57. QUICK, A. J., and GROSSMAN, A. M., Proc. Soc. Exper. Biol. & Med., **41**: 227, 1939.
58. WADDELL, W. W., and GUERRY, DU P., III, J.A.M.A., **112**:2259, 1939.
59. HELLMAN, L. M., and SHETTLES, L. B., Bull. Johns Hopkins Hosp., **65**:138, 1939.
60. SHETTLES, L. B.; DELFS, E.; and HELLMAN, L. M., Bull. Johns Hopkins Hosp., **65**:419, 1939.
61. NYGAARD, K. K., Acta obst. & gynec. Scandinav., **19**:361, 1939.
62. DAM, H.; TAGE-HANSEN, E.; and PLUM, P., Ugesk. f. laeger, **101**:896, 1939; Lancet, **2**:1157, 1939.
63. WADDELL, W. W., JR., and GUERRY, DU P., III, J. Pediat., **15**:802, 1939.
64. SALOMONSEN, L., and NYGAARD, K. K., Acta paediat., **27**: 209, 1939.
65. SALOMONSEN, L., Acta paediat., **27**, Suppl. 1: 5, 1939.
66. QUICK, A. J., and GROSSMAN, A. M., Am. J. M. Sc., **199**:1, 1940.
67. KOLLER, F., and FIECHTER, N., Schweiz. med. Wchnschr., **70**:136, 1940.
68. KELLEY, O. R., and BRAY, W. E., J. Lab. & Clin. Med., **25**:527, 1940.
69. THORDARSON, O., Nature, **145**:305, 1940.
70. KATO, K., and PONCHER, H. G., J.A.M.A., **114**:749, 1940.
71. RUSH, A., Surg., Gynec., & Obst., **70**:922, 1940.
72. MACPHERSON, A. I. S.; MCCALLUM, E.; and HAULTAIN, W. F. T., Brit. M. J., 1940, p. 839.
73. HELLMAN, L. M.; MOORE, W. T.; and SHETTLES, L. B., Bull. Johns Hopkins Hosp., **66**:379, 1940.
74. KUGELMASS, I. N., Arch. Dis. Childhood, **15**:97, 1940.
75. SALOMONSEN, L., Nord. med., **7**:1309, 1940.
76. PLUM, P., and DAM, H., Klin. Wchnschr., **19**:853, 1940.
77. FITZGERALD, J. E., and WEBSTER, A., Am. J. Obst. & Gynec., **40**:413, 1940.
78. JAVERT, C. T., Am J. Obst. & Gynec., **40**:453, 1940.
79. WADDELL, W. W., JR.; GUERRY DU P., III; and BIRDSONG, M., South. M. J., **33**:974, 1940.
80. SALOMONSEN, L., Acta paediat., **28**:1, 1940.
81. WADDELL, W. W., JR., and LAWSON, G. McL., J.A.M.A., **115**:1416, 1940.
82. SNELLING, C. E., J. Pediat., **17**:615, 1940.
83. HELLMAN, L. M.; SHETTLES, L. B.; and EASTMAN, N. J., Am. J. Obst. & Gynec., **40**:844, 1940.
84. PLUM, P., Deutsche med. Wchnschr., **66**:1389, 1940.
85. JAVERT, C. T., and MOORE, R. A., Am. J. Obst. & Gynec., **40**:1022, 1940.
86. MAUMENEE, A. E.; HELLMAN, L. M.; and SHETTLES, L. B., Bull. Johns Hopkins Hosp., **68**:158, 1941.

87. LAWSON, R. B., J. Pediat., **18**:224, 1941.
88. LEIDENHEIMER, H., and ALBRITTON, A. S., New Orleans M. & S. J., **93**: 464, 1941.
89. VAN VYVE, A., Acta brev. Neerland., **11**:101, 1941.
90. HUBER, C. P., and SHRADER, J. C., Am. J. Obst. & Gynec., **41**:566, 1941.
91. BOHLENDER, G. P.; ROSENBAUM, W. M.; and SAGE, E. C., J.A.M.A., **116**: 1763, 1941.
92. NORRIS, R. F., and BENNETT, M. C., Surg., Gynec., & Obst., **72**:758, 1941.
93. EDSALL, G., New England J. Med., **224**:762, 1941.
94. SMITH, H. P.; ZIFFREN, S. E.; OWEN, C. A.; and HOFFMAN, G. R., J.A.M.A., **113**:380, 1939.
95. SMITH, H. P.; ZIFFREN, S. E.; OWEN, C. A.; HOFFMAN, G. R.; and FLYNN, J. E., J. Iowa M. Soc., **29**:377, 1939.
96. ALLEN, J. G., and LIVINGSTONE, H., Anesthesiology, **1**:89, 1940.
97. ASTROWE, P. S.; PALMERTON, E. S.; and HENDERSON, V., J. Pediat., **18**: 507, 1941.

[PRINTED IN U.S.A.]